Chemicals
and Life

DICKENSON SERIES IN BIOLOGY

Elof Axel Carlson, Consulting Editor

Biology of the Oceans   *Donald J. Reish*

Chemicals and Life   *Kenneth E. Maxwell*

Contemporary Readings in Ecology   *Arthur S. Boughey*

CONTEMPORARY THOUGHT IN BIOLOGY SERIES

Molecular and Cell Biology   *Bruce H. Carpenter*

Molecular Approaches to Psycho-Biology   *Edward Glassman*

Gene Theory   *Elof A. Carlson*

Cellular Differentiation   *J. Richard Whittaker*

Population and Environmental Biology   *Arthur S. Boughey*

Molecular Control of Plant Growth   *J. Eugene Fox*

The Adaptations of Organisms   *Rodolfo Ruibal*

Chemicals and Life

Kenneth E. Maxwell

California State College at Long Beach

dickenson publishing company, inc.
belmont, california

L. C. Cat. Card No.: 77–103038

FEB 15 '72

Printed in the United States of America

2 3 4 5 6 7 8 9 10   74 73 72 71 70

Contents

10. *molecular war* *310*

11. *radiation roulette* *333*

Preface

Many of humanity's most pressing problems involve the effects of chemicals on living processes. The four horsemen of the space age, *population, pollution, pestilence,* and *plutonium,* are chemically dependent and in some measure chemically controlled.

In a sense, life is chemistry. Every organism is an enormously complex factory in which millions of ionic actions and reactions take place every split second, and where protons and electrons in response to the natural laws of the mysterious life-force are shunted from molecule to molecule. Thus, it is not surprising that the highly organized systems of living things are supersensitive to chemicals in the external and internal environment. The results of exposure or administration are profound, often drastic, to the organism. Some chemicals are controllable, others are not; some are harmful, others are beneficial; some that are harmful to one species are beneficial to another; some are man-made, others belong to the multitude of chemicals in the natural environment to which all living things are constantly exposed. Moreover, all organisms through eons of adaptation and evolution have acquired the ability, even the necessity, to use or reject (or frequently to succumb to) the chemicals that impinge on their existence.

That scientists differ in their interpretations of experimental and observational data is confusing if not amusing to nonscientists and sometimes to scientists of different persuasion. But it could not be otherwise. Tunnel vision is a by-product of the specialization brought about by the knowledge explosion. Perspective can be achieved only by lively communication and full expression. With this in mind, some of the topics in this book are discussed from two or more points of view.

Urgent decisions concerning man's future existence are impending. Many of the decisions are destined to be made by legislative bodies, politicians, and others of limited scientific background. Even technical advisors are increasingly restricted by their narrow specialties. The objective of this book is to contribute to a better understanding by the reader of those natural and man-made chemicals that affect our lives beneficially and adversely, and some of the problems inherent in their use with which present and future generations may be cursed or blessed.

—KENNETH E. MAXWELL

1

Living Molecules

Out of water all life is created.
—THE KORAN

The mystery of creation has intrigued men from early times. Theories of the Garden of Eden or its counterpart were embodied in almost all of the ancient religions, and symbolic representations of procreation were, and are, more or less realistically portrayed in primitive rites.

Among scientists two hundred years ago, the question of whether life originates spontaneously and continuously around us was one of the most bitterly debated topics. John Needham and others said that it does, Lazzaro Spallanzani said that it doesn't, and Pasteur proved that it can't.

In 1953, Stanley Miller, with imagination and a modern scientific approach, showed that it can—but only under conditions that long ago ceased to exist naturally on Earth. He set up within a flask a miniature Garden of Eden, in reality a hostile primordial world, where the events of eons were telescoped into a few dramatic hours during which nonliving substances reformed into life-oriented amino acids. By similar techniques other living molecules, including the code of life, DNA, were subsequently synthesized.

As scientists see it, life must have sprung painfully and convulsively from the hostile environment of the young Earth. At first a molten speck of dust among the stars, eventually—so slowly that to us it almost seems that time stood still—the infernally hot blob of whirling mineral cooled enough to form a crust, although melted rock still oozed from cracks in the surface. Finally a fog of gaseous water, the giver of life, condensed in the cooler spots and formed a mineral soup in puddles and ponds. Mingled among the swirling vapors were nitrogen and carbon dioxide and, at first, toxic concentrations of methane or marsh gas, ammonia, and deadly hydrogen cyanide. There was also an abundance of hydrogen gas, a residue from the nearest star, the Sun, a small but efficient nuclear reactor. The most energetic rays from the Sun, ultraviolet and deadly gamma rays, struck the Earth almost unimpeded by the light atmosphere of hydrogen gas. Moreover, the now warm vapors convulsed with blow upon blow as electric discharges of incredible violence lashed the planet.

Following the proposals of Oparin, Bernal, and Urey that the early Earth had a reducing atmosphere of hydrogen, Stanley Miller subjected a mixture of methane, ammonia, and water in the presence of hydrogen to electrical discharges and produced life molecules, including many of the amino acid building blocks of proteins. Here, indeed, was substantive proof that living molecules and, hence, living organisms could have been created under conditions presumed to exist on primitive Earth.

Following Miller's breakthrough, others synthesized more complicated living molecules in the laboratory. Klaus Hofmann in 1960 put together the first 23 amino acid units of pig corticotropin. R. Schwyzer and his co-workers in 1963 synthesized the full peptide chain that makes up the pig corticotropin active hormone, containing 39 amino acid units. Y.-T. Kung and his co-workers in Red China constructed in 1966 an even more complex peptide chain to produce crystals of bovine insulin containing 777 atoms, identical with the natural material.

But the nearest approach that scientists have made to the creation of life is the synthesizing of polynucleotides. The nucleotides are the building blocks of the nucleic acids DNA (deoxyribonucleic acid) and RNA (ribonucleic acid). As an outgrowth of the pioneering work of Watson and Crick, we now know that DNA is the genetic substance that not only carries the code for determining the inheritable characteristics of progeny but also lays down the law that controls the functioning of the cell. In short, polynucleotides are the basic stuff of life.

One of the first steps was made by Juan Oro and A. P. Kimball who, apparently inspired by the work of Miller, used as starting materials hydrogen cyanide and ammonia, presumed to exist on primitive Earth. They succeeded in synthesizing adenine, a key component of DNA and

RNA, as well as ATP (adenosine triphosphate), the energy substance that is the cellular equivalent of a combustion engine.

Arthur Kornberg and his co-workers at Stanford extracted and purified enzymes from the common colon bacillus *E. coli*, with which they made the first step toward producing DNA in a test tube. Frederick Bollum did much the same thing with animal cells. The biological mechanism depends on the action of an enzyme that, in company with an existing DNA template, catalyzes a new DNA chain.

Many other workers have uncovered facts that contribute to our knowledge of the still largely mysterious creation of life. Gobind Khorana at the University of Wisconsin, as well as others, has prepared synthetic polynucleotides that can serve to prime DNA and RNA synthesis. The techniques make it possible to produce, in cell-free systems, polynucleotide chains having known sequences of the nucleotide code letters—chains of three-letter words made up of the nucleotide bases adenine, guanine, cytosine, and thymine or, in the case of RNA, uracil.

Since Miller's classic experiment, the production in the laboratory of primordial substances essential to life comes closer and closer to the creation of life itself. One can only speculate what synthetic life will be like and whether it will be for evil or for good.

A Production of Amino Acids under Possible Primitive Earth Conditions

Stanley L. Miller

The idea that the organic compounds that serve as the basis of life were formed when the earth had an atmosphere of methane, ammonia, water, and hydrogen instead of carbon dioxide, nitrogen, oxygen, and water was suggested by Oparin [1] and has been given emphasis recently by Urey [2] and Bernal [3].

In order to test this hypothesis, an apparatus was built to circulate CH_4, NH_3, H_2O, and H_2 past an electric discharge. The resulting mixture has been tested for amino acids by paper chromatography. Electrical discharge was used to form free radicals instead of ultraviolet light, because quartz absorbs wavelengths short enough to cause photo-dissociation of the gases. Electrical discharge may have played a significant role in the formation of compounds in the primitive atmosphere.

The apparatus used is shown in Figure 1. Water is boiled in the flask, mixes with the gases in the 5-1 flask, circulates past the electrodes, condenses and empties back into the boiling flask. The U-tube prevents circulation in the opposite direction. The acids and amino acids formed in the discharge, not being volatile, accumulate in the water phase. The circulation of the gases is quite slow, but this seems to be an asset, because production was less in a different apparatus with an aspirator arrangement to promote circulation. The discharge, a small corona, was provided by an induction coil designed for detection of leaks in vacuum apparatus.

The experimental procedure was to seal off the opening in the boiling

Reprinted from *Science, 117:* 528–29 (1953) with permission of the author and publisher.

flask after adding 200 ml of water, evacuate the air, add 10 cm pressure of H_2, 20 cm of CH_4, and 20 cm of NH_3. The water in the flask was boiled, and the discharge was run continuously for a week.

During the run the water in the flask became noticeably pink after the first day, and by the end of the week the solution was deep red and turbid. Most of the turbidity was due to colloidal silica from the glass. The red color is due to organic compounds absorbed on the silica. Also present are yellow organic compounds, of which only a small fraction

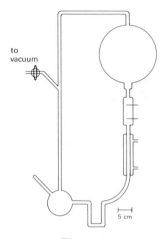

to
vacuum

5 cm

Figure 1

can be extracted with ether, and which form a continuous streak tapering off at the bottom on a one-dimensional chromatogram run in butanol-acetic acid. These substances are being investigated further.

At the end of the run the solution in the boiling flask was removed and 1 ml of saturated $HgCl_2$ was added to prevent the growth of living organisms. The ampholytes were separated from the rest of the constituents by adding $Ba(OH)_2$ and evaporating *in vacuo* to remove amines, adding H_2SO_4 and evaporating to remove the acids, neutralizing with $Ba(OH)_2$, filtering and concentrating *in vacuo*.

The amino acids are not due to living organisms because their growth would be prevented by the boiling water during the run, and by the $HgCl_2$, $Ba(OH)_2$, H_2SO_4 during the analysis.

In Figure 2 is shown a paper chromatogram run in *n*-butanol–acetic acid–water mixture followed by water-saturated phenol, and spraying with ninhydrin. Identification of an amino acid was made when the R_f value (the ratio of the distance traveled by the amino acid to the distance traveled by the solvent front), the shape, and the color of the spot were the same on a known, unknown, and mixture of the known and unknown; and when consistent results were obtained with chromatograms using phenol and 77% ethanol.

On this basis glycine, α-alanine and β-alanine are identified. The identification of the aspartic acid and α-amino-*n*-butyric acid is less certain because the spots are quite weak. The spots marked A and B are unidentified as yet, but may be beta and gamma amino acids. These are the main amino acids present, and others are undoubtedly present but in smaller amounts. It is estimated that the total yield of amino acids was in the milligram range.

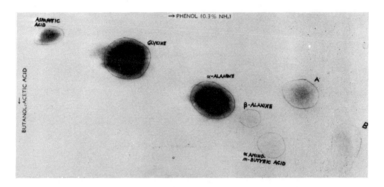

Figure 2

In this apparatus an attempt was made to duplicate a primitive atmosphere of the earth, and not to obtain the optimum conditions for the formation of amino acids. Although in this case the total yield was small for the energy expended, it is possible that, with more efficient apparatus (such as mixing of the free radicals in a flow system, use of higher hydrocarbons from natural gas or petroleum, carbon dioxide, etc., and optimum ratios of gases), this type of process would be a way of commercially producing amino acids.

A more complete analysis of the amino acids and other products of the discharge is now being performed and will be reported in detail shortly.

references

1. A. I. Oparin, *The Origin of Life.* New York: Macmillan (1938).
2. H. C. Urey, *Proc. Natl. Acad. Sci. U.S., 38,* 351 (1952); *The Planets.* New Haven: Yale Univ. Press, Chap. 4 (1952).
3. J. D. Bernal, *Proc. Phys. Soc.* (London), *62A,* 537 (1949); *62B,* 597 (1949); *Physical Basis of Life.* London: Routledge and Kegan Paul (1951).

Biologic Synthesis of Deoxyribonucleic Acid

Arthur Kornberg

The knowledge drawn in recent years from studies of bacterial transformation [1] and viral infection of bacterial cells [2], combined with
other evidence [3], has just about convinced most of us that deoxyribonucleic acid (DNA) is the genetic substance. We shall assume then
that it is DNA which not only directs the synthesis of the proteins and
the development of the cell but which must also be the substance which
is copied so as to provide for a similar development of the progeny of
that cell for many generations. Deoxyribonucleic acid, like a tape
recording, carries a message in which there are specific instructions for
a job to be done. Also, exact copies can be made from it, as from a tape
recording, so that this information can be used again and elsewhere in
time and space.

Are these two functions, the expression of the code (protein synthesis) and the copying of the code (preservation of the race), closely
integrated or are they separable? What we have learned from our
studies over the past 5 years is that the replication of DNA can be
examined and at least partially understood at the enzymatic level even
though the secret of how DNA directs protein synthesis is still locked in
the cell.

structure

First I should like to review very briefly some aspects of DNA structure which are essential for this discussion. Analysis of the composition
of samples of DNA from a great variety of sources, and by many
investigators [4], has revealed the remarkable fact that the purine

Reprinted from *Science, 131:* 1503–08 (1960) with permission of the author, the
publisher and the copyright owner. Copyright © The Nobel Foundation 1960.

content always equals the pyrimidine content. Among the purines, the adenine content may differ considerably from the guanine, and among the pyrimidines, the thymine from the cytosine. However, there is an equivalence of the bases with an amino group in the 6-position of the ring to the bases with a keto group in the 6-position. These facts were interpreted by Watson and Crick [5] in their masterful hypothesis of the structure of DNA. As shown in Figure 1, they proposed in connection with their double-stranded model for DNA, discussed below, that the 6-amino group of adenine is linked by hydrogen bonds to the 6-keto group of thymine and that in a like manner guanine is hydrogen-bonded to cytosine, thus accounting for the equivalence of the purines to the pyrimidines.

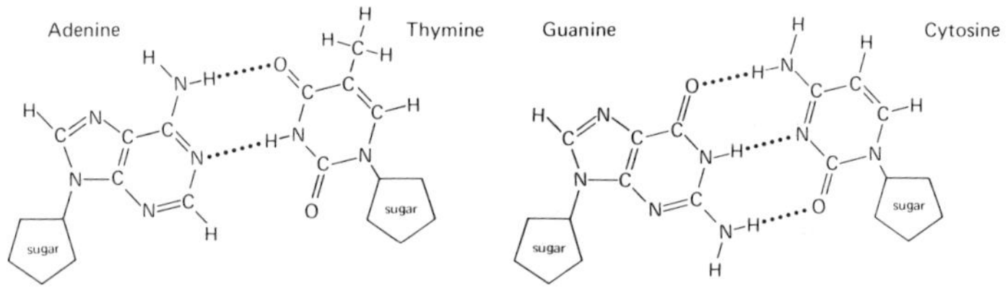

Figure 1. Hydrogen bonding of bases

On the basis of these considerations and the results of x-ray crystallographic measurements by Wilkins and his associates [6], Watson and Crick proposed a structure for DNA in which two long strands are wound about each other in a helical manner. Figure 2 is a diagrammatic representation of a fragment of a DNA chain about 10 nucleotide units long. According to physical measurements, DNA chains are, on the average, 10,000 units long. We see here the deoxypentose rings linked by phosphate residues to form the backbone of the chain; the purine and pyrimidine rings are the planar structures emerging at right angles from the main axis of the chain. Figure 3 is a more detailed molecular model [7] and gives a better idea of the packing of the atoms in the structure. The purine and pyrimidine bases of one chain are bonded to the pyrimidine and purine bases of the complementary chain by the hydrogen bonds described in Figure 1.

The x-ray measurements have indicated that the space between the opposing chains in the model agrees with the calculated value for the hydrogen-bond linkage of a purine to a pyrimidine; it is too small for two purines and too large for two pyrimidines. Most rewarding from the biological point of view, the structure provides a useful model to

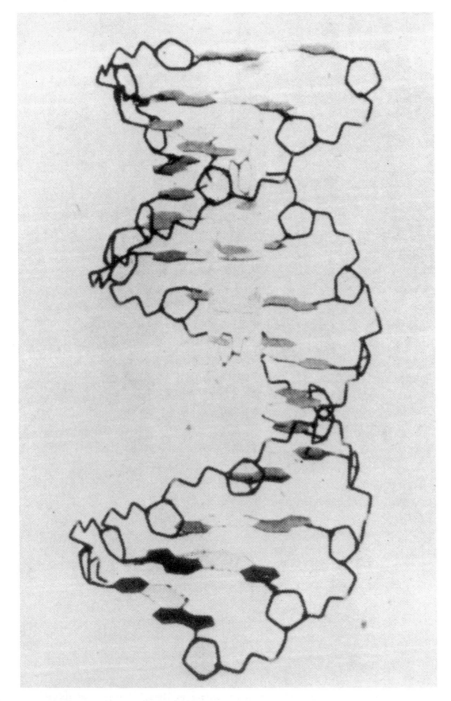

Figure 2. Double helical structure of DNA (Watson and Crick model)

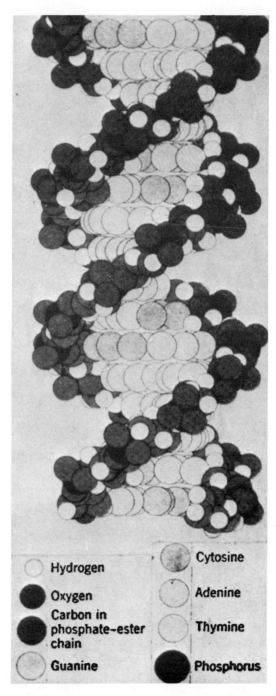

Figure 3. Molecular model of DNA (after M. Feughelman *et al.* [7])

explain how cellular replication of DNA may come about. For, if you imagine that these two chains separate and that a new chain is formed complementary to each of them, the result will be two pairs of strands, each pair identical to the original parent duplex and each member of the pair identical to the other.

enzymatic approach to replication

Although we have in the Watson and Crick proposal a mechanical model of replication, we may at this point pose the question: What is the chemical mechanism by which this super molecule is built up in the cell? Some 60 years ago the alcoholic fermentation of sugar by a yeast cell was a "vital" process inseparable from the living cell, but through the Buchner discovery of fermentation in extracts and the march of enzymology during the first half of this century, we understand fermentation by yeast as a (now familiar) sequence of integrated chemical reactions.

Five years ago the synthesis of DNA was also regarded as a "vital" process. Some people considered it useful for biochemists to examine the combustion chambers of the cell, but tampering with the very genetic apparatus itself would surely produce nothing but disorder. These gloomy predictions were not justified then, nor are similar pessimistic attitudes justified now with regard to the problems of cellular structure and specialized function which face us. High adventures in enzymology lie ahead, and many of the explorers will come from the training fields of carbohydrate, fat, amino acid, and nucleic acid enzymology.

I feel now, as we did then, that for an effective approach to the problem of nucleic acid biosynthesis it is essential to understand the biosynthesis of the simple nucleotides and the coenzymes and to have these concepts and methodology well in hand. It was from these studies that we developed the conviction that an activated nucleoside 5'-phosphate is the basic biosynthetic building block of the nucleic acids [8]. You will recall that the main pathways of purine and pyrimidine biosynthesis all lead to the nucleoside 5'-phosphate [8]; they do not usually include the free bases or nucleosides, except as salvage mechanisms. While the 2' and 3' isomers of the nucleotides are known, they probably arise mainly from certain types of enzymatic degradation of the nucleic acids. You will also recall from the biosynthesis of coenzymes [9], the simplest of the nucleotide condensation products, that

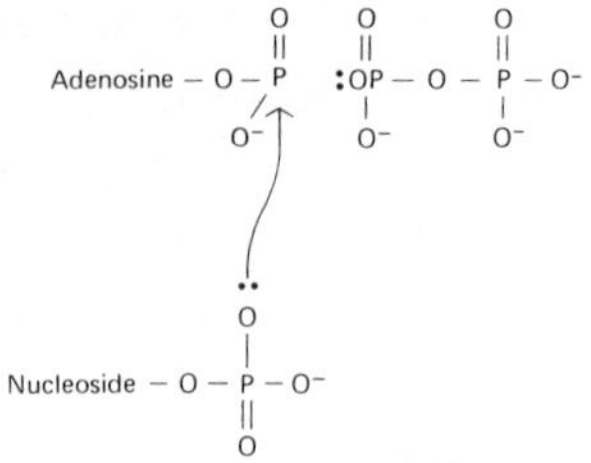

$$
\text{Adenosine} - O - \overset{\overset{\displaystyle O}{\|}}{\underset{\underset{\displaystyle O^-}{\nearrow}}{P}} \quad : O\overset{\overset{\displaystyle O}{\|}}{\underset{\underset{\displaystyle O^-}{|}}{P}} - O - \overset{\overset{\displaystyle O}{\|}}{\underset{\underset{\displaystyle O^-}{|}}{P}} - O^-
$$

$$
\text{Nucleoside} - O - \overset{\overset{\displaystyle \cdot\cdot}{\displaystyle O}}{\underset{\underset{\displaystyle O}{\|}}{\underset{\displaystyle P}{|}}} - O^-
$$

Figure 4. Nucleophilic attack of a nucleoside monophosphate on ATP

it is adenosine triphosphate (ATP) which condenses with nicotinamide mononucleotide to form diphosphopyridine nucleotide, with riboflavin phosphate to form flavine adenine dinucleotide (FAD), with pantetheine phosphate to form the precursor of coenzyme A, and so forth. This pattern has been amplified by the discovery of identical mechanisms for the activation of fatty acids and amino acids, and it has been demonstrated further that uridine, cytidine, and guanosine coenzymes are likewise formed from the respective triphosphates of these nucleosides.

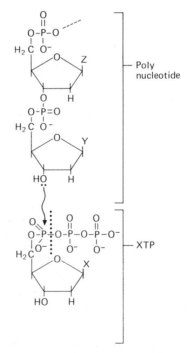

Figure 5. Postulated mechanism for extending a DNA chain

This mechanism (Figure 4), in which a nucleophilic attack [10] on the pyrophosphate-activated adenyl group by a nucleoside monophosphate leads to the formation of a coenzyme, was adopted as a working hypothesis for studying the synthesis of a DNA chain. As illustrated in Figure 5, it was postulated that the basic building block is a deoxynucleoside 5′-triphosphate which is attacked by the 3′-hydroxyl group at the growing end of a polydeoxynucleotide chain; inorganic pyrophosphate is eliminated, and the chain is lengthened by one unit. The results of our studies of DNA synthesis, as is shown below, are in keeping with this type of reaction.

properties of the enzyme

First let us consider the enzyme and comment on the way in which it was discovered [8, 11]. Mixing the triphosphates of the four deoxynucleosides which commonly occur in DNA with an extract of thymus or of bone marrow or of *Escherichia coli* would not be expected to lead to the net synthesis of DNA. Instead, as might be expected, the destruction of DNA by the extracts of such cells and tissues was by far the predominant process, and one had to resort to more subtle devices to detect such a biosynthetic reaction. We used a C^{14}-labeled substrate of high specific radioactivity and incubated it with adenosine triphosphate and extracts of *Escherichia coli*, an organism which reproduces itself every 20 minutes. The first positive results represented the conversion of only a very small fraction of the acid-soluble substrate into an acid-insoluble fraction (50 or so counts out of a million added). While this represented only a few micromicromoles of reaction, it was something. Through this tiny crack we tried to drive a wedge, and the hammer was enzyme purification [12].

This has been and still is a major preoccupation. Our best preparations are several thousand-fold enriched with respect to protein over the crude extracts, but there are still contaminating quantities of one or more of the many varieties of nuclease and diesterase present in the *E. coli* cell. The occurrence of what appears to be a similar DNA-synthesizing system in animal cells as well as in other bacterial species has been observed [13]. We must wait for purification of the enzymes from these sources in order to make valid comparisons with the *E. coli* system.

The requirements for net synthesis of DNA with the purified *E. coli* enzyme [14] are shown in the equation in Figure 6. All four of the deoxynucleotides which form the adenine-thymine and guanine-cytosine couples must be present. The substrates must be the tri- and not the diphosphates, and only the deoxy sugar compounds are active. Deoxyribonucleic acid, which must be present, may be obtained from animal, plant, bacterial, or viral sources, and the best indications are that all these DNA samples serve equally well in DNA synthesis provided their molecular weight is high. The product, which I discuss below in further detail, accumulates until one of the substrates is exhausted and may be 20 or more times greater in amount than the DNA added, and thus is composed to the extent of 95 percent or more of the substrates added to the reaction mixture. Inorganic pyrophosphate is released in quantities equimolar to the deoxynucleotides converted to DNA.

Should one of these substrates be omitted, the extent of the reaction

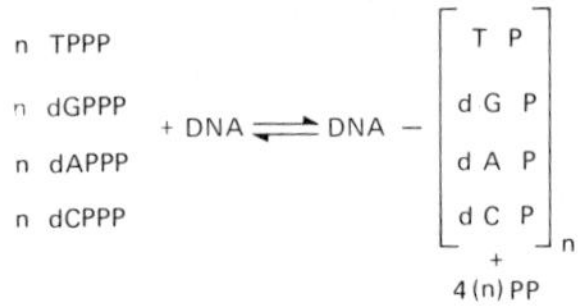

$$
\begin{array}{l}
n \ \text{TPPP} \\
n \ \text{dGPPP} \\
n \ \text{dAPPP} \\
n \ \text{dCPPP}
\end{array}
+ \text{DNA} \rightleftharpoons \text{DNA} -
\begin{bmatrix}
\text{T} & \text{P} \\
\text{dG} & \text{P} \\
\text{dA} & \text{P} \\
\text{dC} & \text{P}
\end{bmatrix}_n
$$
$$
+ \\
4(n)\,\text{PP}
$$

Figure 6. Equation for enzymatic synthesis of DNA

is diminished by a factor of more than 10^4, and special methods are then required to detect it. It turns out that when one of the deoxynucleotide substrates is lacking, an extremely small yet significant quantity of nucleotide is linked to the DNA primer. My co-workers and I have described this so-called "limited reaction" [15] and have shown that under these circumstances a few deoxynucleotides are added to the nucleoside ends of some of the DNA chains but that further synthesis is blocked for lack of the missing nucleotide. Current studies suggest that this limited reaction represents the repair of the shorter strand of a double helix in which the strands are of unequal length, and that the reaction is governed by the hydrogen-bonding of adenine to thymine and of guanine to cytosine.

When all four triphosphates are present, but when DNA is omitted, no reaction takes place at all. What is the basis for this requirement? Does the DNA function as a primer in the manner of glycogen, or does it function as a template in directing the synthesis of exact copies of itself? We have good reason to believe that it is the latter, and as the central and restricted theme of this article, I should like to emphasize that it is the capacity for base pairing by hydrogen-bonding between the pre-existing DNA and the nucleotides added as substrates that accounts for the requirement for DNA.

The enzyme we are studying is thus unique in our experience to date in that it takes directions from a template—it adds the particular purine or pyrimidine substrate which will form a hydrogen-bonded pair with a base on the template (Figure 7). There are five major lines of evidence that support this thesis.

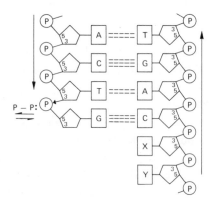

Figure 7. Mechanism for enzymatic DNA replication

physical properties of enzymatically synthesized DNA

The first line of evidence is derived from studies of the physical nature of the DNA produced by the enzyme. I might mention again that in these descriptions as in those of the chemical nature of DNA, discussed below, 90 to 95 percent of the DNA sample comes from the substrates used in the reaction. From collaborative studies with Howard K. Schachman, to whom we are greatly indebted, it can be said that the enzymatic product is indistinguishable from high-molecular-weight, double-stranded DNA isolated from natural sources [16]. It has sedimentation coefficients in the neighborhood of 25 and reduced viscosities of 40 deciliters per gram, and on the basis of these measurements we believe it to be a long, stiff rod with a molecular weight of about 6 million. When the DNA is heated, the rod collapses and the molecule becomes a compact, randomly coiled structure; it may be inferred that the hydrogen bonds holding the strands together have melted, and this is borne out by characteristic changes in the viscometric and optical properties of the molecule. Similar results are found upon cleavage of the molecule by pancreatic deoxyribonuclease. In all these respects the enzymatically synthesized DNA is indistinguishable from the material isolated from natural sources and may thus be presumed to have a hydrogen-bonded structure similar to that possessed by natural DNA.

Would one imagine that the collapsed, jumbled strands of heated DNA would serve as a primer for DNA synthesis? Very likely one would think not. Guided by everyday experience with a jumbled strand of twine, one might regard this as a hopeless template for replication. It turns out that the collapsed DNA is an excellent primer and that the nonviscous, randomly coiled, single-stranded DNA leads to the synthesis of highly viscous, double-stranded DNA [17]. Sinsheimer has isolated from the tiny ΦX174 virus a DNA which appears to be single-stranded [18]. Like heated DNA, it has proved to be an excellent primer [17] and a useful material in current studies [19] for demonstrating in density-gradient sedimentations its progressive conversion to a double-stranded condition during the course of enzymatic synthesis.

While a detailed discussion of the physical aspects of replication is not feasible in this article, it should be mentioned that the DNA in the single-stranded condition is not only a suitable primer but is the only active form when the most purified enzyme preparations are used. With such preparations of *E. coli*, the native, double-stranded DNA is inert unless it is heated or pretreated very slightly with deoxyribonuclease. Bollum has made similar observations with the enzyme that he has purified from calf thymus [20].

substitution of analogs

The second line of evidence is derived from studies of the activity of the substrates when substitutions are made in the purine and pyrimidine bases. From the many interesting reports on the incorporation of bromouracil [21], azaguanine [22], and other analogs into bacterial and viral DNA, it might be surmised that some latitude in the structure of the bases can be tolerated provided there is no interference with their hydrogen bondings. When experiments were carried out with deoxyuridine triphosphate or 5-bromodeoxyuridine triphosphate, it was found that these compounds supported DNA synthesis when used in place of thymidine triphosphate but not when substituted for the triphosphates of deoxyadenosine, deoxyguanosine, or deoxycytidine. As already described [23], 5-methyl- and 5-bromocytosine specifically replaced cytosine; hypoxanthine substituted only for guanine; and, as just mentioned, uracil and 5-bromouracil specifically replaced thymine. These findings are best interpreted on the basis of hydrogen bonding of the adenine-thymine and guanine-cytosine type.

Along these lines it is relevant to mention the existence of a naturally occurring "analog" of cytosine, hydroxymethyl cytosine (HMC), which is found in place of cytosine in the DNA of the *E. coli* bacteriophages of the T-even series [24]. In this case the DNA contains equivalent amounts of HMC and guanine and, as usual, equivalent amounts of adenine and thymine. Of additional interest is the fact that the DNA's of T2, T4, and T6 bacteriophages contain glucose linked to the hydroxymethyl groups of the HMC in characteristic ratios [25, 26], although it is clear that in T2 and T6 some of the HMC groups contain no glucose [26].

These characteristics have posed two problems regarding the synthesis of these DNA's which might appear to be incompatible with the simple base-pairing hypothesis. First, what mechanism is there for preventing the inclusion of cytosine in a cell which under normal conditions has deoxycytidine triphosphate and incorporates it into its DNA? Second, how does one conceive of the origin of the constant ratios of glucose to HMC in DNA if the incorporation occurs via glucosylated and nonglucosylated HMC nucleotides? Our recent experiments have shown that the polymerase reaction in the virus-infected cell is governed by the usual hydrogen-bonding restrictions but with the auxiliary action of several new enzymes developed specifically in response to infection with a given virus [27, 28]. Among the new enzymes is one which splits deoxycytidine triphosphate and thus removes it from the sites of polymerase action [28]. Another is a type of glucosylating enzyme that transfers glucose from uridine diphosphate glucose directly and specifically to certain HMC residues in the DNA [28].

chemical composition

The third line of evidence is supplied by an analysis of the purine and pyrimidine base composition of the enzymatically synthesized DNA.

We may ask two questions. First, will the product have the equivalence of adenine to thymine and of guanine to cytosine that characterizes natural DNA? Second, will the composition of the natural DNA used as primer influence and determine the composition of the product? In Table 1 are the results which answer these two questions [29]. The experiments are identical except that in each case a different DNA primer was used: *Mycobacterium phlei, Escherichia coli,* calf thymus, and phage T2 DNA, respectively.

Table 1.
Chemical Composition of Enzymatically
Synthesized DNA, Synthesized with Different Primers.
A, Adenine; *T*, Thymine; *G*, Guanine; *C*, Cytosine

DNA	*A*	*T*	*G*	*C*	$\dfrac{A+G}{T+C}$	$\dfrac{A+T}{G+C}$
Mycobacterium phlei						
Primer	0.65	0.66	1.35	1.34	1.01	0.49
Product	0.66	0.65	1.34	1.37	0.99	0.48
Escherichia coli						
Primer	1.00	0.97	0.98	1.05	0.98	0.97
Product	1.04	1.00	0.97	0.98	1.01	1.02
Calf thymus						
Primer	1.14	1.05	0.90	0.85	1.05	1.25
Product	1.12	1.08	0.85	0.85	1.02	1.29
Bacteriophage T2						
Primer	1.31	1.32	0.67	0.70	0.98	1.92
Product	1.33	1.29	0.69	0.70	1.02	1.90
A-T copolymer	1.99	1.93	<0.05	<0.05	1.03	40

In answer to the first question, it is clear that in the enzymatically synthesized DNA, adenine equals thymine and guanine equals cytosine, so the purine content is in every case identical to the pyrimidine. In answer to the second question, it is again apparent that the characteristic ratio of adenine-thymine pairs to guanine-cytosine pairs of a given DNA primer is imposed rather faithfully on the product that is synthesized. Whether the net DNA increase is only 1 percent, as measured with isotopic tracers, or 1000 percent, the results are the same.

It can be said further that it has not been possible to distort these base ratios by using widely differing molar concentrations of substrates or by any other means. In the last line of Table 1 is a rather novel

"DNA" which is synthesized under conditions that I will not describe here [17, 30]. Suffice it to say that after very long lag periods, a copolymer of deoxyadenylate and thymidylate (A-T) develops which has the physical size and properties of natural DNA and in which the adenine and thymine are in a perfectly alternating sequence. When this rare form of DNA-like polymer is used as a primer, new A-T polymer synthesis starts immediately, and even though all four triphosphates are present, no trace of guanine or cytosine can be detected in the product. The conclusion thus seems inescapable that the base composition is replicated in the enzymatic synthesis and that hydrogen-bonding of adenine to thymine and of guanine to cytosine is the guiding mechanism.

enzymatic replication of nucleotide sequences

The fourth line of evidence which I should like to cite is drawn from current studies of base sequences in DNA and their replication. As I have suggested already, we believe that DNA is the genetic code; the four kinds of nucleotides make up a four-letter alphabet, and their sequence spells out the message. At present we do not know the sequence; what Sanger has done for peptide sequence in protein remains to be done for nucleic acids. The problem is more difficult, but not insoluble.

Our present attempts at determining the nucleotide sequences [31] will be described in detail elsewhere, and I will only summarize them here. Deoxyribonucleic acid is enzymatically synthesized, with phosphorus-32 as label, in one of the deoxynucleoside triphosphates; the other three substrates are unlabeled. This radioactive phosphorus, attached to the 5-carbon of the deoxyribose, now becomes the bridge between that substrate molecule and the nucleotide at the growing end of the chain with which it has reacted (Figure 8). At the end of the synthetic reaction (after some 10^{16} diester bonds have been formed), the DNA is isolated and digested enzymatically to yield the 3'-deoxynucleotides quantitatively. It is apparent (Figure 8) that the phosphorus atom formerly attached to the 5-carbon of the deoxynucleoside triphosphate substrate is now attached to the 3-carbon of the nucleotide with which it reacted during the course of synthesis of the DNA chains. The phosphorus-32 content of each of the 3'-deoxynucelotides, isolated by paper electrophoresis, is a measure of the relative frequency with which a particular substrate reacted with each of the four available nucleotides in the course of synthesis of the DNA chains. This procedure, when carried out four times with a different labeled substrate in each case, yields the relative frequencies of all the 16 possible kinds of dinucleotide (nearest neighbor) sequences.

Such studies have, to date, been carried out with **DNA** primer samples from six different natural sources. The conclusions are as follows: (i) All **16** possible dinucleotide sequences are found in each

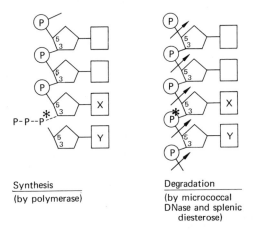

Synthesis
(by polymerase)

Degradation
(by micrococcal
DNase and splenic
diesterose)

Figure 8. Method for determining sequences in DNA

case; (ii) the pattern of relative frequencies of the sequences is unique and reproducible in each case and is not predicted from the base composition of the **DNA**; (iii) enzymatic replication involves base pairing of adenine to thymine and of guanine to cytosine; and, most significantly (iv) the frequencies also indicate clearly that the enzymatic replication produces two strands of opposite direction, as predicted by the Watson and Crick model.

These studies and anticipated extensions of them should yield the dinucleotide frequencies of any **DNA** sample which can serve as an effective primer for enzymatic replication and thus provide some clues for deciphering the **DNA** code. Unfortunately, this method does not provide information about trinucleotide frequencies, but we are hopeful that, with the improvement of enzymatic tools for analysis and chromatographic techniques for isolation, some start can be made in this direction.

requirement for four triphosphates and *DNA* for *DNA* synthesis

Returning to the earlier-stated requirement for all four deoxynucleo-side triphosphates and DNA for DNA synthesis, we can now regard and understand this requirement as another and final line of evidence for hydrogen bonding. Without added DNA there is no template for hydrogen bonding, and without all four triphosphates, synthesis stops early and abruptly for lack of a hydrogen-bonding mate for one of the bases in the template.

summary

I have sketched the enzymatic approaches to the problem of DNA replication and the properties of the DNA-synthesizing enzyme purified from *Escherichia coli*. The unifying and basic generalization about the action of this enzyme is that it catalyzes the synthesis of a new DNA chain in response to directions from a DNA template; these directions are dictated by the hydrogen-bonding relationship of adenine to thymine and of guanine to cytosine. The experimental basis for this conclusion is derived from the observations of: (i) the double-stranded character of the enzymatically synthesized DNA and its origin from a single-stranded molecule, (ii) the pattern of substitution of analogs for the naturally occurring bases, (iii) the replication of the chemical composition, (iv) the replication of the nucleotide (nearest neighbor) sequences and the antiparallel direction of the strands, and (v) the requirement for all four deoxynucleoside triphosphates (adenine, thymine, guanine, and cytosine) and for DNA for DNA synthesis [32].

references and notes

1. O. T. Avery, C. M. MacLeod, M. McCarty, *J. Exptl. Med. 79,* 137 (1944); R. D. Hotchkiss, in *The Chemical Basis of Heredity,* W. D. McElroy and B. Glass, Eds. (Johns Hopkins Press, Baltimore, 1957), p. 321.

2. A. D. Hershey, *Cold Spring Harbor Symposia Quant. Biol. 18,* 135 (1953).

3. G. W. Beadle, in *The Chemical Basis of Heredity,* W. D. McElroy and B. Glass, Eds. (Johns Hopkins Press, Baltimore, 1957), p. 3.

4. E. Chargaff, in *Nucleic Acids,* E. Chargaff and J. N. Davidson, Eds. (Academic Press, New York, 1955), vol. 1, pp. 307–371.

5. J. D. Watson and F. H. C. Crick, *Nature 171,* 737 (1953); *Cold Spring Harbor Symposia Quant. Biol. 18,* 123 (1953).

6. M. H. F. Wilkins, *Biochem. Soc. Symposia* (Cambridge, England) *14,* 13 (1957).

7. M. Feughelman, R. Langridge, W. E. Seeds, A. R. Stokes, H. R. Wilson, C. W. Hooper, M. H. F. Wilkins, R. K. Barclay, L. D. Hamilton, *Nature 175,* 834 (1955).

8. A. Kornberg, in *The Chemical Basis of Heredity,* W. D. McElroy and B. Glass, Eds. (Johns Hopkins Press, Baltimore, 1957), p. 579; *Rev. Modern Phys. 31,* 200 (1959).

9. A. Kornberg, in *Phosphorus Metabolism,* W. D. McElroy and B. Glass, Eds. (Johns Hopkins Press, Baltimore 1951), p. 392; *Advances in Enzymol. 18,* 191 (1957).

10. D. E. Koshland, Jr., in *The Mechanism of Enyzme Action,* W. D. McElroy and B. Glass, Eds. (Johns Hopkins Press, Baltimore, 1954), p. 608.

11. A. Kornberg, I. R. Lehman, E. S. Simms, *Federation Proc. 15,* 291 (1956); A. Kornberg, *Harvey Lecture Ser. 53,* 83 (1957–58).

12. I. R. Lehman, M. J. Bessman, E. S. Simms, A. Kornberg, *J. Biol. Chem. 233,* 163 (1958).

13. F. J. Bollum and V. R. Potter, *J. Am. Chem. Soc. 79,* 3603 (1957); C. G. Harford and A. Kornberg, *Federation Proc. 17,* 515 (1958); F. J. Bollum, *ibid. 17,* 193 (1958); ———, *ibid. 18,* 194 (1959).

14. M. J. Bessman, I. R. Lehman, E. S. Simms, A. Kornberg, *J. Biol. Chem. 233,* 171 (1958).

15. J. Adler, I. R. Lehman, M. J. Bessman, E. S. Simms, A. Kornberg, *Proc. Natl. Acad. Sci. U.S. 44,* 641 (1958).

16. H. K. Schachman, I. R. Lehman, M. J. Bessman, J. Adler, E. S. Simms, A. Kornberg, *Federation Proc. 17,* 304 (1958).

17. I. R. Lehman, *Ann. N.Y. Acad. Sci. 81,* 745 (1959).

18. R. L. Sinsheimer, *J. Mol. Biol. 1,* 43 (1959).

19. I. R. Lehman, R. L. Sinsheimer, A. Kornberg, unpublished observations.

20. F. J. Bollum, *J. Biol. Chem. 234,* 2733 (1959).

21. F. Weygand, A. Wacker, H. Dellweg, *Z. Naturforsch. 7b,* 19 (1952); D. B. Dunn and J. D. Smith, *Nature 174,* 305 (1954); S. Zamenhof and G. Griboff, *ibid. 174,* 306 (1954).

22. M. R. Heinrich, V. C. Dewey, R. E. Parks, Jr., G. W. Kidder, *J. Biol. Chem. 197,* 199 (1952).

23. M. J. Bessman, I. R. Lehman, J. Adler, S. B. Zimmerman, E. S. Simms, A. Kornberg, *Proc. Natl. Acad. Sci. U.S. 44,* 633 (1958).

24. G. R. Wyatt and S. S. Cohen, *Biochem. J. 55,* 774 (1953).

25. R. L. Sinsheimer, *Science 120,* 551 (1954); E. Volkin, *J. Am. Chem. Soc. 76,* 5892 (1954); G. Streisinger and J. Weigle, *Proc. Natl. Acad. Sci. U.S. 42,* 504 (1956).

26. R. L. Sinsheimer, *Proc. Natl. Acad. Sci. U.S. 42,* 502 (1956); M. A. Jesaitis, *J. Exptl. Med. 106,* 233 (1957); *Federation Proc. 17,* 250 (1958).

27. J. G. Flaks and S. S. Cohen, *J. Biol. Chem. 234,* 1501 (1959); J. G. Flaks, J. Lichtenstein, S. S. Cohen, *ibid. 234,* 1507 (1959).

28. A. Kornberg, S. B. Zimmerman, S. R. Kornberg, J. Josse, *Proc. Natl. Acad. Sci. U.S. 45,* 772 (1959).

29. I. R. Lehman, S. B. Zimmerman, J. Adler, M. J. Bessman, E. S. Simms, A. Kornberg, *ibid. 44*, 1191 (1958).

30. C. M. Radding, J. Adler, H. K. Schachman, *Federation Proc. 19*, 307 (1960).

31. J. Josse and A. Kornberg, *ibid. 19,* 305 (1960).

32. Any credit for the work cited here is shared by my colleagues in New York, Bethesda, St. Louis, and Stanford, and by the whole international community of chemists, geneticists, and physiologists, which is truly responsible for the progress in nucleic acid biochemistry.

2

Prevention of People

The world is much with us.
—OLD SAYING

Homo sapiens is among the most fertile of the higher animals. Whereas humans populating the world before the invention of agriculture 8000 years ago totaled only a few million, the population now has grown to a few billion and is generating babies at a terrifying rate.

The gloomy prospect of overpopulation was predicted in 1798 by the Reverend Thomas Robert Malthus,[1] the first professor of economics. Malthus contended that the struggle up the human ladder is a losing game in which the reproductive urge will ultimately outrun all possible sources of subsistence. In short, said Malthus, there are too many people. Malthus, from his vantage in fertile eighteenth-century England, not only saw with perceptive insight the world's future food problem but must have had as well a precognition of the insurmountable congestion, industrial pollution, and discouraging waste-disposal problems of modern life.

In Malthus' day, the population of the British Isles was reckoned to be about six million individuals. At that time, the population of the entire planet must have been less than a billion, as against 1965's lusty population of three and one-third billion. The population curve follows what is called an *exponential increase*; that is, as the population rises, the rate of increase is accelerated. Whereas the population of stone-age

---

[1] *"An Essay on the Principle of Population as It Affects the Future Improvement of Society."*

man is said to have doubled every 30,000 years, the population at the current rate of increase is calculated to double every 30 or 40 years. By the year 2000, projection gives a world population of six to seven billion,[2] and further extrapolation predicts better than 50 billion humans on earth by the year 2100.

The chilling specter of an unmanageable, insupportable, immovable, and psychologically unrecognizable mass of humanity within two or three generations poses problems at least as great as the awful prospect of unleashed nuclear energy. Clearly, until or unless wise men can devise ways to relieve congestion, provide transportation, dispose of waste products, and prevent air, water, and soil pollution while feeding several billion more people, human fertility will have to be effectively, cheaply, and, above all, promptly curbed.

Sperm control and germ control share honors for the most spectacular achievements in biological science, even though they are mutually defeating. Actually, birth control is not a modern invention. Onan, as related in Genesis, was ordered by the patriarch Judah to marry the widow of Onan's slain brother in order to perpetuate the family. But Onan balked at the responsibility and resentfully prevented conception by the practice of *coitus interruptus*, which made Jehovah so angry that he killed Onan also. The ancient Romans knew that the scrotum is an air-conditioning device and that viable sperm can be produced by human male gonads only when cooled below body temperature. They effectively employed hot compresses. Preliterate people in the past as well as in some parts of the world today did and do practice infanticide, particularly in times of famine or other hardship. The ancient Spartans, soldiers to the core, were equally pragmatic in disposing of deficient newborn males.

Historically, wars, often combined with famine and pestilence, have frequently been a significant check on population size. Warfare as a population control has been highly effective as recently as World War I, when the Axis and Allied invasions, air raids, and blockades resulted in the deaths from starvation and disease of millions of people, particularly children and the elderly. Hitler's genocidal policy of "Aryan purification" might abstractly be considered another approach to effective population control, but he set out to destroy some of the best genetic material in Europe, and, even if he had been a better biologist,

---

[2] The World Food Problem, A Report of the President's Science Advisory Committee, *Vol. I (Washington, D.C.: U.S. Government Printing Office, 1967), 1–127.*

his methods of sterilization and mass murder are abhorrent to civilized people.

Mechanical birth control devices have been popular in recent times, but their various disadvantages made "the pill" a dream that stimulated imaginative researchers into a frenzied quest for the universal contraceptive. Julian Huxley, writing in 1955,[3] predicted that a massive research effort on the scale of the atom bomb project would provide the answer within 10 years or, at most, a generation. He was nearly correct, for, while we have the pill, the chemicals that are used are expensive and too hazardous to use except under medical supervision. However, the concept and the practice are new, and there is no reason to doubt that present and future research will bring to light a plethora of substances, some of which will almost certainly fulfill the urgent world-wide need for a cheap, safe, and effective chemical.

---

[3] *Julian Huxley, "World Population,"* Scientific American *(March 1956), reprinted in* Three Essays on Population *(New York: The New American Library of World Literature, Inc., 1960), 61–81.*

World Population Growth: An International Dilemma

Harold F. Dorn

During all but the most recent years of the centuries of his existence man must have lived, reproduced, and died as other animals do. His increase in number was governed by the three great regulators of the increase of all species of plants and animals—predators, disease, and starvation—or, in terms more applicable to human populations—war, pestilence, and famine. One of the most significant developments for the future of mankind during the first half of the 20th century has been his increasing ability to control pestilence and famine. Although he has not freed himself entirely from the force of these two regulators of population increase, he has gained sufficient control of them so that they no longer effectively govern his increase in number.

Simultaneously he has developed methods of increasing the effectiveness of war as a regulator of population increase, to the extent that he almost certainly could quickly wipe out a large proportion, if not all, of the human race. At the same time he has learned how to separate sexual gratification from reproduction by means of contraception and telegenesis (that is, reproduction by artificial insemination, particularly with spermatozoa preserved for relatively long periods of time), so that he can regulate population increase by voluntary control of fertility. Truly it can be said that man has the knowledge and the power to direct, at least in part, the course of his evolution.

This newly gained knowledge and power has not freed man from the inexorable effect of the biological laws that govern all living organisms.

The evolutionary process has endowed most species with a reproductive potential that, unchecked, would overpopulate the entire globe within a few generations. It has been estimated that the tapeworm, *Taenia*, may lay 120,000 eggs per day; an adult cod can lay as many as 4 million eggs per year; a frog may produce 10,000 eggs per spawning. Human ovaries are thought to contain approximately 200,000 ova at puberty, while a single ejaculation of human semen may contain 200 million spermatozoa.

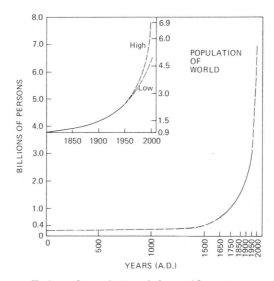

Figure 1. Estimated population of the world, A.D. 1 to A.D. 2000

This excessive reproductive potential is kept in check for species other than man by interspecies competition in the struggle for existence, by disease, and by limitation of the available food supply. The fact that man has learned how to control, to a large extent, the operation of these biological checks upon unrestrained increase in number has not freed him from the necessity of substituting for them less harsh but equally effective checks. The demonstration of his ability to do this cannot be long delayed.

Only fragmentary data are available to indicate the past rate of growth of the population of the world. Even today, the number of inhabitants is known only approximately. Regular censuses of populations did not exist prior to 1800, although registers were maintained for small population groups prior to that time. As late as a century ago, around 1860, only about one-fifth of the estimated population of the world was covered by a census enumeration once in a 10-year period [1]. The commonly accepted estimates of the population of the world prior to 1800 are only informed guesses. Nevertheless, it is possible to piece together a consistent series of estimates of the world's population during the past two centuries, supplemented by a few rough guesses of the number of persons alive at selected earlier periods. The most generally accepted estimates are presented in Figure 1.

These reveal a spectacular spurt during recent decades in the increase of the world's population that must be unparalleled during the preceding millennia of human existence. Furthermore, the rate of increase shows no sign of diminishing (Table 1). The period of time

Table 1.
The Number of Years Required to Double the Population of the World (from United Nations Data [9, 14])

Year (A.D.)	Population (Billions)	Number of Years to Double
1	0.25 (?)	1650 (?)
1650	0.50	200
1850	1.1	80
1930	2.0	45
1975	4.0	35
2010	8.0[a]	?

[a] A projection of United Nations estimates.

required for the population of the world to double has sharply decreased during the past three centuries and now is about 35 years.

Only a very rough approximation can be made of the length of time required for the population of the world to reach one-quarter of a billion persons, the estimated number at the beginning of the Christian era. The present subgroups of *Homo sapiens* may have existed for as long as 100,000 years. The exact date is not necessary, since for present purposes the evidence is sufficient to indicate that probably 50,000 to 100,000 years were required for *Homo sapiens* to increase in number until he reached a global total of one-quarter of a billion persons. This number was reached approximately 2000 years ago.

By 1620, the year the Pilgrims landed on Plymouth Rock, the population of the world had doubled in number. Two hundred years later, shortly before the Civil War, another 500 million persons had

been added. Since that time, additional half billions of persons have
been added during increasingly shorter intervals of time. The sixth half
billion, just added, required slightly less than 11 years, as compared to
200 years for the second half billion. The present rate of growth
implies that only 6 to 7 years will be required to add the eighth half
billion to the world's population. The change in rate of growth just
described has taken place since the first settlers came to New
England.

implications

The accelerating rate of increase in the growth of the population of the
world has come about so unobtrusively that most persons are unaware
of its implications. There is a small group who are so aroused by this
indifference that, like modern Paul Reveres, they attempt to awaken the
public with cries of "the population bomb!" or "the population explosion!"

These persons are called alarmists by those who counter with the
assertion that similar warnings, such as "standing-room only" and
"mankind at the crossroads," have been issued periodically since Malthus wrote his essay on population, about 200 years ago. Nevertheless,
says this group, the level of living and the health of the average person
has continued to improve, and there is no reason to believe that advances in technology will not be able to make possible a slowly rising
level of living for an increasing world population for the indefinite
future. Furthermore, the rate of population increase almost certainly
will slow down as the standard of education and living rises and as
urbanization increases.

A third group of persons has attempted to estimate the maximum
population that could be supported by the world's physical resources
provided existing technological knowledge is fully utilized. Many of
these calculations have been based on estimates of the quantity of food
that could be produced and a hypothetical average daily calorie consumption per person.

As might be expected, the range of the various estimates of the
maximum world population that could be supported without a lowering
of the present level of living is very wide. One of the lowest, 2.8 billion,
made by Pearson and Harper in 1945 on the assumption of an Asiatic
standard of consumption, already has been surpassed [2]. Several
others, ranging from 5 to 7 billion, almost certainly will be exceeded by

the end of this century. Perhaps the most carefully prepared estimate as well as the largest—that of 50 billions, prepared by Harrison Brown —would be reached in about 150 years if the present rate of growth should continue [3].

I believe it is worth while to prepare estimates of the maximum population that can be supported and to revise these as new information becomes available, even though most of the estimates made in the past already have been, or soon will be, demonstrated to be incorrect (in most instances too small), since this constitutes a rational effort to comprehend the implications of the increase in population. At the same time it should be recognized that estimates of the world's carrying capacity made in this manner are rather unrealistic and are primarily useful only as very general guidelines.

In the first place, these calculations have assumed that the earth's resources and skills are a single reservoir available to all. In reality this is untrue. The U.S. government attempts to restrict production of certain agricultural crops by paying farmers not to grow them. Simultaneously, in Asia and Africa, large numbers of persons are inadequately fed and poorly clothed. Except in a very general sense there is no *world* population problem; there are population problems varying in nature and degree among the several nations of the world. No single solution is applicable to all.

Since the world is not a single political unity, the increases in production actually achieved during any period of time tend to be considerably less than those theoretically possible. Knowledge, technical skill, and capital are concentrated in areas with the highest level of living, whereas the most rapid increase in population is taking place in areas where such skills and capital are relatively scarce or practically nonexistent.

Just as the world is not a single unit from the point of view of needs and the availability of resources, skills and knowledge to meet these needs, so it also is not a single unit with respect to population increase. Due to political barriers that now exist throughout the entire world, overpopulation, however defined, will become a serious problem in specific countries long before it would be a world problem if there were no barriers to population redistribution. I shall return to this point later, after discussing briefly existing forecasts or projections of the total population of the world.

Most demographers believe that, under present conditions, the future population of areas such as countries or continents, or even of the entire world, cannot be predicted for more than a few decades with even a moderate degree of certainty. This represents a marked change from the view held by many only 30 years ago.

In 1930 a prominent demographer wrote, "The population of the United States ten, twenty, even fifty years hence, can be predicted with a greater degree of assurance than any other economic or social fact, provided the immigration laws are unchanged" [4]. Nineteen years later, a well-known economist replied that "it is disheartening to have to assert that the best population forecasts deserve little credence even for 5 years ahead, and none at all for 20–50 years ahead" [5].

Although both of these statements represent rather extreme views, they do indicate the change that has taken place during the past two decades in the attitude toward the reliability of population forecasts. Some of the reasons for this have been discussed in detail elsewhere and will not be repeated here [6].

It will be sufficient to point out that knowledge of methods of voluntarily controlling fertility now is so widespread, especially among persons of European ancestry, that sharp changes in the spacing, as well as in the number, of children born during the reproductive period may occur in a relatively short period of time. Furthermore, the birth rate may increase as well as decrease.

forecasting population growth

The two principal methods that have been used in recent years to make population forecasts are (i) the extrapolation of mathematical curves fitted to the past trend of population increase and (ii) the projection of the population by the "component" or "analytical" method, based on specific hypotheses concerning the future trend in fertility, mortality, and migration.

The most frequently used mathematical function has been the logistic curve which was originally suggested by Verhulst in 1838 but which remained unnoticed until it was rediscovered by Pearl and Reed about 40 years ago [7]. At first it was thought by some demographers that the logistic curve represented a rational law of population change. However, it has proved to be as unreliable as other methods of preparing population forecasts and is no longer regarded as having any unique value for estimating future population trends.

A recent illustration of the use of mathematical functions to project the future world population is the forecast prepared by von Foerster,

Mora, and Amiot [8]. In view of the comments that subsequently were published in this journal, an extensive discussion of this article does not seem to be required. It will be sufficient to point out that this forecast probably will set a record, for the entire class of forecasts prepared by the use of mathematical functions, for the short length of time required to demonstrate its unreliability.

The method of projecting or forecasting population growth most frequently used by demographers, whenever the necessary data are available, is the "component" or "analytical" method. Separate estimates are prepared of the future trend of fertility, mortality, and migration. From the total population as distributed by age and sex on a specified date, the future population that would result from the hypothetical combination of fertility, mortality, and migration is computed. Usually, several estimates of the future population are prepared in order to include what the authors believe to be the most likely range of values.

Such estimates generally are claimed by their authors to be not forecasts of the most probable future population but merely indications of the population that would result from the hypothetical assumptions concerning the future trend in fertility, mortality, and migration. However, the projections of fertility, mortality, and migration usually are chosen to include what the authors believe will be the range of likely possibilities. This objective is achieved by making "high," "medium," and "low" assumptions concerning the future trend in population growth. Following the practice of most of the authors of such estimates, I shall refer to these numbers as population projections.

The most authoritative projections of the population of the world are those made by the United Nations [9, 10] (Table 2). Even though the most recent of these projections were published in 1958, only 3 years ago, it now seems likely that the population of the world will exceed the high projection before the year 2000. By the end of 1961 the world's population at least equaled the high projection for that date.

Although the United Nations' projections appear to be too conservative in that even the highest will be an underestimate of the population only 40 years from now, some of the numerical increases in population implied by these projections will create problems that may be beyond the ability of the nations involved to solve. For example, the estimated increase in the population of Asia from A.D. 1950 to 2000 will be roughly equal to the population of the entire world in 1958! The population of Latin America 40 years hence may very likely be four times that in 1950. The absolute increase in population in Latin America during the last half of the century may equal the total increase in the population of *Homo sapiens* during all the millennia from his origin until about 1650, when the first colonists were settling New England.

Increases in population of this magnitude stagger the imagination. Present trends indicate that they may be succeeded by even larger increases during comparable periods of time. The increase in the rate of growth of the world's population, shown by the data in Table 1, is still

Table 2.

Estimated Population of the World for A.D. 1900, 1950, 1975, and 2000 (from United Nations Data [9], Rounded to Three Significant Digits)

Area	Estimated Population (Millions)		Projected Future Population (Millions)			
			Low Assumptions		High Assumptions	
	1900	1950	1975	2000	1975	2000
World	1550	2500	3590	4880	3860	6900
Africa	120	199	295	420	331	663
North America	81	168	232	274	240	326
Latin America	63	163	282	445	304	651
Asia	857	1380	2040	2890	2210	4250
Europe including U.S.S.R.	423	574	724	824	751	987
Oceania	6	13	20	27	21	30

continuing. This rate is now estimated to be about 2 percent per year, sufficient to double the world's population every 35 years. It requires only very simple arithmetic to show that a continuation of this rate of growth for even 10 or 15 decades would result in an increase in population that would make the globe resemble an anthill.

But as was pointed out above, the world is not a single unit economically, politically, or demographically. Long before the population of the entire world reaches a size that could not be supported at current levels of living, the increase in population in specific nations and regions will give rise to problems that will affect the health and welfare of the rest of the world. The events of the past few years have graphically demonstrated the rapidity with which the political and economic problems of even a small and weak nation can directly affect the welfare of the largest and most powerful nations. Rather than speculate about the maximum population the world can support and the length of time before this number will be reached, it will be more instructive to examine the demographic changes that are taking place in different regions of the world and to comment briefly on their implications.

decline in mortality

The major cause of the recent spurt in population increase is a world-wide decline in mortality. Although the birth rate increased in some countries—for example, the United States—during and after World War II, such increases have not been sufficiently widespread to account for more than a small part of the increase in the total population of the world. Moreover, the increase in population prior to World War II occurred in spite of a widespread decline in the birth rate among persons of European origin.

Accurate statistics do not exist, but the best available estimates suggest that the expectation of life at birth in Greece, Rome, Egypt, and the Eastern Mediterranean region probably did not exceed 30 years at the beginning of the Christian era. By 1900 it had increased to about 40 to 50 years in North America and in most countries of northwestern Europe. At present, it has reached 68 to 70 years in many of these countries.

By 1940, only a small minority of the world's population had achieved an expectation of life at birth comparable to that of the population of North America and northwest Europe. Most of the population of the world had an expectation of life no greater than that which prevailed in western Europe during the Middle Ages. Within the past two edcades, the possibility of achieving a 20th-century death rate has been opened to these masses of the world's population. An indication of the result can be seen from the data in Figure 2.

In 1940, the death rate in Mexico was similar to that in England and Wales nearly 100 years earlier. It decreased as much during the following decade as did the death rate in England and Wales during the 50-year period from 1850 to 1900.

In 1946–47 the death rate of the Moslem population of Algeria was higher than that of the population of Sweden in the period 1771–80, the earliest date for which reliable mortality statistics are available for an entire nation. During the following 8 years, the drop in the death rate in Algeria considerably exceeded that in Sweden during the century from 1771 to 1871 [11].

The precipitous decline in mortality in Mexico and in the Moslem population of Algeria is illustrative of what has taken place during the past 15 years in Latin America, Africa, and Asia, where nearly three out of every four persons in the world now live. Throughout most of this area the birth rate has changed very little, remaining near a level

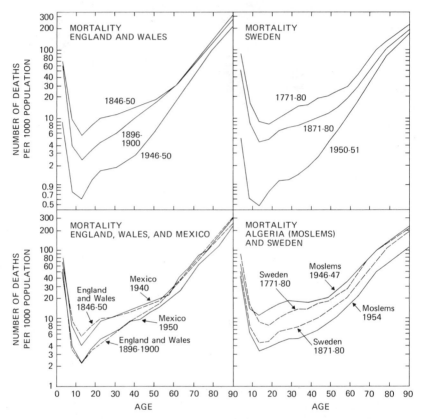

Figure 2. Age-specific death rates per 1000 per year for Sweden, England, Wales, and Mexico, and the Moslem population of Algeria for various time periods from 1771 to 1954

of 40 per 1000 per year, as can be seen from Figure 3, which shows the birth rate, death rate, and rate of natural increase for selected countries.

Even in countries such as Puerto Rico and Japan where the birth rate has declined substantially, the rate of natural increase has changed very little, owing to the sharp decrease in mortality. A more typical situation is represented by Singapore, Ceylon, Guatemala, and Chile, where the crude rate of natural increase has risen. There has been

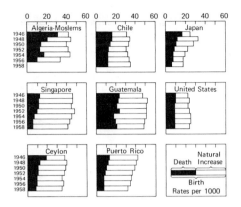

Figure 3. Birth rate, death rate, and rate of natural increase per 1000 for selected countries for the period 1946–58

a general tendency for death rates to decline universally and for high birth rates to remain high, with the result that those countries with the highest rates of increase are experiencing an acceleration in their rates of growth.

regional levels

The absolute level of fertility and mortality and the effect of changes in them upon the increase of population in different regions of the world can be only approximately indicated. The United Nations estimates that only about 33 percent of the deaths and 42 percent of the births that occur in the world are registered [12]. The percentage registered ranges from about 8 to 10 percent in tropical and southern Africa and Eastern Asia to 98 to 100 percent in North America and Europe. Nevertheless, the statistical staff of the United Nations, by a judicious combination of the available fragmentary data, has been able to prepare estimates of fertility and mortality for different regions of the world that are generally accepted as a reasonably correct representation of the actual but unknown figures. The estimated birth rate, death rate, and crude rate of natural increase (the birth rate minus the death rate) for eight regions of the world for the period 1954–58 are shown in Figure 4.

The birth rates of the countries of Africa, Asia, Middle America, and South America average nearly 40 per 1000 and probably are as high as they were 500 to 1000 years ago. In the rest of the world—Europe, North America, Oceania, and the Soviet Union—the birth rate is slightly more than half as high, or about 20 to 25 per 1000. The death rate for the former regions, although still definitely higher, is rapidly approaching that for people of European origin, with the result that the highest rates of natural increase are found in the regions with the highest birth rates. The most rapid rate of population growth at

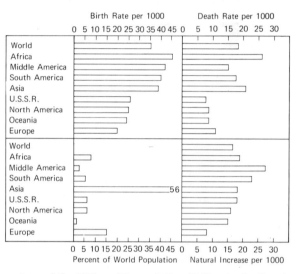

Figure 4. Percentage of the 1958 world population, birth rate, death rate, and rate of natural increase, per 1000, for the period 1954–58 for various regions of the world

present is taking place in Middle and South America, where the population will double about every 26 years if the present rate continues.

These regional differences in fertility and mortality are intensifying the existing imbalance of population with land area and natural resources. No matter how this imbalance is measured, that it exists is readily apparent. Two rather crude measures are presented in Figures 4 and 5, which show the percentage distribution of the world's population living in each region and the number of persons per square kilometer.

An important effect of the decline in mortality rates often is overlooked—namely, the increase in effective fertility. An estimated 97 out of every 100 newborn white females subject to the mortality rates pervailing in the United States during 1950 would survive to age 20, slightly past the beginning of the usual childbearing age, and 91 would survive to the end of the childbearing period (Figure 6). These esti-

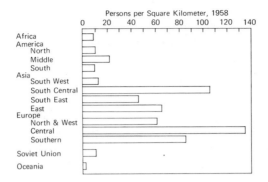

Figure 5. Number of persons per square kilometer in various regions of the world in 1958

mates are more than 3 and 11 times, respectively, the corresponding estimated proportions for white females that survived to these ages about four centuries ago.

In contrast, about 70 percent of the newborn females in Guatemala would survive to age 20, and only half would live to the end of the childbearing period if subject to the death rates prevailing in that country in 1950. If the death rate in Guatemala should fall to the level of that in the United States in 1950—a realistic possibility—the number of newborn females who would survive to the beginning of the childbearing period would increase by 36 percent; the number surviving to the end of the childbearing period would increase by 85 percent. A corresponding decrease in the birth rate would be required to prevent this increase in survivorship from resulting in a rapid acceleration in the existing rate of population growth, which already is excessive. In

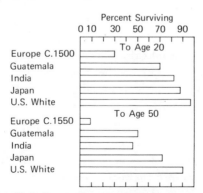

Figure 6. Percentage of newborn females who would survive to the end of the reproductive period according to mortality rates in Europe around A.D. 1500 and in selected countries around 1950

other words, this decrease in the death rate would require a decrease in the birth rate of more than 40 percent merely to maintain the status quo.

As can be seen from Figure 3, the birth rate in countries with high fertility has shown little or no tendency to decrease in recent years. Japan is the exception. There, the birth rate dropped by 46 percent from 1948 to 1958—an amount more than enough to counterbalance the decrease in the death rate, with the result that there was a decrease in the absolute number of births. As yet there is very little evidence that

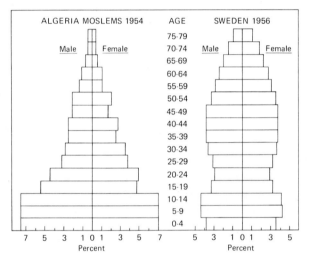

Figure 7. Percentage distribution by age of the population of Sweden in 1956 and the Moslem population of Algeria in 1954

other countries with a correspondingly high birth rate are likely to duplicate this in the near future.

Another effect of a rapid rate of natural increase is demonstrated by Figure 7. About 43 percent of the Moslem population of Algeria is under 15 years of age; the corresponding percentage in Sweden is 24, or slightly more than half this number. Percentages in the neighborhood of 40 percent are characteristic of the populations of the countries of Africa, Latin America, and Asia.

This high proportion of young people constitutes a huge fertility potential for 30 years into the future that can be counterbalanced only by a sharp decline in the birth rate, gives rise to serious educational problems, and causes a heavy drain on the capital formation that is necessary to improve the level of living of the entire population. A graphic illustration of this may be found in the recently published

5-year plan for India for 1961–66, which estimates that it will be necessary to provide educational facilities and teachers for 20 million additional children during this 5-year period [13].

historical pattern in western Europe

Some persons, although agreeing that the current rate of increase of the majority of the world's population cannot continue indefinitely without giving rise to grave political, social, and economic problems, point out that a similar situation existed in northwestern and central Europe during the 18th and 19th centuries. Increasing industrialization and urbanization, coupled with a rising standard of living, led to a decline in the birth rate, with a consequent drop in the rate of increase of the population. Why should not the rest of the world follow this pattern?

There is small likelihood that the two-thirds of the world's population which has not yet passed through the demographic revolution from high fertility and mortality rates to low fertility and mortality rates can repeat the history of wesern European peoples prior to the development of serious political and economic problems. A brief review of the circumstances that led to the virtual domination of the world at the end of the 19th century by persons of European origin will indicate some of the reasons for this opinion.

Around A.D. 1500 the population of Europe probably did not exceed 100 million persons (perhaps 15 to 20 percent of the population of the world) and occupied about 7 percent of the land area of the earth. Four hundred years later, around 1900, the descendants of this population numbered nearly 550 million, constituted about one-third of the world's population, and occupied or controlled five-sixths of the land area of the world. They had seized and peopled two great continents, North and South America, and one smaller continent, Australia, with its adjacent islands; had partially peopled and entirely controlled a third great continent, Africa; and dominated southern Asia and the neighboring islands.

The English-, French-, and Spanish-speaking peoples were the leaders in this expansion, with lesser roles being played by the Dutch and Portuguese. The Belgians and Germans participated only toward the end of this period of expansion. Among these, the English-speaking people held the dominant position at the end of the era, around 1900.

The number of English-speaking persons around 1500, at the start of this period of expansion, is not known, but it probably did not exceed 4 or 5 million. By 1900 these people numbered about 129 million and occupied and controlled one-third of the land area of the earth and, with the non-English-speaking inhabitants of this territory, made up some 30 percent of the population of the world.

This period was characterized by an unprecedented increase in population, a several-fold expansion of the land base for this population, and a hitherto undreamed of multiplication of capital in the form of precious metals, goods, and commodities. Most important of all, the augmentation in capital and usable land took place more rapidly than the growth in population.

A situation equally favorable for a rapid improvement in the level of living associated with a sharp increase in population does not appear likely to arise for the people who now inhabit Latin America, Africa, and Asia. The last great frontier of the world has been closed. Although there are many thinly populated areas in the world, their existence is testimony to the fact that, until now, these have been regarded as undesirable living places. The expansion of population to the remaining open areas would require large expenditures of capital for irrigation, drainage, transportation facilities, control of insects and parasites, and other purposes—capital that the rapidly increasing populations which will need these areas do not possess.

In addition, this land is not freely available for settlement. The entire land surface of the world is crisscrossed by national boundaries. International migration now is controlled by political considerations; for the majority of the population of the world, migration, both in and out of a country, is restricted.

The horn of plenty, formerly filled with free natural resources, has been emptied. No rapid accumulation of capital in the form of precious metals, goods, and commodities, such as characterized the great 400-year boom enjoyed by the peoples of western-European origin, is possible for the people of Africa, Asia, and Latin America.

Last, but not least, is the sheer arithmetic of the current increase in population. The number of persons in the world is so large that even a small rate of natural increase will result in an almost astronomical increment over a period of time of infinitesimal duration compared to the duration of the past history of the human race. As was pointed out above, continuation of the present rate of increase would result in a population of 50 billion persons in another 150 years. A population of this magnitude is so foreign to our experience that it is difficult to comprehend its implications.

Just as Thomas Malthus, at the end of the 18th century, could not foresee the effect upon the peoples of western Europe of the exploration of the last great frontier of this earth, so we today cannot clearly foresee the final effect of an unprecedented rapid increase of population within closed frontiers. What seems to be least uncertain in a future full of uncertainty is that the demographic history of the next 400 years will not be like that of the past 400 years.

world problem

The results of human reproduction are no longer solely the concern of the two individuals involved, or of the larger family, or even of the nation of which they are citizens. A stage has been reached in the demographic development of the world when the rate of human reproduction in any part of the globe may directly or indirectly affect the health and welfare of the rest of the human race. It is in this sense that there is a world population problem.

One or two illustrations may make this point more clear. During the past decade, six out of every ten persons added to the population of the world live in Asia; another two out of every ten live in Latin America and Africa. It seems inevitable that the breaking up of the world domination by northwest Europeans and their descendants, which already is well advanced, will continue, and that the center of power and influence will shift toward the demographic center of the world.

The present distribution of population increase enhances the existing imbalance between the distribution of the world's population and the distribution of wealth, available and utilized resources, and the use of nonhuman energy. Probably for the first time in human history there is a universal aspiration for a rapid improvement in the standard of living and a growing impatience with conditions that appear to stand in the way of its attainment. Millions of persons in Asia, Africa, and Latin America now are aware of the standard of living enjoyed by Europeans and North Americans. They are demanding the opportunity to attain the same standard, and they resist the idea that they must be permanently content with less.

A continuation of the present high rate of human multiplication will act as a brake on the already painfully slow improvement in the level of living, thus increasing political unrest and possibly bringing about eventual changes in government. As recent events have graphically demonstrated, such political changes may greatly affect the welfare of even the wealthiest nations.

The capital and technological skills that many of the nations of Africa, Asia, and Latin America require to produce enough food for a rapidly growing population and simultaneously to perceptibly raise per capita income exceed their existing national resources and ability. An immediate supply of capital in the amounts required is available only from the wealthier nations. The principle of public support of social welfare plans is now widely accepted in national affairs. The desirability of extending this principle to the international level for the primary purpose of supporting the economic development of the less advanced nations has not yet been generally accepted by the wealthier and more advanced countries. Even if this principle should be accepted, it is not as yet clear how long the wealthier nations would be willing to support the uncontrolled breeding of the populations receiving this assistance. The general acceptance of a foreign-aid program of the extent required by the countries with a rapidly growing population will only postpone for a few decades the inevitable reckoning with the results of uncontrolled human multiplication.

The future may witness a dramatic increase in man's ability to control his environment, provided he rapidly develops cultural substitutes for those harsh but effective governors of his high reproductive potential—disease and famine—that he has so recently learned to control. Man has been able to modify or control many natural phenomena, but he has not yet discovered how to evade the consequences of biological laws. No species has ever been able to multiply without limit. There are two biological checks upon a rapid increase in number—a high mortality and a low fertility. Unlike other biological organisms, man can choose which of these checks shall be applied, but one of them must be. Whether man can use his scientific knowledge to guide his future evolution more wisely than the blind forces of nature, only the future can reveal. The answer will not be long postponed.

references and notes

1. *Demographic Yearbook* (United Nations, New York, 1955), p. 1.

2. F. A. Pearson and F. A. Harper, *The World's Hunger* (Cornell Univ. Press, Ithaca, N.Y., 1945).

3. H. Brown, *The Challenge of Man's Future* (Viking, New York, 1954).

4. O. E. Baker, "Population trends in relation to land utilization," *Proc. Intern. Conf. Agr. Economists, 2nd Conf.* (1930), p. 284.

5. J. S. Davis, *J. Farm Economics* (Nov. 1949).

6. H. F. Dorn, *J. Am. Statist. Assoc. 45*, 311 (1950).

7. R. Pearl and L. J. Reed, *Proc. Natl. Acad. Sci. U.S. 6,* 275 (1920).

8. H. von Foerster, P. M. Mora, L. W. Amiot, *Science 132,* 1291 (1960).

9. "The future growth of world population," *U.N. Publ. No. ST/SOA/Ser. A/28* (1958).

10. "The past and future growth of world population—a long-range view," *U.N. Population Bull. No. 1* (1951), pp. 1–12.

11. Although registration of deaths among the Moslem population of Algeria is incomplete, it is believed that the general impression conveyed by Figure 2 is essentially correct.

12. *Demographic Yearbook* (United Nations, New York, 1956), p. 14.

13. New York *Times* (5 Aug. 1961).

14. "The determinants and consequences of population trends," *U.N. Publ. No. ST/SOA/Ser. A/17* (1953).

Control of Conception by Hormonal Steroids

Gregory Pincus

It is sometimes difficult to be decisive about the exact date marking the advent of a particular era in experimental science. Although there was a well-established background for its launching, the initiation of the present-day practice of oral contraception may fairly be marked by the publication in 1953 [1] of a report by Chang and me on the ovulation-inhibiting potency of progesterone and some of its derivatives as administered by several routes (subcutaneous, intravaginal, oral). Although inhibition of ovulation by administered sex steroids (and particularly by injected progesterone in the rabbit [2]) had been previously demonstrated [see 3], our express objective was to discover a·means of oral contraception [4]. Our findings in the rabbit were soon extended to the rat [5] and to humans [6]. In the course of screening approximately 200 steroids in the rabbit for ovulation-inhibiting activity, we discovered, among the neutral 19-norsteroids with progestational activity, several outstanding ovulation inhibitors that were effective when administered orally [1]. The establishment of the roles of these inhibitors in the control of human ovulation and menstruation [8] led to their use as contraceptive agents [9]. Projects established in Puerto Rico and Haiti soon demonstrated the extraordinary contraceptive effectiveness of a combination of a 19-norsteroid and an estrogen [10], and this finding was confirmed and amplified by projects in Los Angeles [11] and England [12].

In addition to the 19-norsteroids, a group of highly potent oral progestins was found in various derivatives of 17-acetoxyprogesterone [13]. Some of these progestins when administered orally inhibit ovula-

Reprinted from *Science, 153:* 493–500 (1966) with permission of the publisher and Mrs. Gregory Pincus. Copyright 1966 by the American Association for the Advancement of Science.

tion, particularly when combined with an estrogen [14]. The progestins now available in contraceptive preparations are derivatives of 19-norsteroids or 17-acetoxyprogesterone. Their structural formulas are presented in Figure 1. All the available preparations require the action of both progestin and estrogen for maximum contraceptive

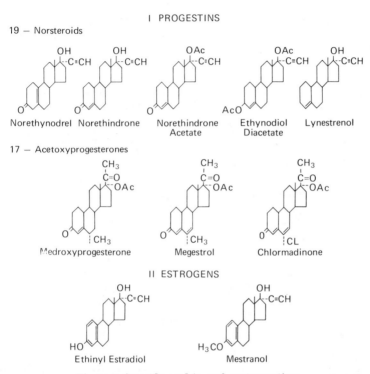

Figure 1. Steroids used in oral contraceptives

efficiency, as well as for optimum control of menstrual periodicity. The drugs are administered orally for 20 or 21 days beginning on day 5 of the menstrual cycle. The estrogen employed is either 17α-ethinyl-estradiol or its 3-methyl ether, mestranol (see Figure 1).

methods of oral contraception

Progestin-estrogen combinations are used according to one of two regimens, combined therapy or sequential therapy. Combined therapy involves the use of the combination throughout the monthly medication period; sequential therapy, introduced in 1963 [15], involves administration of the estrogen alone for 10 or 15 successive days and use of the combination for the remaining period of 10 or 5 successive days. The combined therapy is undoubtedly the most efficient contraceptive method; a somewhat variable failure rate has been reported for the sequential method [see 16], but on the average it appears to permit ovulation and some pregnancies. The pregnancy rates for a number of contraceptive methods are presented in Table 1, which demonstrates very clearly the superior efficiency of oral contraceptives. Indeed, it has

Table 1.
Number of Pregnancies per 100 Years of Exposure for Various Methods of Contraception

Method	Pregnancy Rate
Douche	31[a]
Rhythm	24[a]
Jelly Alone	20[a]
Withdrawal	18[a]
Condom	14[a]
Diaphragm	12[a]
Intrauterine Devices	5[b]
Sequential Steroids	5[c]
Combined Steroids	0.1

[a] Data of Venning [47].
[b] Estimated from data summarized by Pincus [17, p. 297].
[c] Data of Mears [48].

been alleged that the failures reported for the combined administration method are due to patients' failing to follow the directions for regular daily use [16]. Perhaps the only other experimental contraceptive method which approaches the oral contraceptives in efficiency is that involving the insertion of a plastic or metal intrauterine device. Although long-term data are still being collected, pregnancy rates in users of such devices in various localities vary from approximately 1 to 9 per 100 women-years [17].

Special interest attaches to the physiological actions of the oral contraceptives for several reasons. First, they involve the daily use of synthetic steroids having significant hormonal action. Second, they are being taken by women during their fertile premenopausal years. And third, they are being taken for many months or many years by normal healthy women, not as correctives to or therapy for obvious endogenous hormonal deficiencies or aberrations, but specifically as antifertility agents. Each of these considerations implicates concern for the safety with which these preparations can be used. Apprehension has been expressed because of possible effects of an altered hormonal balance [18], with perhaps irreversible effects on pituitary function [19]. Induced temporary or even permanent sterility has been considered possible [20]. The occurrence of a variety of "adverse reactions" in women taking or ceasing to take oral contraceptives has led to the allegation of "side effects" varying from thromboembolism to hair loss, from retinopathy to hyperpigmentation. Except for clear and expected hormonal actions of progestins and estrogens I know of no scientifically valid demonstration of significant pathological effects of their use in contraceptive doses and regimens. I have presented a detailed discussion elsewhere [17].

Here I propose to present a précis of the available information on the physiological actions of these preparations. Implicit in what follows is that all of the various progestin-estrogen combinations have quite similar biological properties. It should be recognized that the extent to which this is true is limited. For example, we recognized early that in test animals orally administered norethynodrel is a progestin with weak intrinsic estrogenic action whereas norethindrone is a weakly androgenic progestin [21]. However, in women taking these various preparations at the currently used dosages a number of effects clearly attributable to intrinsic hormonal properties appear to be common properties. These properties are clearly divisible into three categories: (i) actions on reproductive tract and allied organs, (ii) effects on other endocrine systems, and (iii) effects on systems and functions not ordinarily associated with sex hormone action. Most of the data given here are derived from observations made by my colleagues and myself with volunteer patients in several study projects over the past 9 years.

Here I shall consider ovarian, uterine, cervical, vaginal, and mammary-gland functions.

We have observed oocyte numbers and cytology in ovaries from experimental animals receiving various dosages of oral contraceptives over periods ranging from months to years. In rats, for example, we have seen no significant differences between ovaries from controls and those from females to which drugs have been administered [22, 23, 24]. Reporting on a 3-year period of cyclical administration of norethynodrel-mestranol (Enovid, 10 milligrams per 60 kilograms of body weight) to prepubertal female rhesus monkeys, Kar *et al.* [25] state that

Enovid "has not been found to cause any change in the ovary except a consistent increase in weight. The follicular development proceeds uninterrupted, culminating in the appearance of typical Graafian follicles towards the terminal stage of the drug regime. No noteworthy effect on the number of primordial oocytes has been observed." In ovarian biopsies taken at laparotomy from women using Enovid and from control non-users we have found no differences in the proportions of atretic follicles and have found a tendency in Enovid users toward increased density of oocytes, attributable to the absence of corpora lutea and of large follicles (Table 2). Effects of oral contraceptives on the secre-

Table 2.
Frequency of Atresia and Densities of Follicles in Ovarian Biopsies from Users of Enovid and Control Patients

Age Range (yr)		Controls			Enovid Users	
	No.	Atretic Follicles (%)	Follicles per mm²	No.	Atretic Follicles (%)	Follicles per mm²
18–25	15	80 ± 3.3	0.79 ± 0.13	9	63 ± 8.0	1.77 ± 0.75
26–29	5	67 ± 8.7	0.39 ± 0.12	8	47 ± 8.2	1.78 ± 0.72
30–33	13	58 ± 6.8	0.38 ± 0.16	9	67 ± 9.0	0.31 ± 0.11
34–37	27	61 ± 4.6	0.22 ± 0.05			
38–42	7	67 ± 4.5	0.09 ± 0.03	5	53 ± 7.3	0.31 ± 0.07[a]

[a] Value significantly different from value for controls ($p < .01$).

tory activity of the ovaries have been reported by Loraine *et al.* [26] and are illustrated in Figure 2. A decrease in the urinary output of estrogens and pregnanediol is not accompanied by a decrease in the total amount of gonadotropic activity detectable in the urine, and a direct action on the secretory tissues of the ovaries is deducible. However, specific inhibition of pituitary luteinizing-hormone secretion may underlie a diminished ovarian steroid production.

Because it is a major target organ for the ovarian hormones, the uterus and its functions have been subjects of especial study in users of oral contraceptives. In Table 3 are presented data on uterine size as determined by manual palpation. Except for a significant low incidence of large uteri in 1- to 2-year users of Enovid, no significant differences have been found between long-term and short-term users and a group of former users examined some time after discontinuance of use. Our data on the nature of the endometria of users of Enovid as determined from

biopsies taken before use, during use, and after cessation of use are
presented in Tables 4 and 5. The relative reduction in proliferative and
secretory specimens and the increase in the proportion of specimens
exhibiting "hormonal effect" are obvious. This "effect" is characterized
by a relative predominance of stromal edema and by a degree of

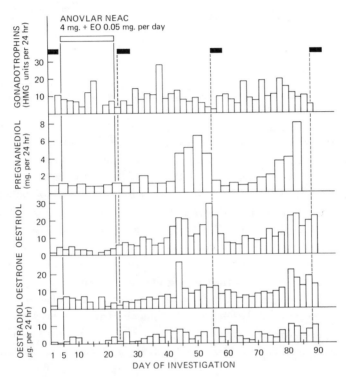

Figure 2. Excretion of hormones in urine of a patient treated with Anovlar. Black
areas indicate the duration of menstrual bleeding (from Loraine *et al.* [*26*]).

glandular involution. Most significant is that the proportions of these
endometria are identical in 1- to 2-year users and in longer-term users.
The hormonal effect tends to persist in uteri after discontinuance of
medication, but a lessening in incidence is obvious. The data of Table 5
are noteworthy in indicating that the incidence of cystic and adenomatous hyperplasia and of endometritis tends to be diminished in users of
Enovid, the decrease in endometritis persisting into the period after
medication has been discontinued. These may be considered therapeutic
actions.

Uterine function is reflected in the nature of the menstrual cycles.

Table 3.
Uterine Size in Users of Enovid, as Determined by Manual Palpation

Lunar Years of Use	No. of Patients	Size of Uterus			
		Normal (%)	Subnormal (%)	Large (%)	Ill-Defined (%)
1–2	901	88.3 ± 1.07	3.3 ± 0.60	5.1 ± 0.73[a]	3.2 ± 0.59
3–4	837	86.7 ± 1.17	1.7 ± 0.45	8.7 ± 0.98	3.0 ± 0.59
5–9	465	85.4 ± 1.64	0.6 ± 0.36	11.0 ± 1.45	3.0 ± 0.79
Medication Discontinued	242	81.0 ± 2.53	2.9 ± 1.08	12.4 ± 2.12	3.7 ± 1.22

[a] Value significantly different from postmedication value ($p < .02$).

That the use of oral contraceptives from day 5 through day 24 imposes a fairly specific pattern of menstrual periodicity was evident early. This is clearly illustrated in the data on relative frequencies of various cycle lengths in users of Enovid and in a group of control patients in the same locality who used vaginal spermicidal jellies and foams as contraceptives (Table 6). The tendency in Enovid users for the great majority of cycle lengths to fall between 25 and 30 days is obvious, as is the relatively narrow distribution of frequencies about this mode. Again, it should be noted that no significant differences in cycle-length distributions are seen between long-term and short-term users.

Table 7 presents data on two phenomena that have been associated with the use of oral contraceptives, breakthrough bleeding, and amenorrhea. "Breakthrough bleeding" refers to menstrual spotting or

Table 4.
Analysis of Endometrial Biopsies in Users of Enovid; "Normal" Endometrial States

Lunar Years of Use	No.	Patients			Hormonal Effect
		Endometrial State (%)			
		Proliferative	Secretory	Menstrual	
0	2013	54.6 ± 1.11	19.4 ± 0.88	5.4 ± 0.51	5.9 ± 0.53
1–2	492	9.2 ± 1.30[a]	10.2 ± 1.37[a]	6.1 ± 1.08	72.4 ± 2.02[a]
3–4	434	13.8 ± 1.66[a]	14.7 ± 1.70[a]	8.1 ± 1.31	58.3 ± 2.37[a]
5–9	258	11.2 ± 1.97[a]	12.3 ± 2.05[a]	4.3 ± 1.27	65.5 ± 2.97[a]
Medication Discontinued	134	33.5 ± 4.09[a]	24.6 ± 3.73	6.0 ± 2.06	25.4 ± 3.78[a]

[a] Values differ significantly from premedication values ($p < .05$).

Table 5.
Analysis of Endometrial Biopsies in Users
of Enovid; "Abnormal" Endometrial States

		Patients				
		Percentage with Abnormalities				
Lunar Years of Use	No.	Cystic and Adenomatous Hyperplasia	Atrophy	Endometritis	Anaplasia	Carcinoma in Situ
0	2013	5.0 ± 0.49	0.9 ± 0.21	8.6 ± 0.63	0.14 ± 0.08	0.09 ± 0.07
1–2	492	0.8 ± 0.40ª	0.6 ± 0.35	0.6 ± 0.35ª	0.0	0.0
3–4	434	2.8 ± 0.79ª	0.9 ± 0.45	1.2 ± 0.52ª	0.20 ± 0.22	0.0
5–9	258	3.5 ± 1.15	1.9 ± 0.85	0.8 ± 0.56ª	0.40 ± 0.39	0.0
Medication Discontinued	134	6.0 ± 2.06	1.5 ± 1.05	3.0 ± 1.48ª	0.0	0.0

ª Values differ significantly from premedication values ($p < .05$).

bleeding occurring during medication days and presumably representing incomplete control of endometrial vasculature by the drug. Amenorrhea refers to the absence of the menstrual flow that usually occurs in days 1 to 7 following the taking of the last dose in any given month (if no flow occurs by the seventh day, medication is reinstituted). The data of Table 7 exhibit the reduction, noted by many investigators, in frequency of breakthrough bleeding after the first year of use and the relative stabilization in the frequency from the end of the second year on. The frequency of amenorrhea, on the other hand, is identical from year to year over the 8 years of study. We have attributed this first-year frequency of breakthrough bleeding in part to forgetfulness

Table 6.
Cycle Lengths in Users of Enovid. Controls Used Vaginal Spermicidal Jellies and Foams as Contraceptives. All Values Differ Significantly from Those for Controls ($p < .05$)

Lunar Years of Use	No. of Patients	No. of Cycles	Percentage of Patients			
			Cycle <25 Days	Cycle 25–30 Days	Cycle 31–36 Days	Cycle >37 Days
1–2	2,682	25,158	6.9 ± 0.49	84.5 ± 0.70	7.6 ± 0.51	1.1 ± 0.20
3–4	2,310	15,636	4.0 ± 0.41	91.2 ± 0.51	4.4 ± 0.43	0.5 ± 0.15
5–10	952	8,652	4.2 ± 0.65	90.6 ± 0.95	4.9 ± 0.70	0.4 ± 0.20
Control	455	6,242	10.5 ± 1.44	56.0 ± 2.33	27.3 ± 2.09	7.8 ± 1.26

in pill-taking (a "withdrawal" flow may occur if pills are missed for even 1 day and almost certainly after two or more days) which characterizes the period of learning to use the pills properly, and in part to a physiological adjustment of the endometrial vasculature to the imposed levels of circulating progestin and estrogen. It should be noted, however, that in the control patients breakthrough bleeding (cycles shorter than 25 days) occurs more frequently than in users of oral contracep-

Table 7.

Menstrual Phenomena Reported by
Volunteer Long-Term Users of Enovid. Controls, Who Used
Vaginal Contraceptives, Reported Data for up to 4 Years

Lunar Year of Use	No. of Patients	Cycles		
		No.	Breakthrough Bleeding[a] (%)	Amenorrhea (%)
1st	1,591	14,957	7.4 ± 0.20	0.8 ± 0.07
2nd	1,091	12,480	5.0 ± 0.20	0.7 ± 0.07
3rd	827	8,875	3.8 ± 0.18	0.9 ± 0.10
4th	655	7,492	3.3 ± 0.21	0.9 ± 0.11
5th	474	4,692	2.7 ± 0.24	1.0 ± 0.15
6th	283	2,763	2.4 ± 0.29	1.1 ± 0.20
7th	124	1,054	3.0 ± 0.53	1.6 ± 0.39
8th	48	387	3.6 ± 0.95	1.8 ± 0.68
9th	19	125		
10th	6	22		
Total	5,118	52,847	4.8 ± 0.09	0.9 ± 0.04
Controls	455	6,809	10.0 ± 0.36	4.7 ± 0.26

[a] Cycles less than 25 days in length.

tives. This illustrates the relatively tight control of menstrual bleeding exercised by the exogenous steroid. Indeed, the use of oral contraceptives in the control of hypermenorrhea is now commonplace. We have several times presented data demonstrating reduced duration of menstruation in users of Enovid, and also a clear reduction in the quantity of menstrual fluid [17, 27]. This has been observed in users of practically all the presently available preparations, and there is a tendency for the amount of the effluvium to decrease with increasing dose. The rather constant frequency of "amenorrhea" observed from year to year probably also reflects a constant level of progestin and estrogen month in and month out. The higher frequency of amenorrhea in users of vaginal contraceptives may reflect in part the occurrence of pregnancy but primarily reflects the degree of irregularity encountered in menstrual cyclicity in our Puerto Rican subjects.

Our studies of vaginal and cervical responses to the oral contraceptives have involved primarily the study of Papanicolaou smears and of cervical biopsies from patients with confirmed suspicious smears. We have elsewhere discussed the type of data obtained [28]. Table 8 illustrates the incidence of suspicious smears for users of vaginal contraceptives, of three oral contraceptives, and of plastic intrauterine devices. The lower rates for the oral contraceptives may be due to lack

Table 8.

Incidence of Suspicious Papanicolaou Smears in Subjects with Negative Smears before the Use of Various Contraceptives

	Patients	
Contraceptive	No.	Percentage with Suspicious Smears
Vaginal	208	7.2 ± 1.8
Enovid	580	2.6 ± 0.6[a]
Ovulin	188	2.1 ± 1.0[a]
Orthonovum	105	2.8 ± 1.6
Intrauterine	500	5.4 ± 1.0

[a] Incidence differs significantly ($p < .05$) from that for users of vaginal contraceptives.

of irritative or inflammatory reactions that occur in some users of local materials, or there may be a genuine suppression by the steroids of dysplasia or anaplasia such as is found in the uterine endometrium (Table 5). Our data on the occurrence of carcinoma in cervical biopsies are too scant to afford statistically significant figures; thus far, users of oral contraceptives have had the lowest rates [see 17, p. 257].

If we take the breasts as reproductive-system target organs, the available data for users of oral contraceptives indicate the following: (i) there is no significant average increase in breast size, although some individuals claim a mild hypertrophy or an increase in breast sensitivity [17, pp. 260–261]; (ii) there is no increase, over a 9-year period, in the occurrence of mastalgia (observed in about 0.5 percent of the subjects); (iii) lactation appears to be reduced by large doses but is unaffected at the lower contraceptive doses, although certain preparations appear to be much less potent inhibitors than others [see 16, pp. 64–65]; (iv) the frequency of breast nodularities is significantly reduced compared to the frequency before medication and to that in users of vaginal contraceptives; this suggests inhibition of a potential precancerous state.

Table 9.
Urinary Excretion of Gonadotropin in Six Patients

Age of Patient	Cycle		Activity	Remarks
	No.	*Days*	*(mg/Day)*[a]	
	No Medication			
37	[b]	6–8	0.53	Mid-Cycle
		16–18	3.14	Rise
		22–24	1.41	
41	[b]	7–9	0.58	Mid-Cycle
		18–20	.75	Rise
		25–27	.47	
	Enovid, 10 Milligrams			
24	98	7–9	0.25	No Mid-
		13–15	.12	Cycle Rise
		23–25	.29	
42	96	11–13	0.26	No Mid-
		14–16	.22	Cycle Rise
		23–25	.21	
34	61	7–9	0.77	No Mid-
		14–16	.35	Cycle Rise
		22–24	.29	
36	107	5–7	0.11	No Mid-
		16–18	.10	Cycle Rise
		21–23	.36	

[a] Activity is given in estrone equivalents.
[b] Ovulatory cycle.

We have data on aspects of the activity of three endocrine organs, the anterior pituitary, the thyroid, and the adrenal cortex. I early reported effective suppression of urinary gonadotropin activity in users of a norethynodrel-estrogen combination [29], especially in post-menopausal women, in whom gonadotropin output is relatively high. Other preparations have appeared to be ineffective suppressors of urinary gonadotropic activity. Since, however, this activity is the result of the combined action of follicle-stimulating and luteinizing gonadotropins, the method of assay may affect the findings. Most

Table 10.
Protein-Bound Iodine (PBI) in the Blood
of Users of Enovid

		Percentage of Patients		
Lunar Years of Use	*No. of Patients*	*PBI < 4.0 µg/100 ml*	*PBI 4.0–8.8 µg/100 ml*	*PBI ≥ 9 µg/100 ml*
1–2	69	0	82.7 ± 4.59	17.3 ± 4.59[a]
3–4	113	0	84.1 ± 3.46	15.9 ± 3.46[a]
5–9	58	1.7 ± 1.71	75.8 ± 5.67[a]	22.4 ± 5.52[a]
Medication Discontinued	49	4.1 ± 2.86	93.9 ± 3.45	2.0 ± 2.02

[a] Values differ significantly from postmedication values ($p < .05$).

observers agree that excretion of luteinizing gonadotropins tends to peak most markedly at mid-cycle, and separate assay for partially purified luteinizing gonadotropins shows abolition of this peak in users of synthetic progestins or progestin-estrogen mixtures [30]. Data on long-term users of Enovid certainly indicate absence of this mid-cycle peak (Table 9), which is evident in the control patients. Whatever the degree of suppression, a rapid recovery following cessation of use of oral contraceptives is clearly indicated by the practically immediate return of normal ovarian secretory activity [26] and the almost hyper-normal fertility [31].

I know of no studies of the production or secretion of other anterior pituitary hormones. It should be noted that young animals fed fairly high doses of progestin-estrogen combinations continuously for many months tend to have lower body weights than control animals. This is in

Table 11.
Comparison of Average Thyroid Uptake
in Patients Who Used Enovid for 3 Years or
Longer and in Control Groups (Users of Vag-
inal Contraceptives)

No. of Patients	*Medication*	*Average Uptake (% of Administered Dose)*
50	Enovid, 5 mg	19.97 ± 0.59[a]
56	Enovid, 2.5 mg	20.88 ± 1.07[a]
52	Control	20.84 ± 0.81[a]

[a] Mean ± standard error.

large measure due to an inhibition of appetite, as our feeding records have shown [24]. However, a limited inhibition of production or release of pituitary growth hormone cannot be excluded. Studies of the histology and cytology of pituitaries taken from rats fed varying doses of a combination of ethynodiol diacetate and mestranol over a 2-year period disclosed no significant differences from controls [23].

Two measures of thyroid function commonly used in human subjects have been applied to users and nonusers of Enovid. The first of these,

Table 12.

Concentration of Cortisol in Plasma in
Pregnant and in Nonpregnant Women Taking Oral
Estrogens and Progestins

| | | Cortisol | |
| | No. of | Endogenous | Bound (% of |
Group	Patients	(μg/ml)	Tracer Dose)
Control	8	13.7 ± 4.3[a]	78 ± 3.7
Pregnancy, 3rd Trimester	3	40.0 ± 1.8[b]	86 ± 2.5[c]
Enovid, 10 mg/day	8	30.8 ± 8.4[c]	91 ± 1.5[c]
Ethinylestradiol-3-Methyl Ether,			
0.1 mg/day	5	24.0 ± 3.7[c]	85 ± 5.1[c]
Ethinylestradiol-3-Methyl Ether,			
0.3 mg/day	5	32.0 ± 4.7[b]	89 ± 2.1[b]
Progesterone, 300 mg/day	5	7.5 ± 4.2	75 ± 3.0
Norethynodrel, 10 mg/day	5	25.5 ± 6.1[c]	88 ± 3.6[b]

[a] Standard error.
[b] Significantly different from control group ($p = .01$).
[c] Significantly different from control group ($p = .02$).

the amount of protein-bound iodine in blood, exhibits an average increase during medication [17, p. 266]. This skewing of frequencies toward higher values is shown in Table 10. There is no systematic alteration with increasing years of use. Presumably this is a characteristic estrogen effect seen in pregnancy [32] and after administration of exogenous estrogen [33] and reflects the activity of the estrogen component in increasing the amount of thyroxin-binding globulin in the blood [34]. The prompt return to normal values which we have noted on discontinuance of use has been confirmed in users of several oral contraceptives [34] and indicates that there is no permanent alteration in the iodine-binding systems.

The second measure of thyroid function that we have studied is the uptake of administered radioactive iodine. Here we have seen no difference in percentages of uptake between users of oral contraceptives and users of vaginal contraceptives. Moreover, as is evident in the data of Table 11, there is no significant difference between long-term users and controls. Employing much larger than normal dosages of medroxy-progesterone alone or in combination with estradiol, Maneschi *et al.* [35] have found a decrease in uptake of radio-iodine and other evidence of depressed thyroid function.

Our data on adrenocortical function in users of oral contraceptives tend to parallel those obtained on thyroid function. First of all, at high

Table 13.
Rates of Cortisol Production in Long-Term Users of Enovid and in Control Patients

Months of Therapy	Cortisol (μg/hr)
Control	412
Control	536
Control	493
Control	731
Mean ± S.D.	543 ± 135
93	540
59	294
104	460
94	861
Mean ± S.D.	538 ± 238

doses of Enovid or either of its components, there is a clear increase in concentrations of cortisol in plasma. As may be seen in Table 12, this increase appears to be attributable to an increase in plasma transcortin, the cortisol-binding protein. In contrast, in several long-term users, there has been no apparent change in the rate of cortisol production (Table 13) as determined by studies with radioisotopes. Furthermore, responsivity to administration of adrenocorticotropic hormone is undiminished in Enovid users [36].

other potential targets

Since all of the 19-norsteroids and estrogens combined in contraceptive preparations are alkylated at carbon 17 of the steroid skeleton, an effect on one aspect of liver function as determined by retention of bromsulfophthalein may be expected [37]. This is indeed shown in the data of Table 14 by the average increase in the percentage of bromsulfophthalein retained. In contrast, two other tests of liver function show no alteration during medication, and the data for bromsulfophthalein clearly indicate no very marked alteration. Return to lower percentages of bromsulfophthalein retained is prompt on cessation of medication [16, p. 49]. Other tests of liver function (for example, thymol turbidity, cephalin flocculation) give no indication of significant

Table 14.
Results of Three Tests of Liver Function in Users of Ovulen

Test	No. of Patients	Before Medication	No. of Patients	During Medication
Bromsulfophthalein Retention (Milligrams per 100 ml at 45 Minutes)	44	3.1 ± 0.40[c]	32	4.9 ± 0.56[c]
Transaminase (TransAc Units)[a]	46	12.3 ± 0.62[c]	63	14.6 ± 0.98[c]
Alkaline Phosphatase (KBR Units)[b]	45	3.3 ± 0.10[c]	62	3.7 ± 0.20[c]

[a] Twenty-five TransAc units are defined as the amount of enzyme that will form 25 micromoles of oxalacetic acid per minute per liter of serum under the specific conditions (pH 7.40, 37°C).

[b] Klein-Babson-Read unit is the number of micrograms of phenolphthalein released when phenolphthalein phosphate is incubated with serum or plasma at 37°C for 30 minutes. The free phenolphthalein is liberated by the alkaline phosphatase present.

[c] Mean $\pm$ standard error. All values are within the range for normal individuals.

change during use of oral contraceptives. An odd exception appears to occur in the first cycle of use by postmenopausal women in Finland, but this "may indicate no more than that the livers of postmenopausal Finnish women are less well adapted to estrogen inactivation than those of women during the reproductive years" [16, p. 48].

We have seen no very consistent changes in hematological functions studied in users of oral contraceptives. Thus the hematocrit values and the white blood counts are fairly constant from year to year in any given woman, and no meaningful trends occur in long-term users. In view of the claims of thromboembolic effects of progestin-estrogen combinations, a number of studies have been made of clotting factors in the blood of women taking oral contraceptives. Most observers agree that the concentration of certain clotting factors (for example, the factor VII-X complex) in the blood increases [see 38]. The general conclusion from the available data has been well expressed by Miller *et al.* [39]: "Although the occurrence of thromboembolic phenomena suggests a disturbance of the blood coagulation system, no reliable evidence has established a connection between increase in coagulation factors and an increased incidence of such phenomena. Thus, although the present study demonstrates changes in the coagulation mechanism similar to those seen in pregnancy, no implications can be drawn regarding the relationship of these findings to the clinical tendency toward thromboembolic disease." Indeed, apprehensions expressed by some of thromboembolic effects of oral contraceptives [40] are unsupported not only by these coagulation-factor studies but also by careful analysis of the epidemiology of thromboembolism. Winter [41] has

Table 15.
Blood Pressures in Users of Enovid

Lunar Years of Use	*No.*	Patients		
		Hypotensive (%)	*Normotensive* (%)	*Hypertensive* (%)
1–2	342	1.5 ± 0.66	97.4 ± 0.86	1.2 ± 0.59
3–4	467	1.1 ± 0.48	97.2 ± 0.76	1.7 ± 0.60
5–9	394	0.8 ± 0.45	95.7 ± 1.02	3.5 ± 0.93
Medication Discontinued	134	1.5 ± 1.05	93.2 ± 2.18	5.2 ± 1.93

reviewed the data on thromboembolic mortality rates in Enovid users and in the female population generally for the years 1961, 1962, and 1963. He concludes that "no significant increase in the risk of thromboembolic death from the users of Enovid has been demonstrated," which is the conclusion also of the Food and Drug Administration committee which reviewed the 1962 data for the United States [42].

Studies of the cardiovascular system have revealed no significant trends in blood pressures. This is illustrated in Table 15, which lists the proportions of patients classifiable as hypotensive, normotensive, and hypertensive in our long-term study of Enovid. There are no statistically significant trends in these data. Table 16 demonstrates that there tend to be fewer varices in Enovid users than in women who have ceased taking Enovid. We have elsewhere noted this phenomenon and attributed it to the absence of pregnancy [43].

A number of miscellaneous physical and physiological conditions have been studied in users of oral contraceptives, particularly when an occasional report of phenomena such as hair loss or increased hirsutism is made. Thus degrees of hirsutism and chloasma have been attributed

Table 16.
Varices in Users of Enovid

		Patients
Lunar Years of Use	No.	With Varices (%)
1–2	108	24.1 ± 4.13
3–4	320	23.1 ± 2.36
5–9	380	22.9 ± 2.16
Medication Discontinued	96	33.3 ± 4.84

to the use of these drugs, but adequately controlled studies give no support to such actions. A tendency to lowered glucose tolerance has been reported [44] in some users of Enovid, with a high frequency in women with a family history of diabetes. This is the type of change in glucose tolerance that occurs in pregnancy and may be attributed to an estrogen-progestin balance similar to that in pregnancy. In any event, the diagnosis of true diabetes is not justified. A number of uncontrolled observations of users of oral contraceptives have led to claims of the induction of leg cramps, various types of headache, edema, and so on. Exceptional weight gain has been attributed to some but not all of the oral contraceptives. This is illustrated in Table 17, taken from Satterthwaite [see 27], which summarizes significant weight gains and losses (2.7 kilograms or more) at annual examination of three groups of women taking the three drugs indicated. Orthonovum is more obviously stimulative of weight gain than of weight loss.

The psychological effects of the use of oral contraceptives have been

Table 17.
Weight Changes in Users of Oral Contraceptives after 1 Year of Use. Weight Changes of Less than 2.7 Kilograms Are Not Included [from 26]

		Patients	
Drug	No.	Gaining (%)	Losing (%)
Enovid, 2.5 mg	95	19	20
Orthonovum, 2 mg	106	24	6.6
Ovulen, 1 mg	87	18	22

much discussed. A good proportion of the "reactions" reported by users appear to be of this nature. The types of such reactions and the proportions of women reporting them are presented in Table 18 [27]. Listed as subjective have been such complaints as headache, nervousness, and so on. In the first year about one-fourth to one-third of the women complain of undesirable effects.

I have been struck by the finding of practically all investigators that

Table 18.
Results of a Comparative Study of Symptoms Produced by Three Oral Contraceptives during the First Year of Use. Patients Were the Same as Those for Whom Data Are Reported in Table 17

| | Patients Complaining (%) | | |
| | | Ortho- | |
Symptom	*Enovid*	*novum*	*Ovulen*
Gastrointestinal	13	10	10
Subjective	20	19	14
Vaginal and Lower Abdominal Distress	6	7	6
Breakthrough Bleeding	6	1	2
All Symptoms[a]	28	32	28

[a] Some patients complained of more than one symptom; therefore this is not additive of the data in the preceding columns.

these complaints are most evident early during the use of the drugs and tend to be reported at a rather low, fairly constant level thereafter [17, p. 301]. This is illustrated by the data of Table 19 for women in Rio Piedras, Puerto Rico. Every one of the alleged reactions to Enovid declines in frequency after the first year. We therefore suspected that apprehension occasioned by the use of a new (and often unknown) drug might underlie these symptoms. Accordingly, we tested the putative psychogenic action (i) in 15 women in a city many kilometers away from Rio Piedras who were offered an effective contraceptive to be taken by mouth, with no admonition concerning possible side effects, and (ii) in 28 women in Rio Piedras who were asked not to abandon their use of vaginal (diaphragm and jelly) contraceptives for several months and to take pills by the usual regime to see if the pills were "fit" to continue such use. They were asked to report any untoward reac-

Table 19.
Complaints by Patients Taking Enovid
in Rio Piedras, Puerto Rico

			Cycles	
				With
Lunar		With	With	Dysmenor-
Year	No. of	Nausea	Headache	rhea
of Use	Patients	(%)	(%)	(%)
0				52.0
1st	744	1.20	2.83	27.5
2nd	450	0.57	2.24	25.0
3rd	321	0.65	1.85	22.3
4th	237	0.26	0.84	23.9
5th	176	0.33	0.98	16.9
6th	118	0.25	0.91	12.8
7th	68	0.00	1.08	20.5
8–10th	65	0.40	0.40	9.2

tions. By random assignment, 15 of the women in the second group received placebos identical in appearance with the true medication taken by the other 13 in the group. The data from this study, presented in Table 20, demonstrate no statistically significant difference in the percentage of reactions reported by placebo users as compared to the 13 matched, randomized Enovid users, a much reduced "reaction rate" in women who had not been admonished, and definite occurrence of breakthrough bleeding in those who had been given placebos and had been admonished.

Table 20.
Results of Administration of Enovid with
and without Admonitions and of Placebos with Admonitions

			Cycles			
			Mean		Breakthrough	Amen-
	No. of		Length	Reactions[a]	Bleeding	orrhea
Group	Patients	No.	(days)	(%)	(%)	(%)
No Admonition,						
Effective Drug	15	48	29.2	6.3 ± 3.5[b]	2.1 ± 2.1[a]	0.0
Admonition, Placebo	15	41	31.6	17.1 ± 5.9	4.9 ± 3.2	9.8
Effective Drug	13	30	25.5	23.3 ± 7.7	16.7 ± 6.8	3.3

[a] Includes complaints of physical ill-being such as nausea, vomiting, headache, vertigo, gastralgia, and malaise.
[b] Standard error.

A number of additional effects with psychological bases have been studied. Thus premenstrual tension has been found to decrease in users of oral contraceptives [45], and both increases and decreases in libido have been reported, although generally the frequency of coitus tends to increase and to remain somewhat higher than prior to use of oral contraceptives. For comments on subjective symptoms, see Puddy [46].

conclusions

Experience with the use of progestin-estrogen preparations as oral contraceptives indicates that they inhibit fertility by preventing ovulation and that their action is clearly a physiological process. Their efficiency as antifertility agents is extraordinary. An examination of their physiological effects over many years of use indicates that actions to be expected from the hormonal properties of the steroidal components occur but that none of these constitute pathological phenomena. Rather, we observe a state conditioned by the rather constant hormonal milieu resulting from the particular dosages and regimes of use. Thus far, despite use by millions of women, none of the alleged pathological adverse reactions (such as thromboembolism) to the drugs have been established as more than coincidental. Clearly beneficial effects are inherent not only in the avoidance of risks attendant upon pregnancy but also in improvements in menstrual function (regularity, reduction of hypermenorrhea and dysmenorrhea) and perhaps in a prophylactic effect upon certain abnormalities of the reproductive tract (cervical anaplasia, endometrial cystic and adenomatous hyperplasia). Psychogenic phenomena due to use of oral contraceptives are difficult to measure, but beneficial effects would seem to outweigh adverse ones.

references and notes

1. G. Pincus and M. C. Chang, *Acta Physiol. Latinoam. 3,* 177 (1953).
2. S. W. Makepeace, G. L. Weinstein, M. W. Friedman, *Am. J. Physiol. 119,* 512 (1937).
3. J. W. Everett, in *Sex and Internal Secretions,* W. C. Young, Ed. (Williams and Wilkins, Baltimore, 1961), vol. 1, p. 497.
4. Experimental work was supported by a grant from the Planned Parenthood Federation made possible through the kind offices of Margaret Sanger.
5. R. F. Slechta, M. C. Chang, G. Pincus, *Fertil. Steril. 5,* 282 (1954).
6. G. Pincus, in *Proc. Intern. Conf. Planned Parenthood, 5th, Tokyo, 1955,* p. 175.

7. ——, M. C. Chang, E. S. E. Hafez, M. X. Zarrow, A. Merrill, *Science 124,* 890 (1956).

8. J. Rock, G. Pincus, C. R. Garcia, *ibid.,* p. 891; J. Rock, C. R. Garcia, G. Pincus, *Recent Progr. Hormone Res. 13,* 323 (1957); C. R. Garcia, G. Pincus, J. Rock, *Am. J. Ostet. Gynecol. 75,* 82 (1958).

9. G. Pincus, J. Rock, C. R. Garcia, E. Rice-Wray, M. Paniagua, I. Rodriguez, *Am. J. Obstet. Gynecol. 75,* 82 (1958).

10. G. Pincus, C. R. Garcia, J. Rock, M. Paniagua, A. Pendleton, F. Laraque, R. Nicolas, R. Borno, V. Pean, *Science 130,* 81 (1959).

11. E. T. Tyler and H. S. Olson, *J. Am. Med. Assoc. 169,* 1843 (1959).

12. E. Mears, *Brit. Med. J. 1961-I,* 1318 (1961).

13. T. Miyake and G. Pincus, *Endocrinology 63,* 816 (1958).

14. G. I. M. Swyer and V. Little, *Proc. Roy. Soc. Med. 55,* 861 (1962).

15. J. W. Goldzieher, J. Martinez-Manatou, N. B. Livingston, Jr., L. E. Moses, E. Rice-Wray, *Western J. Surg. 71,* 187 (1963).

16. E. Mears, Ed., *Handbook on Oral Contraception* (Little, Brown, Boston, 1965).

17. G. Pincus, *The Control of Fertility* (Academic Press, New York, 1965).

18. E. C. Dodds, *J. Endocrinol. 23,* 1 (1961).

19. R. L. Holmes and M. Mandl, *Lancet 1962-I,* 1174 (1962).

20. M. J. Whitelaw, V. F. Nola, C. F. Kalman, *J. Am. Med. Assoc. 195,* 781 (1966).

21. G. Pincus, M. C. Chang, M. X. Zarrow, E. S. E. Hafez, A. Merrill, *Endocrinology 59,* 695 (1956).

22. G. Pincus and A. Merrill, in *Control of Ovulation,* C. Villee, Ed. (Pergamon, New York, 1961), p. 37.

23. L. W. Self, *Metabolism 14,* 311 (1965).

24. S. M. Husain and G. Pincus, *Am. Zoologist 5,* 660 (1965).

25. A. B. Kar, R. P. Chandra, V. P. Kamboj, F. R. Choudhury, *Indian J. Exp. Biol. 3,* 69 (1965).

26. J. A. Loraine, E. T. Bell, R. A. Harkness, E. Mears, M. C. N. Jackson, *Lancet 1963-II,* 902 (1963).

27. C. R. Garcia, A. P. Satterthwaite, G. Pincus, *Addendum Proc. Intern. Planned Parenthood, Fed. Intern. Congr. Ser. 72* (Excerpta Medica Foundation, Amsterdam, 1964), p. 3.

28. G. Pincus and C. R. Garcia, *Symp. Cancer Utero, 16th. Rev. Inst. Nac. Cancerol.* (Mexico City, 1964), p. 3. *Metabolism 14,* 344 (1965).

29. G. Pincus, *Proc. Symp. 19-Nor Progestational Steroids* (Searle Research Laboratories, Chicago, 1957), p. 105.

30. M. L. Taymor, *J. Clin. Endocrinal. Metab. 24,* 803 (1965); V. C. Stevens, N. Vorys, P. K. Besch, R. D. Barry, *Metabolism 14,* 327 (1965).

31. C. R. Garcia, in *Human Fertility and Population Problems,* R. O. Greep, Ed. (Schenkman, Cambridge, Mass., 1963), p. 43; S. W. Goldzieher, E. Rice-Wray, M. Schulz-Conteras, A. Aranda-Rosell, *Am. J. Obstet. Gynecol. 84,* 1474 (1962).

32. J. P. Peters, E. B. Man, M. Heinemann, in *The Normal and Pathological Physiology of Pregnancy* (Williams and Wilkins, Baltimore, 1948).

33. J. T. Dowling, N. Freinkel, S. H. Ingbar, *J. Clin. Endocrinol. Metab. 16,* 1491 (1965).

34. W. H. Florsheim and M. A. Faircloth, *Proc. Soc. Exp. Biol. Med. 117*, 56 (1964).

35. M. Maneschi, E. Cittadini, P. Quartararo, *Sicilia Sanit. 4*, 135 (1962).

36. E. E. Wallach, C. R. Garcia, R. W. Kistner, G. Pincus, *Am. J. Obstet. Gynecol. 87*, 991 (1963).

37. I. M. Arias, in *Ciba Symposium on Protein Metabolism* (Springer, Berlin, 1962), p. 434.

38. O. Egeberg and P. A. Owren, *Brit. Med. J. 1963-I*, 220 (1963) ; C. Hongie, R. N. Rutherford, A. L. Banks, W. A. Coburn, *Metabolism 14*, 411 (1965) ; J. Donayre and G. Pincus, *ibid.*, p. 418.

39. S. P. Miller, S. L. Lee, N. Ritz, *ibid. 14*, 398 (1965).

40. W. Jordan, *Lancet 1961-II*, 1146 (1961) ; W. F. Minogue, I. C. Halperin, J. Soler-Bechara, P. Varricle, F. B. Flood, *New Eng. J. Med. 266*, 1037 (1963).

41. I. C. Winter, *Metabolism 14*, 418 (1965).

42. Special Report: FDA on Enovid: Ad hoc Advisory Committee for the Evaluation of a Possible Etiologic Relation with Thromboembolic Conditions, *J. Am. Med. Assoc. 185*, 776 (1963).

43. G. Pincus, *Advan. Chem. Ser. 49*, 177 (1965).

44. H. Gershberg, C. Z. Javier, S. M. Halse, *Diabetes 13*, 378 (1964).

45. A. Wiseman, in *Recent Advances in Ovarian and Synthetic Steroids*, R. P. Shearman, Ed. (G. D. Searle, High Wycombe, 1965), p. 206.

46. E. M. Puddy, *ibid.*, p. 233.

47. G. R. Venning, *Metabolism 14*, 457 (1965).

48. E. Mears, in *Biological Council Symposium on Agents Affecting Fertility*, C. R. Austin and J. S. Perry, Eds. (Churchill, London, 1965), p. 211.

Biochemistry of the Pill
Largely Unknown

The 5 to 7 million women in the U.S. who practice birth control by oral contraception have two new versions of "the pill" to choose from: Ortho's 1-mg. Ortho-Novum and Syntex's 1-mg. Norinyl-1 (see table). Yet, for all the interest and energy that companies are putting into developing oral contraceptives (the Food and Drug Administration is studying about 30 more possibilities), and for all the efforts to upgrade safety surveillance, nobody knows fundamentally how the drugs work. For the biochemistry of inhibiting conception by taking drugs remains one of reproductive physiology's more fogbound research areas.

And little wonder. Each woman who uses the pill is daily swallowing tablets containing various synthetic formulations of sex hormones of the type she would routinely produce during pregnancy. Being biochemically pseudopregnant, therefore, she fails to ovulate. Failing to ovulate, she can't conceive. When faced with comprehending this biochemical interplay of brain, glands, and genitalia, most scientists turn to work that leads to quicker publication—such as extrapolating the results of urine and blood analyses.

Fortunately, all is not blood and urine. Molecular biology and intermediary metabolism are slowly becoming the critical areas for studying the mechanisms of both the natural sex hormones and their oral contraceptive counterparts. Work of this type is moving ahead at such centers as the Population Council in New York City; the Universities of Chicago, Wisconsin, and Michigan, and Washington University in St. Louis. Also, to a limited extent, at FDA, the National Institutes of Health, the Worcester Foundation for Experimental Biology, Oxford University (England), San Diego Naval Hospital, and Canada's Food and Drug Directorate.

Several laboratories are probing the action of estrogens and progesterone at the protein synthesis level. Some are at long last tracing

Reprinted from *Chemical & Engineering News:* 44–49 (March 27, 1967) with permission of the publisher.

steroidal pathways through the cell with tritiated agents. Other groups are trying to relate neurochemical triggering mechanisms to hormone production. Still others are studying the effects of estrogens, progesterone, and their synthetic counterparts on the structural chemistry of target tissue such as uterus, ovary, and pituitary. All this activity, though really just beginning, could one day lead to a sort of biochemical systems analysis of steroidal interactions. It also could help to clear up the mass of confusion over the pill's long-term effects in connection with diabetes, cancer, diseases' of the circulatory system, and various interactions possibly too subtle to be noticed now.

And confusion there is. The chemical manipulation of the woman's sex cycle by synthetic estrogens, synthetic progesterones (progestins), and future nonsteroidal contraceptives has posed questions of ultimate effects on her biochemistry and physiology. Moral questions aside, millions of women, their husbands, and a high percentage of their physicians express qualms over whether several unresolved possible risks outweigh the convenience.

The World Health Organization lent authority to such apprehension in a report on oral contraceptives about 18 months ago. "There is at present no adequate explanation for the oral activity of these compounds or of their influence on secretion and metabolism. There have been reports of an apparent rise in pregnancy rates after cessation of combined treatment, an increase in glucose tolerance (with consequent risks of diabetes mellitus), an increase in coagulability of blood, and liver disturbance. All these phenomena need to be investigated."

In contrast, however, clinical data gleaned from observation and research on thousands upon thousands of women point to no apparent relationship between contraceptive therapy and cancer, circulatory system blockages (thromboembolic diseases), thyroid gland abnormalities, and damage to the ovaries, uterus, or Fallopian tubes. This enormous outpouring of safety data lead a special FDA panel on oral contraceptives last August to declare the pills "not unsafe" for human use (C&EN, Aug. 15, 1966, page 19). But it didn't close the door on the possibility of such effects on some particularly susceptible women.

Pharmacologists assert that the oral contraceptives occupy a new niche in drug use. Their presence, in many cases for years, affects the sex endocrinology of healthy women during the prime of their reproductive lives. Not only do they substitute for woman's natural hormonal secretions but, in suppressing ovulation, they also jam the production

Synthetics more active orally than natural agents

Natural progesterone

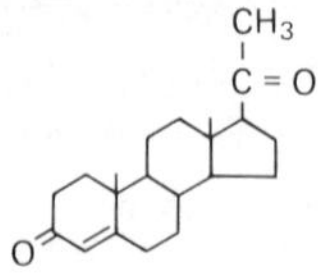

Synthetic progesterones

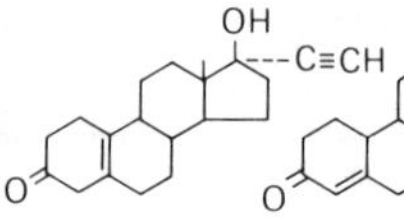

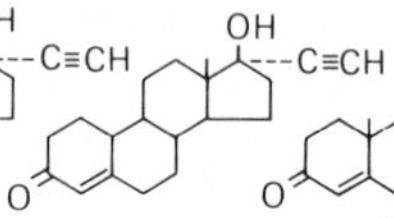

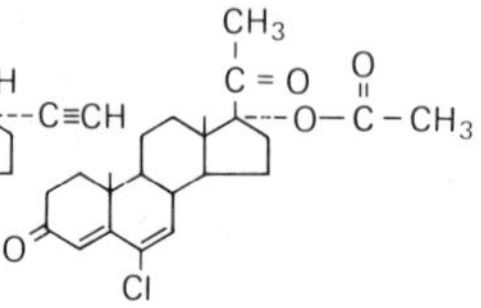

Norethynodrel   Norethindrone   Chlormadinone acetate

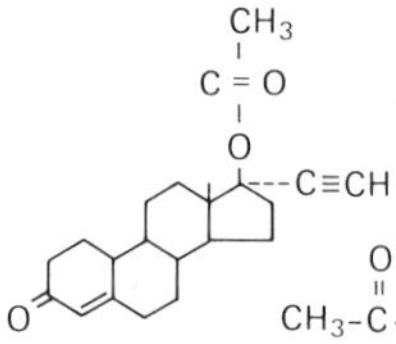

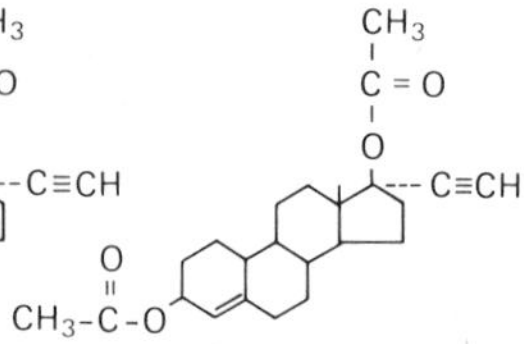

Norethindrone acetate   Ethynodiol diacetate

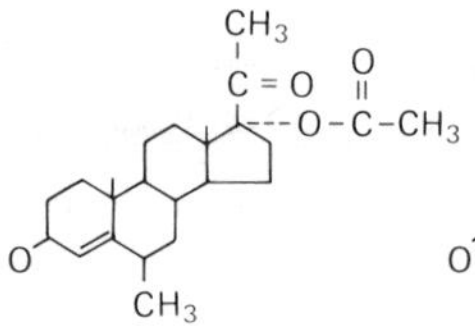

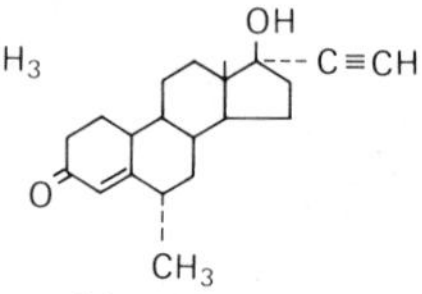

Medroxyprogesterone acetate   Dimethisterone

Natural estrogens

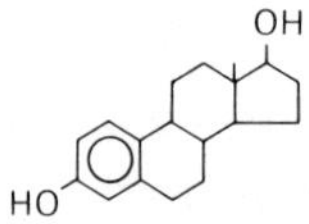

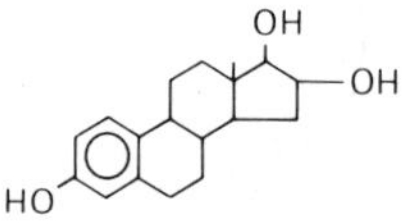

Estriol

Synthetic estrogens

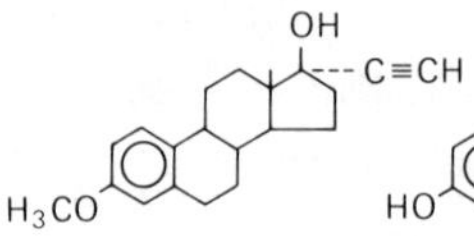

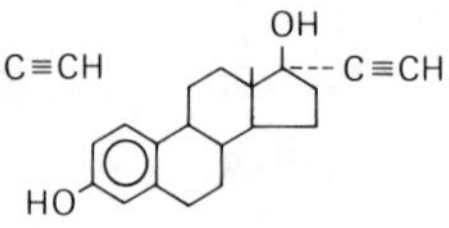

Mestranol   Ethnynylestradiol

Progesterone is weak when taken orally. The ethynyl and other changes at C-17, plus removal of the angular methyl between rings A and B, impart oral activity of progestins. Chlorine or methyl at C-6 also adds to oral potency. Position of norethynodrel's double bond lessens possible androgenic action. Natural estrogens are also weak acting when taken orally. Adding an ethynyl at C-17 eases passage of the compound from the intestines into the blood stream, one concept holds, allowing low dosages.

Seven Drug Firms Market Oral Contraceptives under Eight Brand Names

Product	Manufacturer	FDA clearance	Progestin		Estrogen	
Enovid	G. D. Searle	June 1960	Norethynodrel	9.85 mg.	Mestranol	0.15 mg.
Enovid	G. D. Searle	March 1961	Norethynodrel	5 mg.	Mestranol	0.075 mg.
Enovid-E	G. D. Searle	Feb. 1964	Norethynodrel	2.5 mg.	Mestranol	0.1 mg.
Ortho-Novum	Ortho Pharmaceutical	May 1962	Norethindrone	10 mg.	Mestranol	0.06 mg.
Ortho-Novum	Ortho Pharmaceutical	Oct. 1963	Norethindrone	2 mg.	Mestranol	0.1 mg.
Norinyl	Syntex	March 1964	Norethindrone	2 mg.	Mestranol	0.1 mg.
Norlestrin	Parke-Davis	March 1964	Norethindrone Acetate	2.5 mg.	Ethynyl-Estradiol	0.05 mg.
Provest	Upjohn	Aug. 1964	Medroxyprogesterone Acetate	10 mg.	Ethynyl-Estradiol	0.05 mg.
Oracon[a]	Mead Johnson	April 1965	Dimethisterone	25 mg.	Ethynyl-Estradiol	0.1 mg.
C-Quens[a]	Eli Lilly	April 1965	Chlormadinone Acetate	2.0 mg.	Mestranol	0.08 mg.
Ovulen	G. D. Searle	March 1966	Ethynodiol Diacetate	1 mg.	Mestranol	0.1 mg.
Ortho-Novum SQ[a]	Ortho Pharmaceutical	Dec. 1966	Norethindrone	2 mg.	Mestranol	0.08 mg.
Ortho-Novum-1	Ortho Pharmaceutical	Feb. 1967	Norethindrone	1.0 mg.	Mestranol	0.05 mg.
Norinyl-1	Syntex	Feb. 1967	Norethindrone	1.0 mg.	Mestranol	0.05 mg.

[a] Sequential; all others are combination type.

of her gonadotropic (fertility regulating) hormones: follicle stimulating hormone (FSH) and luteinizing hormone (LH), both glycoproteins. Also, they alter carbohydrate metabolism. And chances are that they affect the pattern of cholesterol metabolism, since that sterol plays such a central and critical role in the synthesis of all body steroids. In short, the ramifications of oral contraceptive use are immensely widespread.

The problem with studying the pill is that little enough is known about normal steroid metabolism per se. Progestin function, for example, seems to differ from dose to dose, from animal to animal, and even from ethnic group to ethnic group, says Dr. Gabriel Bialy of the Worcester Foundation for Experimental Biology. Moreover, the effects on target tissue aren't clearly mapped out.

Effects of the synthetic estrogens—mestranol and ethynylestradiol —are a little less fuzzy. These do indeed suppress ovulation, probably via the hypothalamus, by inhibiting production of a protein that triggers secretion of gonadotropin in the pituitary. And they're considerably more powerful than the progestins (see dosages on table).

With this background—the question of subtle dangers and the purely academic fascination—specifically what headway are scientists making toward unraveling this complex biochemistry? The story might well begin at the University of Chicago's Ben May Laboratory for Cancer Research, in the laboratory of Dr. Elwood V. Jensen.

Organic chemist Jensen was the first to demonstrate the existence of a substance he calls estrogen receptor in the cells of certain target tissue. He remembers his surprise at the swiftness and intensity with which the receptor collected and concentrated estradiol in uterine, vaginal, pituitary, and estrogen-dependent tumor tissue.

"We studied testosterone and progesterone, too," he adds, "but found that only estrogen had such remarkable affinity for this material, as well as certain synthetic estrogens such as hexesterol. Estrogens seem to bind to the receptor and exert their action without undergoing chemical transformation."

Recent studies by Dr. Jensen and colleague Peter Jungblutt indicate that the receptor is a macromolecule containing protein, phosphorus, ribose, and sulfhydryls (which appear essential to the binding). The receptor also seems to be part of the nuclear membrane. As an interesting sidelight, Dr. Jensen recently reported on the interaction between the receptor protein and the oral contraceptive estrogen, mestranol. It turns out that mestranol itself has little affinity for the receptor, but undergoes demethylation in the liver to form ethynylestradiol, which does bind.

Dr. Jensen's studies have helped build the base for the work on the cellular dynamics of estrogens being pursued a quick hop away in Madison, Wis. There, Dr. Gerald C. Mueller of the McArdle Laboratory for Cancer Research at the University of Wisconsin is using uterine tissue as a model system for studying Jensen's hormone-receptor complex in the broader context of the role of estrogens in protein synthesis.

Some months ago, Dr. Mueller and his group showed that estrogen sparked the growth of uterine tissue by direct effect on protein synthesis, through stepped-up production of RNA (ribonucleic acid) in the nucleus. They noticed that there was an increase in RNA polymerase activity—the enzyme which catalyzes the RNA synthesis—just after estrogen was added. But of much interest, in their opinion, is that this higher polymerase activity correlated with the production of protein elsewhere in the cell. In other words, two events were taking place: Protein was being produced somewhere else in the cell; it was affecting the synthesis of RNA via its polymerase.

"We interpret this to mean," Dr. Mueller says, "that this other protein is modifying the activity of the polymerase because if we decrease protein we stop the activity of the polymerase."

Where does estrogen fit into this process? Mueller thinks that it's either facilitating the manufacture of the other protein or helping to transport it to the polymerase area. As for the receptor protein, it could well be acting as a carrier of the estrogen to the site of action.

Progesterone's action is an even bigger mystery. But work by Dr. Walter G. Weist of Washington University (St. Louis) medical school is uncovering some clues. In labeling experiments, he has found that progesterone, like estrogen, also encounters a receptor in uterine cells during the progesterone-dependent proliferative phase of endometrial growth (when the endometrium is being readied to receive the fertilized egg).

Studies of the type being done by Dr. Jensen, Dr. Mueller, and Dr. Weist—as well as the related research of Jack Gorski of the University of Illinois and Sheldon Segal of the Population Council—are indeed scarce in endocrinology today because they're at the level of molecular biology. But this is the trend, and rather a necessary one, in the opinion of Dr. Weist. "Steroid distribution studies, too, are a must," he says. "That is, it must be determined where they tend to distribute in

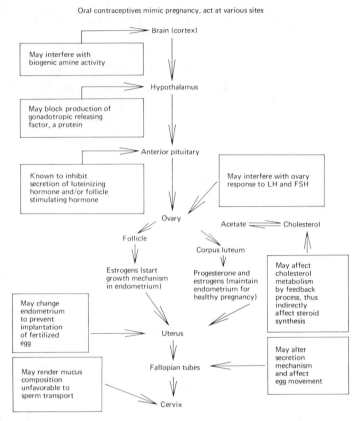

Oral contraceptives mimic pregnancy, act at various sites

All of the oral contraceptives now on the market are designed to mimic pregnancy. Since a pregnant woman does not ovulate, there are no subsequent eggs to fertilize and hence no multiple pregnancies. Normally, the female part of the reproductive process starts with physiologically timed stimuli that reach the brain (cortex), which, via the hypothalamus, stimulates the pituitary to secrete follicle-stimulating and luteinizing hormones (FSH and LH). These hormones are involved in the growth of ovarian follicles, rupture of the follicle to release its egg, secretion of the female sex hormone estradiol (an estrogen), change of the follicular cell into the corpus luteum, and secretion of progesterone. Estradiol is involved in the growth of the uterine lining (endometrium); progesterone is involved in preparing the lining for implantation and nutritive support of the fertilized egg and in preventing the development of more follicles and eggs. The natural estrogens and progesterone, secreted by the ovary and later the placenta, inhibit the secretion of FSH and LH during pregnancy and thus prevent ovulation. When a nonpregnant woman ovulates and fertilization does not take place, secretion of progesterone stops, the uterine lining breaks down, and sloughs off. This is menstruation. The entire cycle in the nonpregnant woman takes about 28 days. The synthetic estrogens and progestins in the birth control pills produce the same effects as the natural hormones. Their basic difference is that they are modified chemically so that they can enter the woman's system when taken orally. Two types of birth control pills (and treatments) are on the market: combined and sequential. In combined treatment, each pill conthe target cell, how and to what they are bound, and their metabolic fate. The big hooker is how you assess the physiological results of cell-hormone interaction."

Hookers do indeed abound in this field. For example, in vitro studies of steroid metabolism could clear away dozens of parameters that muddy results obtained with whole tissue. But all attempts to isolate reaction systems in the necessary lipid environment have meant destruction of one enzymic component or another. Moreover, cell biologists haven't succeeded in growing target tissue outside the cell. Some work along this line is being pursued at Worcester Foundation, but so far without astonishing success. Needed is a chemical medium that prevents the cells from reverting as they do with maddening routine to a primitive, unrecognizable state.

But metabolic studies are beginning to emerge from the what-goes-in-what-comes-out stage into the what-happens-inside phase.

Dr. Donald S. Layne of Canada's Food and Drug Directorate, Ottawa (a counterpart of the U.S.'s FDA), is examining changes in the chemical structure of progestins by some inherent action in the tissues that localize them (liver, kidney, and target organs).

He has found, in one study, that norethynodrel is peroxidized in the blood stream shortly after administration. "This could implicate the blood as an important site of metabolism of norethynodrel," he reported recently. "Further," he says, "the hydroperoxy intermediate has recently been shown to be as potent an ovulation inhibitor as norethynodrel itself, although it has little progesterone-like activity. This indicates that classical progestogenic action is not necessary for contraceptive action."

Work on how the steroids affect the structural chemistry of target tissue has come out of the U.S. Naval Hospital in San Diego, Calif., under Dr. Thomas B. Lebherz. His group has found, for example, that the normal buildup of endometrium involves polymerization of acid mucopolysaccharides, the so-called "ground substance" material that structurally fortifies living tissue. Such a physical framework is needed to support the thickening web of blood vessels that bring nourishment to the fertilized egg after implantation.

---

tains both estrogen and progestin. Generally, the woman takes one pill a day for 21 days, stops for seven days (menstruation period), and resumes taking the pills. In sequential treatment, she takes only an estrogen for 16 days, then a combination pill for five or six days (depending on the product). She then stops until the 28th day before resuming.

With progesterone, Dr. Lebherz has found, the ground substance depolymerizes, a sol state ensues, and the softened endometrium (also undergoing a phase of intense secretion) facilitates implantation of the fertilized egg. Dr. Lebherz theorizes that with oral contraceptive progestins, which in low doses apparently prevent implantation, the sol-gel effect via the acid mucopolysaccharides is thrown out of phase so that, before the sol effect sets in, the egg has already arrived and failed to implant.

FDA's Bureau of Science (now in the process of redefining its mission) is making modest efforts toward getting at some of the scientific issues that could lead to a deeper insight into mechanisms. But much of this work is preliminary and is hindered by FDA's notorious manpower shortage. Anyway, under Dr. Ernest Umberger at the Bureau of Science, scientists are beginning to look into such areas as the effects of steroids on liver enzymes, the role of receptor protein in estrogen and progesterone metabolism, and uptake of estrogen by the hypothalamus. In a study on hamster ovulation, Dr. Umberger's group has found that monoamine oxidase prevents ovulation at the hypothalamus level by blocking release of the luteinizing hormone releasing factor. Several laboratories, incidentally, have tried to characterize this factor but so far can do no better than call it a protein.

What appear now to be the future patterns of basic research in the sex steroid-oral contraceptive field? Dr. Gregory G. Pincus of Worcester Foundation thinks ovulation mechanism studies are the vogue-to-be. "The locus of action seems to be the central nervous system but nobody knows where," he told C&EN. Dr. Geoffrey Harris of Oxford University has recently shown in rabbit studies that the primary site of action could well be at a higher level than the hypothalamus. There seem to be connections between such nervous system metabolites as serotonin, noradrenaline, and prostaglandin and the hypothalamic control of ovulation. One typical idea is that biogenic amines are responsible for inhibiting ovulation and that the sex steroids block breakdown by amines, thereby causing suppression of gonadotropin. Dr. Pincus thinks such mechanism studies must be related to all types of ovulation inhibitory agents alone and combined.

The overall picture that can be drawn after discussions with individuals in basic endocrinology laboratories, in industry, and in Government is lack of agreement on exactly what paths to take in exploring all the ramifications of oral contraception mechanisms. One scientist throws his hands up over the hope of making any immediate headway.

The field is too volatile, he says, products are changing, events in the field don't stand still long enough to even set up the proper experiments. Steroid metabolism work is simply confoundedly difficult. Only clinical studies, at least for this era, yield the quick results most investigators in the field seem to want.

Adds another scientist from a private research foundation: "The trouble in this field is that aside from purely physiological and pharmacological considerations, you know that almost all investigations are done in mutual vacuums. All specify one drug or another; there's little comparative work in the same lab, no unified approach.

"Purely independent work is difficult because so much of it is supported by industry. Government takes months to respond to a proposal. Another hindrance to objective results, and I think this ought to be said, is that too many investigators have too personal an interest in the drugs they work with. All in all I get the feeling that the experimental aspects of this field are so fluid and so controversial that you must be careful over who says what and why he says it."

Whether the scientists do indeed prejudge their studies is something nearly impossible to document. But what is needed is better research coordination and improved rapport between biochemists, clinicians, and physiologists. "Another of the troubles in this field," one scientist told C&EN, "is that many of the big names in steroids frown on basic work on the pill. Those that go ahead with such research immediately get tagged as a toxicologist, or worse yet, a commercial boy. It's ridiculous, but that's the attitude of mind."

Many scientists think the Government is the logical place for a coordinated program to understand all aspects of oral contraceptive action. But no such program exists, despite the recommendation of a special advisory committee to establish one a couple of years ago in the National Institute for Child Health and Human Development. The special advisory committee was asked to suggest research programs in the then new institute, and among the recommendations was a multidisciplined effort at unraveling problems connected with contraception. But the recommendation was turned down by the National Institutes of Health.

Research on the metabolism of the pill seems to be run in scattered fashion at NIH. There appears to be little effort to coordinate NICHHD's oral contraceptive research with that being pursued in considerable volume at the neighboring cancer, heart, general medicine, and allergic and metabolic disease institutes within the organization.

The final note, an ironic one, involves the position of industry. Industry has helped find, and has certainly inspired, some of the research on the frontiers of reproductive biochemistry. Yet, the drug industry is the last to be identified with an aggressive search for solutions to problems of biological science as they relate to public issues. This is unfortunate although consistent with a competitive economy.

One nonindustry chemist commented to C&EN that "Industry isn't shoving very hard to delve into some of these problems because they know that what's found could work against, as well as for, them. Yet I have to say truthfully that they've been quite generous in the support of my work."

The feeling persists that several companies do have significant mechanism data in endocrinology but save it for two reasons: It could lead to new products or, if publicized, could also lead to disfavor on the part of the Government. So industry plays it conservatively.

In FDA's oral contraceptive report last year, Dr. Schuyler G. Kohl of the State University of New York, Brooklyn, suggested that companies pool some of their money and establish a thorough surveillance program of patients under contraceptive therapy. (Surveillance is the biggest drawback to reliable safety data.) The same suggestion might apply to an inter-industry research effort on fundamental problems, perhaps through a special institute of basic studies. The closest approach to this is the Pharmaceutical Manufacturers Association Foundation, which, as of now, is a low-key effort of modest support to some investigators.

3

The Spoilers

I charge and command that, of the city's cost, the
pissing conduit run nothing but claret wine this
first year of our reign.
—JACK CADE, IN *Henry the Sixth*

Man is the most untidy of the higher animals, and the most destructive
of his environment. His gregarious nature seems to be in disharmony
with the tendency to foul his nest, whether it be to throw trash on the
beach, spill his waste in the drinking water, or dump garbage for the
rats to devour. His slovenly habits might suffice for a precarious
existence, even in the congestion of cities, but for the fact that industrialization has enormously aggravated the pollution of his environment.

Actually pollution is neither a new problem nor unique to mankind.
The most primitive one-cell creatures must escape from their wastes or
die. The most successful parasites do not kill their hosts with their
toxins but, instead, permit their victims to survive long enough to
nurture a few generations of the pestilence. Survival of the species is
dependent on such favorable relationships with the environment.

While there is unthinkable disparity in cleanliness between the rich
and the poor of the earth, in those areas where men have become most
affluent we are still little better off than the people in Knossus of
ancient Crete, who had the fresh Mediterranean breeze, flush toilets,
and no refineries. The population explosion has caught us unaware,
while our industry has progressed further and faster than our collec-
tive ability to cope with the headaches and the hangover from our
technological binge.

Air, water, and soil are becoming the dumping grounds for unwanted materials of every conceivable sort. The atmosphere is becoming over-burdened, almost to the limit of human endurance, with the poisonous constituents of smog from industry and automobile exhausts. Water, in ever shorter supply, receives enormous quantities of chemical wastes of known and unknown properties. Rivers, lakes, and oceans are becoming toxic to the point of near extinction for many desirable forms of animal and plant life, to say nothing of the hazards to human health.

Radioactive polonium from fallout is found in tobacco and radioactive strontium in milk. Strontium-90, used by the body in place of calcium, concentrates in the bones; radioactive cesium, also found in the environment after nuclear explosions, is picked up by foodstuffs and behaves like potassium when absorbed by the body. Iodine-131, another residue from radioactive fallout, is absorbed and adversely affects the activity of the thyroid gland. Other radioactive substances, as well, find their way into the food chain where they may in the long run have serious, though as yet undetermined, consequences.

Both soil and water show the presence of agricultural pesticides, as evidenced by concentrations of 30 or more pounds per acre in the marshlands of estuaries and by the recovery of DDT from arctic reindeer and antarctic penguins as well as from temperate land animals and fish in the coastal sea. DDT is found in the body fat of Alaskan natives as well as in the general population of the United States.

Lead from gasoline is found in the ocean off the California coast. Petroleum oil from refineries has made harbor waters unfit for fishing or swimming and threatens some species of commercial and sport fish to the threshold of extinction. Sewage outfalls modify the river and coastal environment and in the latter have slowly caused local, and possibly widespread, extinction of many forms of marine algae, the growth of which is essential for many types of fish and other valuable marine life.

The Battle of Lake Erie: Eutrophication and Political Fragmentation

Kathleen Sperry

Cleveland. As any nose can detect on a warm day, Lake Erie, the oldest and shallowest of the Great Lakes, is an ailing body of water. Its affliction, known as eutrophication, is a natural disease of aging lakes. But, in the case of Lake Erie, the inevitable is being accelerated by a daily overdose of some 150,000 pounds of phosphates, which, ironically, are a by-product of man's penchant for cleanliness. Since most of the phosphates have been traced to expended detergents, it might seem that the problem could be alleviated in one way or another. But, as has been demonstrated on innumerable occasions, the technology of pollution control cannot be considered apart from the economics and politics of pollution.

Eutrophication is characterized by changing biota, and particularly by dense algal blooms that deplete oxygen from the bottom layers of lake water when the algae decay, foul beaches when they wash ashore, and sometimes cause odor and discoloration of drinking water (*Science, 158:* 278, 280, 282 (1967).

Statistics compiled by the Federal Water Pollution Control Administration's (FWPCA) Great Lakes Program in Cleveland indicate that 80 percent of the phosphates entering Lake Erie are first treated by municipal sewer plants. Of those phosphates, 66 percent originate in detergents. The FWPCA takes the position that the eutrophication problem in Erie can be alleviated by removing phosphates from detergents and from treated sewage effluents.

Because no one favors pollution, the soap and detergent industry, which grosses $2 billion annually, has been left in the position of having to favor eutrophication control measures while quietly pointing out that it is not solely to blame. The industry is especially sensitive since just 2 years ago it completed a $150-million changeover to the manufacture of biodegradable detergents. It did this after having been singled out as responsible for turning numerous rivers, lakes, and water supplies into giant bubble baths.

Charles G. Bueltman, technical director of the Soap and Detergent Association, said during an interview with *Science* that the industry is now being cited as the major cause of eutrophication because the government knows the industry will cooperate to find a solution. The industry has already proved its public-spiritedness by voluntarily seeking and finding a substitute for the suds situation, Bueltman says. Critics of the detergent industry assert that the industry came up with a remedy only because legislation was being threatened which would have forced it to do so anyway. Bueltman denies this, saying the industry started a program in 1951 to find a substitute for the surface active agent that was causing the problem. In 1932 it announced that a substitute substance had been found and that an industry-wide changeover would be made. According to Bueltman, most of the legislation threats were not made until after the switch had been announced.

The industry asserts that most of the new burst of finger-pointing in its direction did not begin until 1965, the year of the first Lake Erie Enforcement Conference. Bueltman says that the detergent industry began an intramural program of phosphate research in 1958, and that even if a substitute were discovered today it would be 7 to 10 years before an industry changeover could be completed. Just how much the industry is spending on the research is a secret. Bueltman says no figures are released because they would appear minuscule beside the industry's annual expenditure on advertising. He adds, however, that about 150 people are now working on research for the industry, and that as much money is being spent as can be effectively used.

Bueltman admits the industry has been approached by government agencies regarding federal support for its research, in an attempt to speed solution of the problem. He says his reply has been, "You do not legislate an invention."

Because phosphates have many advantages, they have proved difficult to replace. In detergents, sodium tripolyphosphate acts to soften water; sequester objectionable elements such as iron, thus preventing rust; disperse and suspend dirt; emulsify grease; and buffer alkalinity. When sodium tripolyphosphate is combined with surfactant, the other major ingredient in detergents, the two have a synergic action.

Though the industry has often pointed out that it is not the sole source of phosphates linked with eutrophication, if a substitute product were found, Bueltman says, it probably would be cheaper for the industry to convert to its use than to continue to argue, against public opinion. He notes that the total effects of any phosphate substitute on eutrophication would be unknown, and possibly would be more detrimental than phosphates.

A viable argument for reduction, if not elimination, of phosphates from detergents is the fact that the percentage of phosphates in detergents varies substantially between products designed to perform the same duties. The phosphate content of heavy-duty laundry powders ranges from 35 to 57 percent. That of powders for automatic dishwashers ranges from 25 to 50 percent. Liquid detergents contain the smallest quantities of phosphates; the range is between 15 and 25 percent for heavy-duty cleaners and between 0 and 10 percent for detergents designed for light cleaning.

In Cleveland, where the Cuyahoga River empties into Lake Erie, the problem of pollution is readily apparent. There it is caused not by eutrophication but by the wastes that are commonly associated with biological pollution. Whether eutrophication itself is pollution is a debatable point. George Harlow, who heads the FWPCA's Great Lakes Program, believes it is. He says accelerated eutrophication is caused by man, "and that is pollution."

For Cleveland, as for most of the other cities that lie within the Lake Erie drainage basin, the lake serves not only as a dumping area for sewage but also as the city water supply. It is also valued for providing economic transportation, recreation, esthetic values, and commercial and sports fishing. Transportation suffers little or nothing from eutrophication, but the same cannot be said for the other uses.

The Erie problem is complicated by the sheer size of the lake. Within its drainage area are a Canadian province and five states, only four of which touch the lake's 761-mile shoreline. Only since 1965, when the Department of Health, Education, and Welfare (HEW) called the first Lake Erie Enforcement Conference at the request of Governor James A. Rhodes of Ohio, have the states worked together toward establishing uniform pollution standards. Since that time there have been four Lake Erie Enforcement Conferences, attended by representatives of the five states and observers from Ontario. The FWPCA, which has been transferred from HEW to the Department of the Interior, has acted as sponsor. The conferences have produced a plan designed to curb biological pollution by 1 January 1970. Phosphate removal is one of the objectives of the plan, implementation of which is expected to cost municipalities and industry within the Erie basin $1.2 billion. However, phosphate concentrations are not expected to be substantially reduced as a result of the gigantic expenditure. Similar recommendations have been developed by the United States and Canada under the International Joint Commission, which is concerned with pollution flowing across the international boundary to the injury of health or property on the other side.

Harlow is convinced that a substantial reduction of phosphates in detergents and their removal in waste treatments plants would eventually curb eutrophication in Lake Erie. The "biggest problem in Lake Erie . . . is applying knowledge we already have, not doing more research," Harlow told *Science* during an interview. Although he would like to see the detergent industry come up with a substitute ingredient —possibly a nonsoluble phosphate—he believes sewage-treatment technologists have provided an answer to the problem of removing the bulk of phosphates during the treatment process.

Originally the Lake Erie conferees decided that some 90 percent of the phosphates flowing through treatment plants should be removed, but they considered the task formidable if not impossible, and abandoned it in favor of the edict to "maximize" removal. Neither Detroit nor Cleveland, the two largest cities discharging effluents into Erie, plan to do anything about phosphate removal. Said Walter E. Gerdel, Cleveland's commissioner for water-pollution control, "We don't know how to do it and we don't think anyone else does either."

Somewhat accidentally the FWPCA has come up with a program for phosphate removal. A press release from Interior Secretary Udall's office last year noted that FWPCA scientists and engineers had discovered the process while reviewing operational data of three similar treatment plants in San Antonio, Texas, one of which achieved substantially greater phosphate removal than the other two did. After studies, the FWPCA devised a program designed to obtain the same results in other treatment plants by increasing aeration, concentrating bacteria, and reducing the time for the settling of solids.

It may be that there are a number of accidental combinations of such factors which would maximize phosphate removal. Gerdel said one of Cleveland's two secondary-treatment facilities removes from 60 to 70 percent of the phosphates in the sewage. The other plant removes only 30 percent. Detroit's general manager of the Department of Water Supply, Gerald Remus, said laboratory tests in Detroit indicate that combining pickling acids from steel mills with waste effluents will do a good job of removing phosphates. But, he noted, it may be that the process works because of Detroit's "particular kind of waste." Gerdel said he believes the answer to the problem should come from the federal government, "because they're in the research and development business."

Harlow believes that, because Erie's 125-trillion gallons of water are turned over once every 3 years, much of the algae problem could be eliminated if the entry of phosphates were substantially reduced. In opposition to his position are some authorities who doubt that the algal growth would diminish even if treatment plants achieved 100-percent removal of phosphates. Of the estimated 150,000 pounds of phosphates that enter Lake Erie daily, only 50,000 pounds are discharged from the lake by way of its outlet, the Niagara River. The rest are retained. According to FWPCA data, sources of phosphates entering Erie are as follows: Lake Huron and rural-land runoff, each 20,000 pounds daily; municipal wastes, 70,000 pounds from detergents, 30,000 pounds from human excreta, and 6000 pounds from urban land runoff; direct industrial discharges, 6000 pounds daily.

While admitting that there is much yet to be learned about eutrophication, Harlow says that the algae problem would cease if the phosphate concentrations in Erie could be reduced to 0.01 milligram per liter. Studies of some lakes have revealed conditions that appeared to be right for an extensive algal bloom but none appeared. There have also been reports of blooms when phosphate levels were below those prescribed by Harlow. Despite scattered reports that do not back the FWPCA's diagnosis for Erie, both the phosphate and algal distributions in the lake tend to support the FWPCA's position. In Erie's western basin, where phosphate concentrations are the highest, ranging from 0.05 to 0.15 milligram per liter, the algal blooms are the heaviest. The central basin has lower phosphate concentrations and fewer algae, and the eastern basin, which has the least phosphate, has practically no algae problem.

Effects of eutrophication in Erie have been primarily associated with extensive changes in the fishing industry, with beaches that sometimes have been fouled with from 6 inches to 3 feet of decaying algae, and with odors and discoloration of drinking water. The Fish and Wildlife Service has surveyed the lake extensively in an attempt to analyze the changing fisheries resources. Since the turn of the century, the major commercial species of fish have all but disappeared from the lakes, while catches of medium-quality fish have soared. In addition, the bottom fauna has undergone extensive change. The change in biota has been attributed to decreased amounts of dissolved oxygen in the lower waters —possibly due to decaying algae. However, a report[1] issued by the Fish and Wildlife Service in July indicates that there may be many other factors involved, including a biochemical oxygen demand by the bottom sediments.

Although the changes in fish population have been observed over more than half a century, in Cleveland the water supply problem was first noticed last summer. To date, FWPCA research on eutrophication has been done at Lake Shawaga in Minnesota, at Klamath Lake in Oregon, and at Lake Sabasticook in Maine. But researchers are still a long way from reaching any unanimous conclusions about accelerated eutrophication. Some of them cite the possibility of substances other than phosphates playing a key role. For example, the potential importance of nitrates has been emphasized by several investigators.

Several bills have been introduced into Congress this session calling for additional research on eutrophication, but even without congressional action the problem is likely to come under much closer scrutiny. A task force made up of FWPCA officials and representatives of the detergent and chemical industries was named recently by Secretary Udall to analyze the role of phosphates in eutrophication and to determine what, if any, steps can be taken to stop the process, and how lakes that have already been affected can be rehabilitated.

While the FWPCA's Great Lakes program has been intent on attempting to eliminate phosphates from detergents, several other phosphate contributors have been largely overlooked. Of the 10 million people on the U.S. side of the Erie drainage basin, about half a million rely on septic systems that are not regulated with regard to use of phosphates. Likewise, there are no controls over disposal of wastes from ships, except for prohibitions on the dumping of oil into the lake.

---

[1] *"Fish and Wildlife as Related to Water Quality of the Lake Erie Basin,"* U.S. Fish and Wildlife Service Publication (*1967*).

Shipping tonnage has nearly doubled on Erie in the last 10 years. Agricultural chemicals have been ignored because it is thought that agricultural runoff is largely uncontrollable.

Even with the $1.2-billion program that is supposed to clean up Erie's biological pollution, the largest cities on the lake will continue to dump inadequately processed sewage with high phosphate concentrations into the lake during periods of heavy rain. Both Detroit and Cleveland have combined sanitary and storm sewers that carry untreated waste effluents into the lake along with storm runoff. In Cleveland, two of the overflow storm sewers enter the lake at bathing beaches.

At the moment, most of the talk about the eutrophication around Erie appears to be nothing more than a lot of warm air that is being used to sail incriminating charges back and forth across the lake. In view of the funereal pace at which the problem is being studied, Erie may have passed into its death throes before the doctors are even sure of the disease—let alone the cure.

Implications of Rising Carbon Dioxide Content of the Atmosphere

introduction and summary

Carbon dioxide is not a pollutant in the ordinary sense. It is colorless and odorless. It has no immediate nasty effects. Even the largest amount likely to accumulate in the atmosphere, if the entire reserve of fossil fuels were burned, would not be detrimental to the existence of life; in fact, plant life would be more luxuriant. It is an inevitable product of combustion and cannot be filtered out or precipitated out. Ordinary pollutants are washed out of the atmosphere after a month or so; carbon dioxide will continue to accumulate as long as fossil fuels continue to be burned at present rates.

There is a lack of exact knowledge of the carbon cycle which is part of the general lack of quantitative knowledge of the biogeochemistry of the earth. The increasing funds available for general research and the improving coordination of research effort should help to reduce the uncertainties about the implications of the rise in atmospheric carbon dioxide.

It seems quite certain that a continuing rise in the amount of atmospheric carbon dioxide is likely to be accompanied by a significant warming of the surface of the earth which by melting the polar ice caps would raise sea level and by warming the oceans would change considerably the distributions of marine species including commercial fisheries.

The biogeochemical system of the surface of the earth is, in general, very stable and has persisted with little change over geologically long periods of time. However, the buffering mechanisms which have been

Reprinted by permission from "Implications of Rising Carbon Dioxide Content of the Atmosphere," published by The Conservation Foundation, 1963. Pp. 2–15.

adequate in the past seem unlikely to be able to compensate fully for changes of the magnitude of those now being effected by man.

The effects of a rise in atmospheric carbon dioxide are world-wide. They are significant not to us but to the generations to follow. The consumption of fossil fuel has increased to such a pitch within the last half century that the total atmospheric consequences are matters of concern for the planet as a whole. Although there is the possibility of capturing the CO_2 formed by the burning of fossil fuels and storing it in the form of carbonates, relief is most likely through the development of new sources of power.

the carbon dioxide system

The carbon dioxide (CO_2) in the atmosphere is in constant exchange with the oceans and the biosphere. The amount of CO_2 in the atmosphere is being increased by the burning of fossil fuels; in addition a very small amount is added by volcanic activity. Carbon is removed from the biosphere and indirectly from the atmosphere and oceans by the accumulation of organic remains in sedimentary deposits and from the oceans by the precipitation of carbonate minerals. Carbon is removed from the biosphere by forest fires and by the cultivation of virgin soils and is added to the biosphere by such things as the production of new forest.

Of all the changes in the distribution of CO_2 only those concerning the atmosphere have been studied in any detail. In addition to the average yearly increase in CO_2 in the atmosphere of 0.7 ppm there is a clearly defined seasonal variation of 2.0 ppm in the northern hemisphere between 45° N and 90° N with a winter maximum and a summer minimum. This seasonal variation decreases with increasing altitude and is related to the seasonal changes in the transpiration rates of terrestrial plants. The southern hemisphere with less land and a far smaller terrestrial mass shows almost no seasonal variation. There is also a poleward flux of CO_2 of 5.0 ppm per year which is presumed to be balanced by an equatorward flux of CO_2 in the oceans.

If all the CO_2 added to the atmosphere by the burning of fossil fuels were retained by the atmosphere, the CO_2 content of the atmosphere would be increasing at a rate of 1.6 ppm per year. Studies of the distribution of radioactive carbon have shown that in fact an amount of CO_2 equal to about half of this "new" carbon from fossil fuels is retained in the atmosphere each year. This agrees very closely with the observed rate of increase of 0.7 ppm. The CO_2 content of the atmosphere in 1890 was 290 ppm, or 25 ppm less than the current figure. This again is about half of the amount known to have been produced by the burning of fossil fuels since 1890. It is assumed that the "new" CO_2 not retained by the atmosphere has been absorbed by the oceans, although no measurements have been made which demonstrate this. It should be realized that the man-caused changes when considered on a yearly basis are of smaller magnitude than naturally occurring variations and are, therefore, very difficult to distinguish.

The oceans contain 60 times as much CO_2 as does the atmosphere and would seem capable of absorbing most of any CO_2 which might be added to the atmosphere; however, thousands of years will be necessary for the system to return to equilibrium if CO_2 continues to be added at present rates. There are, as well, physical and chemical limitations to the amount of CO_2 which would be absorbed by the oceans and were a new equilibrium to be reached, the atmosphere would have a greater percentage of the total CO_2 than it does at the present time. The oceans are considered to be divided into a mixed layer at the surface (which is about $\frac{1}{60}$ of the total volume and which contains an amount of CO_2 very nearly equal to that contained in the atmosphere) and the deep sea. (For some purposes it is convenient to consider, as well, an intermediate layer.) The deep sea is assumed to be absorbing about the same amount of the "new" CO_2 as is being retained by the atmosphere but the mechanism by which this CO_2 might be transferred to the deep sea is not known. The deep sea is considered to have an excess of CO_2 (over the value it should have at equilibrium) of around 10 percent which is maintained by the settling of organic remains. The deep sea, in addition, has a greater potential for storing CO_2 than the mixed layer because of its lower temperature (a circulation effect due to the presence of polar ice caps). Knowledge is limited by the difficulty of measuring the amount of CO_2 in the oceans, at least on a scale grand enough to provide a world-wide balance sheet.

The role and importance of the biosphere is less well understood than that of the atmosphere or the oceans. It has been postulated that the marine biota is quite stable in size and is probably nearly unaffected by the current increase in CO_2; however, there is considerable disagreement about this. The terrestrial biota, on the other hand, must be of considerable importance. Productivity of plants is known to be higher in a CO_2 rich atmosphere. Presumably forest productivity is rising with the increase in atmospheric CO_2. This could have the effect of reducing the amount of CO_2 by locking it up in tree trunks. On the other hand, a decrease in the terrestrial biomass, due to the cutting of forests and the cultivation of virgin land, would add CO_2 to the atmosphere and at the same time destroy one of the mechanisms by which CO_2 is removed from the atmosphere.

stability

The CO_2 system is no exception to the general rule that any large natural system which has persisted for a long time is a very stable one. Even rather large changes in temperature or large additions of CO_2 (from fossil fuels) are compensated for with little immediately noticeable change. A warming of the oceans would increase atmospheric CO_2 at a rate of about 5.8 percent for a one degree rise in temperature, but the largest change which might be anticipated within a reasonable range of temperature is about 50 percent. A reduction in the volume of the oceans of the order of that during the maximum extent of Pleistocene glaciation might increase atmospheric CO_2 by about 10 percent but this would be partly compensated for by the lower temperature of the sea. Associated with higher temperature and the accompanying higher absolute humidity would be increased cloudiness which would probably have the effect of reducing the amount of any increase in temperature.

The burning of fossil fuel which adds CO_2 to the atmosphere also adds enough sulphur dioxide so that one third of all atmospheric sulphur (and one quarter of the total sulphur in oceans and atmosphere together) is now man-made. Sulphur dioxide eventually becomes sulphuric acid in the oceans; it is quite possible that the resulting change in alkalinity is enough to enable the surface layer to absorb about 0.5 ppm per year of the atmospheric CO_2, or approximately one third of the yearly addition of CO_2 to the system. This, of course, depends upon the sulphuric acid being retained in the surface layer. Sulphur is also an important fertilizer of the biosphere and the increase in atmospheric sulphur might cause an increase in biologic activity which would further reduce atmospheric CO_2.

Another check is the increase in biologic productivity which accompanies a rise in atmospheric CO_2. An increase in the amount of carbon in the terrestrial biomass would remove carbon from the atmosphere. (If the mixed layer of the oceans is actually taking up 0.5 ppm of CO_2 from the atmosphere each year, then the increase in atmospheric CO_2

could be due to destruction of part of the biosphere.) A considerable part of the addition to the biomass would be wood in trees, and this carbon would, in effect, be unavailable for quite a long time. However, the ratio between carbon in the terrestrial biomass and carbon in the atmosphere is not likely to change much; and, therefore, the biosphere can absorb only a part of any CO_2 added to the atmosphere. If CO_2 is fertilizing the terrestrial plants we should be able to see larger seasonal oscillations in the atmospheric CO_2.

A further possibility of a biologic check is the increased rate of accumulation of organic remains in oceanic sediments which might accompany an increase in marine biological productivity and which would remove CO_2 from the biosphere.

In general, many of the changes in the CO_2 system that have been investigated are believed to be compensated for, at least in part, by some other change (often triggered by the initial change which was being studied). Even though the checks and balances are numerous there are not enough data available to evaluate them with certainty. The present liberation of such large amounts of fossil carbon in such a short time is unique in the history of the earth and there is no guarantee that past buffering mechanisms are really adequate. It is not a cause for complacency that nature seems to have a lot of checks and that these checks seem thus far to be controlling any artificial imbalances. There may be processes presently going on which are due to man's activities and which will eventually be alarming.

the increase of carbon dioxide and its effects

Three of the minor constituents of the atmosphere—carbon dioxide, water vapor and ozone—are very important in the heat balance of the earth because they absorb radiation in a critical part of the spectrum. Any large change in the amounts of these in the atmosphere (even though the overall composition of the atmosphere remains nearly the same) will affect the surface temperature of the earth. An increase in CO_2 is particularly effective since the warming it causes increases as well the amount of water vapor. A doubling of the atmospheric CO_2 is calculated to increase the average surface temperature by 3.8° C under clear sky conditions and about 2° C under conditions of average cloudiness. (These estimates can be questioned; however, they are unlikely to be wrong by a factor of more than two or three.)

The recent systematic atmospheric analyses for CO_2 which began during the International Geophysical Year show consistent increases each year for all parts of the earth. The current rate of increase averages 0.7 ppm per year or about 0.2 percent. The combustion of fossil fuels at current rates adds the equivalent of 1.6 ppm of CO_2 to the atmosphere each year and must therefore be considered to be contributing to the net increase. However, there may be other large sources of CO_2 which are not so easy to distinguish and which are masked by the increase due to the burning of fossil fuels.

If all known reserves of fossil fuel were used within the next 500 years, a very reasonable assumption, and if the CO_2 system reaches $CaCO_3$ equilibrium (reducing atmospheric CO_2 to a minimum—a condition not likely to be reached for several thousand years) then the CO_2 content of the atmosphere would be four times what it is at present and the average surface temperature of the earth would have risen by $7°$ C. (The possible change if $CaCO_3$ equilibrium is not reached is $12.2°$ C.) A change even half this great would be more than sufficient to cause vast changes in the climates of the earth; the polar ice caps would almost surely melt, inundating many densely settled coastal areas, including the cities of New York and London. If the temperature of the equatorial regions were to rise by this amount many life forms would be annihilated both on land and in the sea. The average temperature of the oceans, now maintained at $4°$ C by the ice caps, would rise by at least 15 or 20 centigrade degrees, largely wiping out the world's present commercial fisheries. There has been a well documented warming of oceans of the northern hemisphere (about $2°$ C in the North Atlantic) during the twentieth century, the period of rapidly growing use of fossil fuels, but the temperature rise is too large to be attributed entirely to the concurrent 10 percent rise in atmospheric CO_2. How much the rise in CO_2 may have contributed is not known (or even whether there has been any temperature rise in the tropics or in the southern hemisphere). In any case, the changes in marine life in the North Atlantic which accompanied the temperature change have been very noticeable. The abundance and distribution of a number of important commercial fish species have shifted northwards. These include cod, mackerel, lobster, menhaden, whiting and yellowtail flounder. The green crab has spread far enough north to cause a serious diminution of the soft clam which it feeds upon. The moths and butterflies of England have changed so drastically that descriptions of ranges and habitats done at the end of the nineteenth century are now invalid.

biological productivity

Quantitative knowledge of the biosphere is critical to an understanding of the implications of the increase in atmospheric CO_2. Lack of this knowledge forces assumptions to be made with little besides theory to back them up. Vegetation is a buffer of very considerable magnitude in the CO_2 system. It absorbs and liberates CO_2 at rates which are comparable to the exchange between the atmosphere and upper oceans. Organisms are probably geochemical factors of the same orders of magnitude as the physical chemical factors involved in the exchange of CO_2 in the water and air.

Laboratory experiments have shown that biological productivity increases with a rise in atmospheric CO_2 and also increases with a rise in temperature. Extrapolation from these to the earth's biosphere is not presently possible, because of the lack of world-wide systematic, synoptic measures of productivity.

There is no adequate body of historical data for estimating the size of the earth's biomass; and, therefore, no basis for knowing whether it is increasing or decreasing. Total yearly photosynthesis may use an amount of CO_2 equal to approximately one quarter of the total atmospheric CO_2. At the present time marine biological productivity has been estimated to be about equal to terrestrial biological productivity; tentatively, about 6.7×10^{10} tons of carbon per year for the sea and 7.3×10^{10} tons per year for the land. However, estimates of oceanic productivity are based on very skimpy data. Many researchers have assumed that the marine biomass is nearly stable in size and that other nutrients than CO_2, such as phosphate, may be more important factors in productivity; however, there is little evidence in support of this and the subject is one of considerable controversy.

The marine biota is almost a closed system with very rapid turnover. Production is limited by the tendency of all plankton to sink, carrying with it the nutrient necessary to build up the biomass. (Phosphate removed from the land by erosion should be enriching the sea off river mouths, but the effects of this are often reduced by turbidity.)

The terrestrial biomass should be increasing in size because of the increase in temperature and in atmospheric CO_2. However, it is more likely decreasing due to the activities of man. Forests the world over are being utilized to a greater extent than ever before. In some cases, such as the United States, production of new forest is approximately equal to the destruction of old, but for the whole world, or even just the

North American continent, forests are being cut faster than they grow. To be effective in controlling the rise in CO_2, plants would have to be accumulating organic carbon at the same rate that we are burning fossil carbon.

The increase in land in agriculture which is accompanying the increase in the world's population is almost surely decreasing the total terrestrial biomass. Terrestrial biological productivity is most probably concentrated in the tropical forests which are known to be decreasing markedly. The tropical forest has developed to such a complexity and stratification that the degree of efficiency in photosynthesis is far beyond what any single plant could achieve. The tropical forest is one of the great reserves for making the earth habitable. Its removal and the attempt to grow a mono-crop result in impoverishment. We lose not so much soil, in a tropical forest there is often no soil at all, but the structure of the community in doing the job of photosynthesis—CO_2 consumption and oxygen regeneration.

Lead Isotopes in Gasoline and Aerosols of Los Angeles Basin, California

Tsaihwa J. Chow
M. S. Johnstone

The lead content of rural snow, sampled at Lassen Volcanic National Park, California, is about 1.6 μg/kg [1]. This high concentration of lead could not be accounted for by soil dust, and the contamination was attributed to industrial pollutants. The source of the lead contaminants can be identified by their isotopic composition because each lead ore has its characteristic isotopic composition [2]. We now report on the isotopic composition of leads in antiknock gasoline and in the aerosols of the Los Angeles basin, California. The aerosols were collected from an electrostatic air filter at the Geochemistry Laboratory of the California Institute of Technology (Pasadena) during the spring of 1964. The sooty deposits consisted of about 5 percent ash, which contained about 50,000 parts of lead per million. Gasoline samples were purchased from service stations in the San Diego area in May 1964, and the aerosols were gathered during the same period. The lead content (mean) of antiknock gasoline is 2.1 g per gallon [3]. The lead in the gasoline and in the air filtrate was extracted by refluxing with concentrated hydrochloric acid for several hours. This lead was then isolated and purified by dithizone extraction [4]. Mass spectrometric analyses were performed at the California Institute of Technology with an instrument having a 30-cm radius and solid source (Table 1).

The first four gasoline samples (Table 1) showed a uniform lead

Reprinted from *Science, 147*: 502–503 (1965) with permission of the authors and the publisher. Copyright 1965 by the American Association for the Advancement of Science.

isotopic composition within analytical error. Lead composition of the Shell regular gasoline differed slightly from the average, but this lead alkyl may have been manufactured by another chemical plant. Comparison of the isotopic composition of lead in the Los Angeles basin aerosols with that of the average gasoline lead indicates that these two kinds of lead are identical within the limits of measurement error. The isotopic composition of such lead represents a typical "tertiary" age lead which is less radiogenic than that of the common "modern" lead. The average isotopic composition of the Pacific sediment lead which represents a "quaternary" age [5] is also listed in Table 1 for comparison.

Table 1.
Isotopic Composition of Leads in Gasoline and Aerosols

Sources	Ratio of PB^{206} to		
	Pb^{204}	Pb^{207}	Pb^{208}
Gasolines			
Wilshire D	18.14	1.160	0.4771
Wilshire Regular	18.10	1.156	.4751
Douglas	18.05	1.152	.4745
Standard Oil Regular	17.92	1.142	.4724
Shell Oil Regular	17.38	1.115	.4650
Average	17.92	1.145	.4728
Other Sources			
Los Angeles Aerosols	18.04	1.154	0.4746
Lassen Volcanic Park Snow [1]	18.01	1.144	.4690
1947 Tetraethyl Lead [6]	18.69	1.204	.4880
Pacific Sediment Lead [5]	18.73	1.197	.4836

The isotopic composition of lead in the 1963 winter rural snow [1] is also similar to that of the Los Angeles basin aerosols. The difference between the rural snow and the aerosols with respect to the ratio of Pb^{206} to Pb^{207} was about 0.8 percent. This could be due to the measurement error or to lead alkyls of slightly different lead isotopic composition.

The isotopic composition of lead in the tetraethyl lead manufactured by the Ethyl Corporation in 1947 is given in Table 1. This analysis was performed by Diebler and Mohler [6] on a gas source instrument with errors of about ± 1 percent for Pb^{206}, Pb^{207}, and Pb^{208}, and of about ± 5 percent for Pb^{204}. This antiknock additive which was manufactured 17 years ago had more radiogenic isotopes of lead than some present-day lead alkyls have; this suggests that the isotopic composition of the mixed pool of feed lead has changed slightly with time.

The average annual production of lead alkyls in the northern hemisphere is equivalent to about 2.7×10^{11} g of lead for recent years [7]. If one assumes that this quantity of lead alkyls was combusted and uniformly distributed on the surface of the northern hemisphere, it would amount to an average of 1.1 mg of lead per square meter. The average precipitation at Lassen Volcanic National Park is about 1 m per annum [8]. Thus, the lead contamination from the leaded gasoline alone at Lassen Park is calculated to be 1.1 μg per kilogram of precipitation. A slightly high value for contamination will be obtained because Lassen Park is situated near industrialized regions.

Since the advent of antiknock gasoline in 1923, more than 2.6×10^{12} g of lead in the form of lead alkyls have been marketed and combusted [7]. Thus, the average cumulative contamination from industrial lead on the surface of the northern hemisphere is about 10 mg of lead per square meter from gasoline-burning alone. Within highly industrialized and motorized areas, such as the Los Angeles basin, the content of lead in the air should be several hundredfold higher than this average. Part of this lead has been discharging, directly or through runoff, into the oceans; and as pointed out by Tatsumoto and Patterson [1], only a short time span is required for the abnormal amount of lead now present in the surface sea water of the northern hemisphere to accumulate. Part of this contaminant has undoubtedly been incorporated into plants and animals [7]. Because of the well-known toxicity of lead, the overall effect of lead pollutants in the air and on the ground cannot be ignored.

references and notes

1. M. Tatsumoto and C. C. Patterson, *Nature 199,* 350 (1963).

2. A comprehensive résumé of the isotopic composition of the major lead deposits was compiled by J. S. Brown, *Econ. Geol. 57,* 673 (1962); and that of geochronologic important mineral lead was given by R. D. Russell and R. M. Farquhar, *Lead Isotopes in Geology* (Interscience, New York, 1960).

3. Private communication (1964) with J. Kozikowski of the Ethyl Corporation, Ferndale, Michigan. He stated, "Our records of March 1964 show that the national weighted average of tetraethyl lead content in premium gasoline was 2.49 ml TEL per gallon, and in regular grade gasoline, 1.82 ml TEL per gallon. One ml of TEL is equivalent to 1.057 grams of metallic lead. The ratio of premium-to-regular gasoline sales in the U.S. is about 30 to 70"; (TEL, tetraethyl lead). O. C. Blade [*U.S. Bur. Mines, Rept. Invest.* No. 4702 (1950)] gave the average content of 2.02 ml TEL per gallon of premium gasoline and 1.53 ml per gallon of regular

gasoline, respectively. The averages were based on the analyses of 3659 samples from 135 companies. Evidently the lead alkyl content of gasoline has increased in recent years.

4. T. J. Chow and C. R. McKinney, *Anal. Chem. 30*, 1499 (1958).

5. T. J. Chow and C. C. Patterson, *Geochim. Cosmochim. Acta 26*, 263 (1962).

6. V. H. Diebler and F. L. Mohler. *J. Res. Natl. Bur. Stds. 47*, 337 (1951).

7. C. C. Patterson, *J. Am. Med. Assoc.*, in press. We thank Dr. Patterson for making the statistical data available and also for his suggestions.

8. Based on the data of Manzanita Lake Weather Station, California, *U.S. Weather Bureau Climatological Data*, Washington, D.C. (1963).

9. Supported by the NSF and the ONR.

Climate Modification by Atmospheric Aerosols

Robert A. McCormick
John H. Ludwig

The possibility of deliberate or inadvertent modification of weather and climate from the emission of man-made pollutants into the atmosphere is receiving increased attention by the scientific community [1, 2]. Of those constituents whose concentration and distribution have a bearing on the heat balance of the earth-atmosphere system, particular attention was drawn to CO_2 in a report [3] which concluded that the atmospheric CO_2 has been increasing over the past century and will continue to do so because of the continuing increase in combustion of fossil fuels. However, the worldwide cooling of mean annual air temperature, reported [4, 5] to have started between 1940 and 1950, discouraged the conclusion that there has been a direct effect on climate, that is, atmospheric warming. This enigma led to the further conclusion that ". . . climatic 'noise' from other processes has at least partially masked any effects on climate due to past increases in atmospheric CO_2 content" [3]. Nevertheless, it was suggested that the possibility of inducing "countervailing climatic changes" should be explored by such means as raising the earth's albedo through the spreading of small buoyant reflective particles over large oceanic areas.

We may already be achieving this increased planetary reflectivity by the emission of fine particulate and aerosol pollutants into the atmosphere. The climatic significance of variations in the solar "energy albedo" of the earth by changes in the atmospheric turbidity was studied in some detail by Angstrom [6]. Turbidity was expressed in

Reprinted from *Science, 156:* 1358–59 (1967) with permission of the authors and the publisher. Copyright 1967 by the American Association for the Advancement of Science.

terms of the Angstrom "turbidity coefficient" β, derived some years earlier [7] and defined by the empirical formula,

$$P\lambda = \exp - \beta/\lambda^a \qquad (1)$$

where $P\lambda$ is the solar transmission factor whose values range from 0 to 1 in accordance with the degree of scattering and absorption of solar radiation by atmospheric aerosol, a is called the wavelength factor (apparently related to a particle size), the reference wavelength λ is taken to be 1.0 μ, and β with limiting values lying between ∞ and 0 is related to the "dust" loading of the atmosphere. The quantity β is little affected by selective absorption of solar radiation by permanent gaseous components of the atmosphere, for example, water vapor, CO_2, and O_3, because of the techniques of determination [7–9].

While recognizing the dominating influence of the amount and albedo of clouds on the variations of the planetary albedo, Angstrom presented arguments to the effect that if the cloud amount remains constant, ". . . a change of 10 percent in the turbidity produces a change of about 1.5 percent in the albedo value, or about 0.8 percent in the energy available to warm the earth." Independent empirical evidence from data on solar transmission for the United States supports this conclusion [10]. From 1962 through 1965, on days with 100 percent possible sunshine and no clouds reported (daylight hours) over Washington, D.C., and Cincinnati, Ohio, a 100 percent increase in turbidity produced a 5 percent reduction, on the average, in the transmission of solar radiation to the ground. This loss of transmission was not just that of the direct solar beam, but also that of the total hemispherical solar radiation incident on a horizontal surface, as measured by a 180-degree pyrheliometer.

The direct effect of the above process in lowering the temperature of the earth-atmosphere system cannot be determined within known limits of precision. Angstrom made a "rough estimate" [6] that a ". . . change of 1 percent in the albedo (from 0.40 to 0.41) corresponds to a change . . . (in the mean temperature of the earth) . . . of close to 1° C." Humphreys made similar calculations [11] with about the same results and also showed that the interception of outgoing radiation by fine atmospheric dusts ". . . is wholly negligible in comparison with the interception of solar radiation." Temporal and spatial changes in the atmospheric turbidity of 100 percent, that is, albedo change of 10 to 15 percent, from one day to the next or from one locality to another are very commonplace. Even though these figures may well overestimate the actual changes brought about in atmospheric temperatures, the course of atmospheric turbidity over the earth is an important climatic factor.

There are available data upon which the trend in turbidity during this century can be estimated. Angstrom [7] gave 0.098 as the value of the mean annual turbidity β at Washington, D.C. (1903–1907), and 0.024 as the value at the Davos Observatory, Switzerland (1914–1926). The values for Washington were determined from data on solar transmission (by wavelength) published by the Smithsonian Institution; those for Davos were from data attributed to Lindholm on dust absorption. In 1962, determinations of the atmospheric turbidity were begun at the Continuous Air Monitoring Program station [12] of the Public Health Service, just a few blocks away from the Smithsonian Institution; the mean annual turbidity for 1962–1966 was 0.154. From 1957 to 1959, determinations of atmospheric turbidity were again made for Davos by Valko [13] and were given as 0.043. The $\Delta\beta$ was 0.056 for Washington and 0.021 for Davos; the percentage of increase was 57 for Washington and 88 for Davos. The later Washington and Davos data are published in terms of the "Schüepp coefficient" B, but were transformed into β by the relation

$$B = 1.07\beta \tag{2}$$

for average conditions [8].

When the scattering theory with a Junge distribution of particle size [14] is used, the values of $\Delta\beta$ imply an increase in the average annual number of aerosol particles, in the range of 0.1 to 1.0μ radius, of $2.8 \times 10^7 \text{cm}^{-2}$ and $1.05 \times 10^7 \text{cm}^{-2}$ over Washington and Davos, respectively, during the periods shown. As Davos is at an elevation of somewhat over 1600 m, nearly two-thirds of the Washington increase might be attributed to the increased population and urbanization of the district since the turn of the century. A significant remainder, however, as judged by the Davos increase, may be indicative of a worldwide buildup of atmospheric aerosol.

The increase in atmospheric turbidity due to volcanic eruptions may have temporary effects on atmospheric temperatures. Mitchell [4] concluded that temperatures may be depressed ". . . as much as 0.5° F or more in the first or second year following an unusually violent eruption. . . ." However, we suggest that the effects of man's pollution of his environment are monotonically increasing along with the world population. The emission of long-lived aerosol, keeping pace with the accelerated worldwide production of CO_2 [3] may well be leading to the decrease in worldwide air temperature in spite of the apparent buildup of CO_2. In any case, it is clear that in this "large-scale geophysical experiment" in which human beings are engaged [1], the course of atmospheric turbidity must be documented with concern.

references and notes

1. "Weather and climate modification: problems and prospects," *Nat Acad. Sci. Nat. Res. Council Publ. 1350* (1966), vol. 2, pp. 82–108.

2. R. A. Bryson, *Saturday Review,* 1 April 1967, pp. 52–55.

3. "Restoring the quality of our environment," *Report of the Environmental Pollution Panel* (President's Science Advisory Committee, 1965), pp. 111–131.

4. J. Murray Mitchell, Jr., *Ann. N.Y. Acad. Sci. 95,* 235 (1961).

5. ———, in "Changes of climate," *Arid Zone Research XX* (UNESCO, Paris, 1963).

6. A. Angstrom, *Tellus 14,* 435 (1962).

7. ———, *Geogr. Ann. 11,* 156 (1929); *ibid. 12,* 130 (1930).

8. ———, *Tellus 13,* 214 (1961).

9. ———, *ibid. 16,* 64 (1964).

10. E. C. Flowers, R. A. McCormick, P. A. Starke, in preparation.

11. W. J. Humphreys, *Bull. Mt. Weather Observ. 6,* 1 (1913).

12. *Atmospheric Turbidity Report* (quarterly mimeo.), National Center for Air Pollution Control, Cincinnati.

13. P. Valko, *Arch. Meterol. Geophys. Bioklimatol. Ser. B, 11,* 143 (1961).

14. R. A. McCormick and D. M. Baulch, *J. Air Pollut. Contr. Ass. 12,* 492 (1962).

4

Mind Modifiers

*. . . if it was so, it might be; and if it were so,
it would be; but as it isn't, it ain't.*
—TWEEDLEDUM, IN *Alice in Wonderland*

The use of mind-modifying drugs has an ancient origin. Fermented fruit juices were almost certainly enjoyed, and suffered, by the earliest *Homo sapiens*. Indian hemp, *Cannabis sativa*, preparations of which are variously known as hashish, marijuana, grass, weed, pot, rough stuff, loco weed, mutha, fine stuff, and other gaudy if inaccurate descriptions, was used in the Orient at least 5000 years ago.

The most spectacular use of the hemp drug was by a semireligious cult of ancient Persia known as the Hashishin, a term from which our word *assassin* is derived. The cult was started in the eleventh century by Hassan Sabbah, who had risen and then lost favor in the courts of both Persia and Egypt. He eventually settled in a mountain fortress called Alamut in Persia near Kohistan, where he collected a number of followers to whom he preached a peculiar modification of the Ishmaelite doctrine. He organized them into a secret society, later called the *Assassins*.

The distinctive features of Hassan's sect were its policy of and methods for accomplishing secret assassination of enemies. The *Fedais*, or "devoted ones," were young men constrained to harsh discipline and deprivation. When their services as assassins were required, they were given liberal amounts of hashish, along with an opportunity to experience various sensual pleasures—leading them to believe they were sampling the ecstasies of paradise. This treatment was calculated to make them devoted followers of Hassan, willing to do whatever he desired.

104

The cult continued to flourish after Hassan's death in 1124, and was not destroyed as a major influence in the Middle East until the thirteenth century, when the Mongol, Mangu Khan, and the Sultan of Egypt attacked Hassan's followers in Persia and Syria. However, a small remnant of adherents to the doctrine may still exist in remote regions of Syria.

One of the most recent mind modifiers, lysergic acid and its derivatives, has an equally dramatic if more somber history. During the Middle Ages, and continuing with less frequency to little more than a hundred years ago, epidemics of an indescribably horrible disease, later known as *ergotism*, periodically struck parts of Europe. The pestilence was notably prevalent in the eastern provinces of France. Victims of the disease, called *Holy Fire* or *Hell's Fire*, suffered an agony of disorders so intense and variable as to defy the wisest physicians of the day. The Order of St. Anthony was established by the church to provide for protection of the populace and relief of the victims.

Not until 1597, after a medical study by a team of surgeons at Marburg, confirmed in 1630 by the Duke of Sully in France through animal experiments, was it known that the disease was a form of poisoning from eating rye bread infected with *ergot*. The poisoning is caused by the fungus *Claviceps purpurea*, which eats out the grain and deposits, in its place, a dark *sclerotium* that contains the poisonous substance. The sclerotia contain 30 odd chemical compounds having poisonous or deleterious properties in varying degrees. Lysergic acid is a component of several of the poisonous constituents.

St. Anthony's Fire, as the pestilence came to be known after the eleventh century, was characterized by a number of symptoms, ranging from itching and tingling of the skin, through painful burning sensation and gangrene, to severe mental disturbance, physical deformity, or death. Pregnant women were particularly susceptible to abortion from mild attacks. An extract of ergot, later used medically, is a potent stimulant for contraction of the pregnant uterus.

A puzzling feature of the ergot poisoning is that it is impossible in animal experimentation today to reproduce all of the symptoms that characterized the great epidemics of St. Anthony's Fire. It is supposed that it was primarily an affliction of the poor who subsisted on rye bread, and that starvation from eating fungus-destroyed grain intensified the manifestations of the poison.

The opium poppy, *Papaver somniferum*, and its narcotic effect were known to the Greek medical botanist, Theophrastus, about 300 B.C.

Opium was also described by Dioscorides who practiced during the first century A.D. The following prescription was used to stop a child from crying.

> Pods of the poppy
> Fly specs on the wall
> Stir, strain, and take for four days.

The flower probably originated in southern Europe or Asia and was introduced to China and India centuries later, apparently along with Islam. Trade in the flower drug was prohibited by the Chinese Emperor Yung Chen in 1729. Disputes over its illegal importation, first by the Portuguese then by the East India Company, which smuggled quantities valued at fortunes ashore, eventually led to confiscations by the Chinese, punishment by death for opium smoking, and ultimately to open warfare between the Chinese and the British. The conflict ended by treaty in 1842, and the drug traffic flourished again although it continued to be a sore point with the Chinese government for many years. China again prohibited its use in 1906.

The chief constituent, from among 20 odd alkaloids derived from opium, is morphine. Its subcutaneous injection is cheaper and more effective than opium smoking but is also more dangerous and deleterious. Heroin, the acetic acid ester derivative of morphine, is preferred by addicts. Importation and manufacture of heroin is prohibited in the United States because of its highly addictive nature, although the drug is still legally available in some countries.

The South American coca plant, *Erythroxylon coca*, which contains cocaine and several related alkaloids, has long been known to the Indians of Peru, Bolivia, Ecuador, and Columbia for its narcotic action. The dried leaves are chewed, along with a small quantity of unslaked lime. Unlike opium, coca causes dilation of the pupils instead of contraction, an indication of a stimulant effect resembling that of adrenalin, the "flight or fight" hormone. Small doses of coca stimulate intestinal action, but, in larger amounts, the drug paralyzes the taste buds and anaesthetizes the mucous lining of the stomach so there is no sensation of hunger. Subjective mental powers, however, are enhanced and muscular prowess increases, for which purpose coca was chewed by the Indians of the Andes at the rate of two or three ounces a day.

Mescal buttons, or the flowering heads of the peyote cactus *Lophophora williamsii*, were used by the American Indians partly in connection with religious rites. Peyote contains 15 or 20 alkaloids, the most important of which is mescaline, a close chemical relative of epinephrine (adrenalin) and norephinephrine, powerful stimulant hormones secreted naturally into the blood stream especially at times of stress or excitement.

Also known to the early American Indians was the mind-modifying use of the so-called Mexican mushrooms, *Psilocybe mexicani* and *Stropharia cubensis*. The mushroom alkaloids, psilocybin and psilocin, are less potent than LSD but appear to be nearly identical in their effect.

The new era hallucinogens, besides lysergic acid diethylamide (LSD), include a large number of related synthetic compounds of proved or potential mind-modifying properties: dimethoxymethylamphetamine (STP or DOM), methylenedioxyamphetamine (MDA), methoxymethylenedioxyamphetamine (MMDA) and trimethoxyamphetamine (TMA), the latter being 18 times as active as mescaline. There is also diethyltryptamine DET and the well known methamphetamine (speed). Several hallucinogens of current interest are derivatives of natural products, for example, tetrahydrocannabinol one of the active ingredients of marijuana, dimethyltryptamine MDT or DMT (in cohaba snuff from seeds of *Piptadenia peregrina*), and bufotenine (in cohaba snuff, the toad *Bufo marinus* and the fly agaric mushroom). These and others, especially the synthetics, presage a wave of mind-modifying drugs capable of being mass produced and sold legitimately or bootlegged.

The Problems of
LSD-25 and Emotional
Disorder

J. Thomas Ungerleider
Duke D. Fisher

Over the past year in the United States a new problem has arisen—that of abuse of LSD (lysergic acid diethylamide). The problem seemed to develop rather suddenly in the late summer of 1966 as increasing numbers of persons began to arrive at psychiatric clinics and medical emergency rooms throughout the country with symptoms following LSD ingestion. This occurred at about the same time that the mass media were publicizing LSD—unfortunately often in a seductive, alluring way—as a panacea for man's problems. Most of the major magazines, newspapers and television networks have featured one or another aspect of LSD, including, for example, its alleged use in helping architects build better buildings and enhancing creativity in art and music. It has been publicized as an answer to a variety of sexual problems and problems of living in general, as well as a revolutionizer in the treatment of mental illness.

Then, as the dangers of this drug became recognized, first in Southern California and in New York City, and then throughout the country, particularly on college campuses, a wave of hysteria began to sweep the nation. Federal laws passed early in 1965 making possession of LSD for sale or manufacture illegal (The Drug Abuse Control Amendments of 1965) did not stem the tide. The one legal manufacturer of the drug, Sandoz Laboratories, stopped the production of LSD in May of 1966, and all Sandoz-sponsored grants for research on this drug were cancelled.

Reprinted from *California Medicine, 106:* 49–55 (1967) with permission of the authors and the publisher.

This atmosphere of hysteria continues to pervade the entire LSD problem. Literature has appeared which blames LSD on the Communists and everyone seems to have his own theory on what should be done. In October of 1966, California (along with two other states) made even the possession of this drug illegal. In the meantime, much research into the LSD problems and potentials is being discontinued. Little is really known yet about LSD. This article will attempt to present some of the things that are known, and point up the many areas of uncertainty with particular emphasis on the psychological ramifications connected with the use of LSD.

historical factors

Lysergic acid diethylamide tartrate (LSD-25[1]) was synthesized in 1938 by a Swiss scientist named Hoffman. He recognized its perception-altering properties in 1943. Lysergic acid, the precursor of LSD, is a constituent of ergot, a fungus that grows on rye. The drug is related to psilocybin, the active alkaloid of the Mexican mushroom, and to mescaline which is found in the peyote cactus buttons, except that it is many times stronger than these "hallucinogens." Morning Glory seeds also contain LSD-like compounds, although in milder form.

Man has used drugs which change the state of consciousness for thousands of years. Cannabis (Indian hemp) was brought to Europe in 1500 B.C. from Asia, and to the United States in 1920 as marijuana. Psilocybin and peyote were used by the Aztec Indians in Mexico centuries ago. Now we live in a drug age; it is an age of flagrant drug abuse. Thus perhaps it was only natural, once the word spread about LSD bringing the fountain of youth, for our culture to embrace this drug. Aldous Huxley first described its joys in his *Doors of Perception* in 1954.

The use of LSD was first mainly limited to the upper middle classes, professionals and intellectuals, but gradually its usage has spread from colleges to high schools to junior high schools, and now to lower income groups. This should not surprise us when we have seventy million users of alcohol with five million alcoholics, and when thirteen billion doses of amphetamines and barbiturates are manufactured per year in the United States. The LSD problem has now also spread to England, Holland and France.

---

[1] *Commonly known as LSD, or by users as acid or L.*

The term *psychedelic*, or "mind-manifesting," was coined by Osmond in 1957. To describe LSD as hallucinogenic is not always accurate, although widespread, because persons who see or hear things following LSD ingestion usually perceive *actual* objects or sounds as accentuated and/or distorted. These are then illusions, like a mirage, rather than true hallucinations, although sometimes true hallucinations do occur.

At first these perceptual changes caused by LSD were hailed as offering an experimental way to mimic schizophrenia and thus to study it. The "model psychosis" theory of LSD was thus conceived [1, 2]. This theory died gradually as it was realized that LSD psychosis did not indeed mimic that of schizophrenia. Not only were there such dissimilar factors as the absence of so cardinal a symptom of schizophrenia as autism, but even the nature of the "hallucinations" was fundamentally different.

physiologic effects

Physiologically, LSD has few effects. It is readily absorbed from the intestinal tract. Thus there is little advantage in intravenous injection of the drug, although occasionally a user will try injecting it for a change.

There is usually a loss of appetite, although some studies have reported an increase in appetite following ingestion. Nausea, dizziness, headache and palpitations are often experienced, and periods of shivering alternate with heat flushes. The pupils are dilated and LSD users often wear sun-glasses, even at night, to combat photophobia. Heart rate and both systolic and diastolic blood pressures rise moderately, as does blood sugar. A fine tremor of the fingers and hands may be present. Recently grand mal seizures were observed in a previously non-epileptic person following ingestion of LSD [3].

The drug is not physiologically addicting in that there are no withdrawal symptoms following discontinuation. However, it is psychically addicting in that after taking it the user frequently becomes convinced that he wants to keep taking it. In fact, LSD users, in contrast to hard narcotics addicts, develop a remarkable missionary or proselyting quality.

Laboratory techniques are not sensitive enough to determine the LSD concentration in body fluids and tissues, so C_{14}-labeled LSD has been used in animals. The highest concentration is found in the liver and the kidneys. The highest concentration in the brain is found in the hippocampus, basal ganglia, thalamic nuclei and cerebral cortex [4]. Behavior changes occur after the brain concentration of LSD is decidedly decreased. Most of LSD's metabolites are excreted in the feces [5].

Tolerance to LSD develops rapidly; thus users rarely regularly take LSD more than twice weekly. There is no lethal dosage known in humans. One direct fatality was an elephant that died from an overdose when he was given 100 *milligrams* of LSD per kilogram of body weight in an experimental situation[2] [6]. Monkeys die after receiving 5 mg per kilogram of body weight.

psychologic effects

Sensations become intensified and perceptions are distorted under LSD. One man slept on the floor the night he took LSD because he was sure his bed was only two inches long. Illusory phenomena are common. Another man was restrained from diving off a cliff onto the rocks and the ocean below. Later he explained that he felt the breaking waves were a silk scarf and he wanted to dive into it. Faces often appear to be melting. One high school student cut all the flexor tendons in her wrist when she looked in the mirror and saw her face begin to dissolve. Time sense is especially distorted. We have seen persons under the influence of LSD stare at their fingers or at a leaf for hours. True hallucinations, predominantly visual, also occur.

Delusions are not infrequent. We treated, in crisis intervention, a young man who became convinced, a few hours after ingesting LSD for the first time, that he had to offer a human sacrifice, that is, kill someone, or die himself. He was prevented from throwing his girl friend off the roof of a Hollywood hotel. Additional comments on psychologic effects will be made later in a discussion of side effects.

mode and site of action

Neither the mode nor the site of action of LSD is definitely known. It is even unknown whether the various perceptual distortions—"hallucinations" and the like—can be attributed to a primary action of LSD or whether these different effects involve different mechanisms and sites of action. The perceptual dysfunction itself, unassociated with impair-

---

[2] *Also reported in John Cashman,* The LSD Story *(Fawcett Publications, Greenwich, Conn., 1966), 50–51.*

ment of skilled motor performance, presumably originates at a high level in the nervous system. The hallucinations, intensified with sensory deprivation, also seem to be of central origin, and not an enhancement of responses to peripheral stimuli.

Frontal lobe ablation in chimpanzees does not abolish a previously induced panic reaction in these animals [7]. Implanted cortical electrodes in humans following LSD have revealed paroxysmal electrical activity in the hippocampal gyri, amygdaloid nuclei and septum which parallel the perceptual changes [8].

LSD is a strong antagonist to serotonin both in vitro and in vivo. One hypothesis for the action of LSD is that it antagonizes serotonin in the central nervous system, in which it is found especially in the basal ganglia. Another theory, based on the observation that most of the LSD has left the brain before the mental effects are seen, is that LSD acts as a trigger or is changed into a metabolite which in turn causes the mental changes. LSD also affects various enzyme systems within the body. Inhibition of cholinesterase and monamine oxidase in spinal cord neurons has been demonstrated in animals following LSD administration.

animal experiments

Dogs and cats exhibit behavioral changes, like pawing the air, which suggest they may be hallucinating. They become confused in the performance of various tests. Pigeons become catatonic. Ants attack their nestmates. Spiders spin disorganized webs. Body temperature increases, particularly in rabbits. Large doses of LSD cause complete blindness in cats and monkeys. As was mentioned previously, very large doses kill monkeys.

three areas of research

There have been three main approaches in the work on LSD to date. The first has to do with the controlled administration of a known amount of LSD experimentally, following the screening of subjects by psychiatric interviews and/or psychological testing. Resultant subjective and/or objective effects of the drug are then recorded in this "experimental" study of LSD [6, 9]. There are a number of experimental studies about personality and performance changes under LSD and, particularly with work on LSD, the "set" of the researcher (his attitude toward LSD) may become apparent. For example, in one experiment raters were used who worked gratis, who may have taken LSD themselves, and who were instructed to rate patients as improved if they were "more flexible" and demonstrated less "unrealistic rigidity" [10]. One must be careful and critical in evaluating such studies.

The evaluation of creativity under LSD is extremely difficult. If an artist paints a picture while on LSD it may be rejected by the public and also by art critics and yet it could conceivably be a creative work. Perhaps this reservation also applies when the artist himself (as was once our experience) later terms his artistic effort under LSD "just chicken scratches." But certainly many persons do *feel* that they are more creative under LSD. Subjective feelings of improvement concomitant with objective decrease in performance will be dealt with further under a discussion of side effects later in this article.

The second type of approach with LSD has to do with its therapeutic effectiveness. It has been used for alcoholics to help them stop drinking [11]. It has been used in patients dying of cancer to alleviate the pain and help them die a more "dignified" death [12]. It has been used as a psychotherapeutic aid in general to increase insight and lift repressions [13], and with autistic children to increase socialization [14]. More extensive claims have been made for LSD, and it has been cited as a specific cure for frigidity, impotence and homosexuality.

It is difficult, but essential, to evaluate just what therapeutic efficacy LSD does possess. Extravagant claims and total disclaimers now vie in an atmosphere of hysteria. Several points are noteworthy. For an experiment to be valid, it should be possible to reproduce the results. This has not yet been convincingly done in the therapeutic approach to LSD, in our opinion.

In addition, the attitude of the researcher is vital. We have spoken to researchers, themselves LSD users, who become so enthusiastic that they even refused to consider psychosis and suicide as bad results. Particularly with LSD work, as with hypnosis, one's attitude and expectations are vital factors in the results one achieves.

And finally, it is essential that there be only one variable at a time. In one experiment for example, to find that the recidivism rate among psilocybin-treated prisoners was significantly less than among those not treated sounded encouraging until further scrutiny revealed that the treatment group received many other advantages. These included close relationships with the investigators, a special pre-parole course of instruction, special assistance in obtaining housing and employment and follow-up contact from the researchers. It would be hard to say that it was the LSD alone that helped.

The third approach to LSD has to do with observation of the side effects which occur following the ingestion of the drug. There are both acute and chronic side effects, and their occurrence *cannot* be predicted. Psychiatric interviews and psychological testing do not screen out adverse reactors. Some of the worst reactions have been in persons, often physicians and other professionals, who appeared stable by every indicator. Conversely, others who have had past histories of severe psychiatric problems and have been leading marginal existences have seemed to tolerate LSD without ill effect.

There is some work to show that persons who place a premium on self control, planning, caution and impulse restriction, and who sacrifice spontaneity, do particularly poorly on LSD [15].

acute side effects

Four major types of acute symptoms have been seen. These include, in decreasing frequency, hallucinations (both auditory and visual), anxiety to the point of panic, severe depression with suicidal thoughts or attempts and confusion. These symptoms may occur in patients who have taken the drug once or 60 times. They occur in persons who have only taken LSD as well as in persons who are chronic multiple drug abusers.

At the Psychiatric Emergency Room and Admitting Office of the Neuropsychiatric Institute at the University of California, Los Angeles (UCLA), Medical Center before September of 1965, approximately one problem case associated with LSD ingestion was seen every other month. In the seven months from September 1965 to 1 April 1966, the incidence of "LSD cases" increased to between five and 15 a month and made up 12 per cent of all cases dealt with by the psychiatric emergency service [16]. The 70 "LSD patients" seen in the seven-month period (and in increasing numbers despite the Federal Drug Abuse Control Amendments, effective 1 February 1966) had several characteristics. The group was predominantly single, white, male and young (average age, 21). The members came from throughout the Los Angeles area and most were either unemployed or students. Twenty-eight (40 percent) of the group had taken drugs other than LSD within six weeks of being seen in the emergency room. Twenty-five (36 percent) had a history of chronic marijuana use, but 28 (40 percent) had never taken drugs other than LSD. Our sample contained no professional persons, in contrast to the findings of others that "LSD seems mainly to be used by professionals, intellectuals or middle-class people" [15].

Treatment of the acute symptoms first must be directed toward preventing the patient from physically harming himself or others. Thus the frequent indication for psychiatric hospitalization. Twenty-five of the 70 patients in our study were admitted to hospital. It is important for the therapist not to increase the patient's anxiety by being anxious himself. One patient panicked when he called a center for crisis intervention and was told by the therapist on call that he had "just caused permanent irreversible brain damage" to himself by taking LSD.

Chemical agents are also a vital part of the treatment regime. Chlorpromazine (Thorazine®) is the most effective antagonist to LSD's effects [17]. This is seen clinically by reversal of the hallucinations and can also be demonstrated by reversibility of the electroencephalographic changes [8]. This antagonistic effect of chlorpromazine can also be demonstrated in animal experiments [18]. In contrast, reserpine may actually enhance the effect of LSD [8]. Barbiturates may have some antagonistic effects to LSD, as may azacyclonal (Frenquel®). It should be emphasized however that chlorpromazine is not always effective in treatment of LSD complications. For example, a 22-year-old, single, white man became psychotic approximately 24 hours after the ingestion of LSD. He had both auditory and visual hallucinations. He had used LSD once before without difficulty. Several parenteral doses of 50 mg of chlorpromazine, plus orally administered chlorpromazine up to 2,000 mg per day, and chlorpromazine in conjunction with trifluoperazine hydrochloride (Stelazine®), resulted in no reduction or improvement of the psychosis. The patient improved slowly after a period of six weeks; the improvement was seemingly unrelated to the phenothiazine medication. It is important to note that recurrences of the acute side effects from LSD in all their original intensity often appear up to a year after the ingestion, without further ingestion of the drug. This is regardless of set or setting, which we will elaborate upon further. The efficacy of inducing these side effects in chemical warfare, via contamination of the water supply or as inhalants in the air, is, as far as we know, unproven to date.

chronic side effects

Certain chronic changes have been noted among LSD users. While the authors' initial observations were drawn from patients who had been put in hospital, we have also had the opportunity to observe large numbers of persons in the community who have taken LSD [19]. Many had had bad experiences but had not seen a physician or gone to a hospital. These persons in the community who had the chronic LSD reactions in varying degrees, varied from white collar workers and professional people to unemployed "beatniks," construction workers and longshoremen.

We have observed the ingestion of LSD by individuals and by groups of from two to three to 50 or 60 persons. We have seen it taken indoors and also in scenic surroundings, at "kick-type" Hollywood parties and at quiet religious gatherings, and from Orange County to San Francisco.

An effect of LSD that has been noticed quite frequently and is particularly striking to us is a dramatic shift in one's value systems. Many persons after using LSD are no longer interested in working or playing what they call the "ego games" of society.[3] LSD users often leave their families and become quite withdrawn, devoting most of their time to thinking, writing and talking about LSD. They take quite literally Dr. Timothy Leary's admonition to "turn on, tune in, and drop out." We met one man at an LSD party who had spent the previous two years wandering around the desert with a pack on his back, contemplating the experiences of LSD. Three years before, he had been an international lawyer in New York City. We have talked to students who, after taking LSD, became much less interested in their academic work and preferred to spend their time "thinking kind thoughts." We have seen formerly productive persons who have adopted the attitude that one should live merely for subjective introspective experiences and not play the various "games," like work, that society demands. Since many people who experience this change of attitude are never seen by psychiatrists, one can only speculate as to their frequency.

Another chronic difficulty with LSD is what we would term "perceptual distortion." This refers to a subjective feeling of improvement concomitant with an objective loss of functioning. For example, a band leader phoned us because his drummer was producing such terrible music. He was so out of tune and rhythm that patrons were unable to dance to the band's music. Nevertheless when we interviewed the drum-

---

[3] *Dr. Timothy Leary called ego games "The tribal game . . . mechanized, computerized, socialized, intellectualized, televised, sanforized"* [Playboy *Magazine, September 1966, p. 106*]. *In other words, conformity, work and organization as well as materialism, are all called "ego games" by LSD users.*

mer, he told us that he felt he was playing "like Gene Krupa," and was more than satisfied with his music. A law student told us that LSD had opened such horizons that he felt his legal studies were dull and boring by comparison. He speculated at length (while lying in his room during and between LSD trips) about the advisability of giving the world's leaders LSD so that they would love, not hate or make war. A group of LSD users whom we studied fairly intensively over a period of several months were convinced that they could "pick up vibrations" from other people, and that they could determine if someone else had used LSD merely by casual inspection. When these convictions were put to a test, these persons were completely unable to discriminate as to who had used LSD or what someone else was thinking. In fact we found that they appeared to have actually suffered a loss of their ability to discriminate and to observe.

Unfortunately, the idea of LSD seems to have particular attraction for the adolescent. Most adolescents are struggling with feelings of aggression and sexuality, along with the need to establish an identity, and many of them see LSD as offering a "magic solution" for these struggles. LSD provides an intense introspective experience to the adolescent, and enables him to deny feelings of aggression and sexuality at the same time that it gives him "membership" in the group of LSD users with a common language and dress. But many times the adolescent is so overwhelmed by the LSD experience that his search for identity becomes a florid, psychotic nightmare. Similarly, the attempt to use LSD is a way of denying sexuality and aggression, which robs the adolescent of his chance to work out his conflicts in regard to these instinctual drives in a healthy way. There is probably no other period in our lives more loaded with conflict than adolescence. Yet, it is persons of this very age group that, by virtue of their struggles, are the most attracted to the magic promises of LSD. This is one of the truly great dangers of the drug.

The criteria for mental health, according to Freud, are the ability to work and to love, and LSD users seem to have special difficulties in both of these areas. We have already mentioned the numerous persons we have observed who have lost their incentive to work after using LSD. The ability to love, that is to have psychic intimacy with another person, seems also to be decreased by LSD. In contradiction to the claims that the drug helps one to get closer to other people, we have noticed that users become more introspective and invested in themselves. Several LSD sessions that we have attended were filled with excited individuals proclaiming their feeling of being especially close to various other people in the room. Nevertheless, we were impressed with the number of monologues that were taking place at the sessions. Very few of the participants were at all interested in or relating to others. On the other hand, they seemed to be enjoying their highly introspective experience, the extreme results of which are autism and psychosis.

LSD also seems to provide more primitive defenses against the normal anxiety and depression that most of us face. We have noticed many LSD users who develop a more primitive way of handling their feelings. While many of us get angry, anxious, depressed or even withdrawn when we encounter periods of stress, the LSD user often hallucinates, becomes paranoid or perceives people as caricatures. As was previously mentioned, users frequently experience their psychotic or other symptoms in their original intensity as much as a year after using the drug and without taking the drug again. Thus, many people who have a great deal of difficulty tolerating the anxiety and stress of everyday living anyway are provided, in a sense, with a psychotic defense by LSD. They experience an estrangement from reality with the drug.

Another disturbing aspect of the use of LSD is the missionary quality that develops in many of its users. Many LSD users are so affected by the drug that it becomes impossible for them to be objective when discussing its effects [20]. Unfortunately this lack of objectivity has extended to some researchers in the field, researchers who also are LSD users. There is a great deal of proselyting and insistence on the part of users that other persons must share the same kind of subjective awareness that they experience. We have no doubt that this is a sincere conviction on the part of many LSD users, since in our research we have seen mothers who have given LSD to their infants, brothers who encourage their sisters to take LSD, and individuals who have taken their life's savings and purchased LSD in order to distribute it gratis to complete strangers. Despite all these chronic personality and behavioral changes, organic brain damage has not yet been demonstrated in humans.

the "trip" itself

Users of LSD call themselves "acid heads," and the LSD experience itself is a "trip." (The signs on cars which read "CONSULT YOUR LOCAL

TRAVEL AGENT" refer to the LSD trip.) Many users prefer to have their experience out of doors, particularly by the ocean or a lake, or in the mountains or woods, or in the desert. They usually ingest what has been sold to them as anywhere from 100 to 250 micrograms of LSD, although the amount and purity of the substance is questionable because of its black-market source. It is available at anywhere from 50 cents to 10 dollars. Atropine-like compounds have been substituted for LSD. We recently had one capsule, purchased by a user who paid for 250 micrograms, analyzed. It was found to contain approximately 100 micrograms of LSD.

Users usually like to hear music (particularly played by performers like Ravi Shankar) and to see intense colors (witness the rash of "light shows" and the use of strobe lights) while they have their LSD experience. They often read, especially from the Tibetan Book of the Dead, although often silently. Many chronic users have developed "aids" to help them reverse any bad effects—often reassuring phrases from various psychedelic books. (We have seen a number of users whose aids did not help.) One hundred to 250 micrograms is the usual dosage for an LSD experience although a number of users claim to have ingested 2,000 micrograms daily for a period of weeks.

A great deal has been written about "set" and setting. The set or attitude with which one approaches the LSD experience is extremely important, as with hypnosis. In fact, people are now taking trips *without* drugs [21]. However, set does not completely determine the type of "trip." For, other experiments have recorded subjects who expected psychotic reactions from LSD but experienced only pleasant feelings of relaxation [15]. And we have seen persons who appeared to take the drug under what they felt were ideal conditions, subsequently have a very severe adverse experience.

The setting in which one takes LSD is likewise a very important variable. Persons given LSD without their knowledge are extremely liable to become panicky and have a severe reaction. There are several such incidents recorded and one alleged suicide following a party where the punch had been "spiked" with LSD. However, it is not usual for LSD to be secretly placed in punch or any other liquid. The user wants people to take LSD, but to know that they are taking it. We have seen persons who have taken LSD in what they consider an ideal setting (with one or two good friends, with a guide or "sitter," with soft music playing, and in a relaxed environment) who still had bad experiences.

epilogue

Until more is known about the short- and long-term effects of LSD as well as how to predict who will have a bad experience, it must be considered a very dangerous drug. Unfortunately, the ready market for and the easy manufacture of the drug, have resulted in an almost unlimited black market supply. This colorless, odorless, tasteless liquid will be practically impossible to regulate by law alone. There is no test yet developed to detect the drug inside the body. It can be concealed on the back of an envelope or soaked into a coat, and one can take a trip merely by licking the envelope flap or sucking on the coat lapel. The LSD users are often the very people who have the most to lose from its use. We certainly hope that LSD research will resume, but we appeal to those who loudly proclaim that "everyone" should take LSD to consider the highly subjective and often untoward response to the drug. We have frequently seen the most ardent enthusiast become the most eloquent opponent after just one bad trip.

Man's search for Eldorado continues. LSD will surely become obsolete as other more potent "psychedelics" are developed. Already a compound "DMT" (dimethyltryptamine) is available in limited amount in the black market, and there are now "sophisticated" users who scoff at something as weak and unappealing as LSD.

generic and trade names of drugs

Chlorpromazine—*Thorazine.*
Azacyclonal—*Frenquel.*
Trifluoperazine hydrochloride—*Stelazine.*

references

1. E. J. Tolan and F. A. Lingl, Model Psychosis produced by inhalation of gasoline fumes, *Amer. J. Psychiat., 120,* 757–761 (1964).

2. S. W. Unger: Mescaline, LSD, Psylocybin and personality change, *Psychiat., 26,* 111–125 (1963).

3. D. Fisher and J. T. Ungerleider, Grand Mal seizures after LSD ingestion, in preparation.

4. Erik Jacobsen, The clinical pharmacology of the hallucinogens, *Clin. Pharmacol. Ther., 4,* 480–503 (1963).

5. M. Rinkel, Pharmacodynamics of LSD and Mescaline, *J. Nerv. and Ment. Dis., 125,* 424–427 (1957).

6. S. Cohen, *The Beyond Within,* Atherton Press, New York, 1964.

7. M. Baldwin, S. A. Lewis, and S. A. Bach, The effects of lysergic acid diethylamide after cerebral ablation, *Neurology, 9,* 469–474 (1959).

8. R. R. Monroe, R. C. Heath, W. A. Mickle, and R. C. Llewellyn, Correlation of rhinencephalic electrograms with behavior: A study on humans under the influence of LSD and Mescaline, *Electroencephalog. Clin. Neurophysiol., 9,* 623–642 (1957).

9. L. E. Hollister and A. M. Hartman, Mescaline, LSD and Psilocybin: Comparison of clinical syndromes, effects on color perception and biochemical measures, *Comp. Psychiat., 3,* 235–241 (1962).

10. C. Savage, J. Fadiman, R. Mogar, and Mary H. Allen, The effects of LSD therapy on values, personality and behavior, *Int. J. of Neuropsychiat., 2,* 241–254, (1966).

11. N. Chwelos, D. B. Blewett, C. W. Smish, and A. Hoffer, Use of LSD in the treatment of alcoholism, *Quart. J. Stud. Alc., 20,* 577–590 (1959).

12. E. Kast, *Pain and LSD–25: A theory of attenuation of anticipation, from LSD, the Consciousness-Expanding Drug,* edited by D. Solomon, Putnam Sons, N.Y., 1964, p. 241.

13. D. J. Lewis and R. B. Sloane, Therapy with LSD, *J. Clin. Exp. Psychopath., 19,* 19–27 (1958).

14. J. Q. Simmons, III, S. J. Leiken, O. S. Lovas, B. Shaeffer, and B. Perloff, Modification of autistic behavior with LSD, *A. J. Psychiat., 122,* 1202–1211 (1966).

15. R. Blum (Ed), *Utopiates: The Use and Users of LSD-25,* Atherton Press, New York, 1964.

16. J. T. Ungerleider, D. Fisher, and M. Fuller, The dangers of LSD, *J.A.M.A., 197,* 109–112 (1966).

17. L. D. Clark and E. L. Bliss, Psychopharmacological studies of lysergic acid diethylamide (LSD-25) intoxication, *A.M.A. Arch. Neurol. and Psychiat., 78,* 653–655 (1957).

18. F. M. Sturtevant and V. A. Drill, Effects of mescaline in laboratory animals and influence of ataraxics on mescaline response, *Proc. Soc. Exper. Biol. and Med., 92,* 383–387 (1956).

19. J. T. Ungerleider and D. Fisher, LSD: Research and Joyride, *The Nation,* 16 (1966).

20. J. T. Ungerleider and D. Fisher, LSD: Fact and fantasy, *Arts & Architecture, 83,* 18–20, (1966).

21. The Psychedelic Game: *Mademoiselle,* March 1966, p. 179.

GC Nails Marijuana Isomers

Marijuana and hashish can be analyzed for their physiologically active tetrahydrocannabinol isomers by a gas chromatographic method developed by two chemists at the U.S. Customs Laboratory in Baltimore, Md. The method should give other law enforcement laboratories a fast way to identify samples of marijuana and hashish. It may also help scientists to study changes that occur in a sample's tetrahydrocannabinol composition after long standing, chemical treatment, or smoking.

The Baltimore laboratory's chief chemist, Melvin Lerner, and his coworker, Judith T. Zeffert have used their GC method to determine the ratio of the two isomers, Δ^1-3-4-*trans*-tetrahydrocannabinol and Δ^6-3,4-*trans*-tetrahydrocannabinol. They have used it on 14 marijuana samples, two hashish samples, and two "red oils" (hashish concentrates).

The active component of marijuana has long been known to have the tetrahydrocannabinol carbon skeleton structure. Dr. Raphael Mechoulam and Dr. Y. Gaoni of Weizmann Institute of Science (Rehovoth, Israel) synthesized the Δ^1-trans isomer and stated that it was the active ingredient in hashish. Later, Dr. Edward C. Taylor, Dr. Katherine Lenard, and Dr. Youval Shvo at Princeton University synthesized the Δ^6-trans isomer, and Dr. Richard L. Hively, Dr. William A. Mosher, and Dr. Friedrich W. Hoffmann at the University of Delaware isolated the Δ^6 isomer from naturally occurring marijuana (C&EN, Jan. 24, 1966 page 38). The Δ^6 isomer, although it's usually present in marijuana in smaller amounts than the Δ^1 isomer, is also physiologically active, the Princeton and Delaware groups concluded. More recently, Dr. K. E. Fahrenholtz and his coworkers at Hoffmann-La Roche (Nut-

Reprinted from *Chemical & Engineering News:* 14 (December 26, 1966) with permission of the publisher.

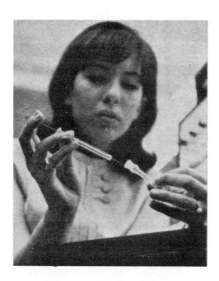

Chromatographer Zeffert
Another sample for injection

ley, N.J.) independently synthesized the two isomers and were able to separate them by GC [*J. Am. Chem. Soc.*, *88*, 2079 (1966)].

Acid catalyzes the isomerization of the Δ^1 to the Δ^6 compound. Dr. Hively has also observed that this isomerization takes place on long standing at room temperature. And Dr. Taylor has concluded that the isomerization also occurs at 280° C. on a chromatographic column (SE-30 on Diatoport S). Because of this observed heat isomerization, he has suggested that the physiological effects of smoking hashish now ascribed to the Δ^1 isomer may actually be due to the Δ^6 isomer.

By contrast, Dr. Mechoulam and Dr. Gaoni have observed none of this isomerization occurring up to 300° C. on a different column (SE-30 on Chromosorb W) [*J. Am. Chem. Soc.*, *88*, 5673 (1966)]. Therefore, they believe that this isomerization does not take place during smoking of marijuana or hashish.

For their GC analyses Mr. Lerner and Miss Zeffert used a flame ionization detector and a ball and disk integrator for quantitative measurements. As references, they used samples of pure Δ^1 and Δ^6 isomers obtained from Dr. Hively. Standards and samples were run at 210° C. in petroleum ether solution on a column using 2% OV-17 (phenyl methyl silicone from Applied Science Laboratories, State College, Pa.). Under these conditions, the Δ^1 and Δ^6 isomer peaks were separated by about

The two active isomers differ
only in location of one bond

Δ^1-3,4-*trans*-Tetrahydrocannabinol

Δ^6-3,4-*trans*-Tetrahydrocannabinol

$2\frac{1}{2}$ minutes with a sharp return to the base line between peaks. The isomers were also separated from cannabidiol, which is present in naturally occurring samples. No Δ^6 isomer was detected in the gas chromatogram of the pure Δ^1 reference sample, nor was any Δ^1 isomer found in the gas chromatogram of the pure Δ^6 reference sample.

The analytical results of Mr. Lerner and Miss Zeffert support the isomerization of Δ^1 to Δ^6 on long standing. For example, their GC analyses showed that the total tetrahydrocannabinol in a freshly prepared "red oil" contained 3% of the Δ^6 isomer. The tetrahydrocannabinol in a four-year-old oil contained 60% of the Δ^6 isomer.

To test whether smoking would actually affect the isomerization of the Δ^1 to the Δ^6 compound, Mr. Lerner and Miss Zeffert used a smoking machine. Regular cigarette tobacco soaked with the "new" red oil and a sample of "Mexican" marijuana, both rolled into cigarettes, were smoked by the machine. The condensed smoke was analyzed by their GC method. The results showed that the proportion of the Δ^6 isomer had increased, but conversion was by no means complete. For example, with the sample containing the "new" red oil, the Δ^6 isomer increased from 3% of the total tetrahydrocannabinol before smoking to 9% after smoking. For the marijuana cigarette, the Δ^6 isomer increased from 0.4% of the total tetrahydrocannabinol before smoking to 0.6% after smoking.

In the 14 marijuana samples analyzed by GC, the average total tetrahydrocannabinol content was 1.2% by weight, Mr. Lerner and Miss Zeffert found. From this they estimated the total weight of tetrahydrocannabinol absorbed by a marijuana smoker if he smokes three cigarettes. Assuming that a cigarette weighs 300 mg, and that 50% of the tetrahydrocannabinol is absorbed by the smoker, the dose would be about 5 mg of tetrahydrocannabinol.

Strychnine: Its Facilitating Effect on the Solution of a Simple Oddity Problem by the Rat

William J. Hudspeth

Primates and higher mammals have demonstrated the ability to solve oddity problems [1]. However, the rat has been singularly unsuccessful in this task [2]. In one previous study [3], rats were successful only after they were given extensive preliminary training with the absolute stimuli later combined into the oddity task. Since the oddity problem is difficult, any method which would facilitate this form of learning in the rat would be of obvious theoretical importance. Such enhancement would provide information concerning individual differences in learning ability and how these differences relate to the rate at which memory storage might occur.

Numerous studies [4] have shown that strains of rats genetically selected for maze-learning ability [5] perform consistently as bright or dull. However, in recent studies the differences observed were not obtained when subjects of the two strains were given injections of strychnine sulfate [6] or a similar compound [7] shortly after, or before, each training session. These studies clearly demonstrated the plausibility of modifying the rate at which demonstrably poor learners will acquire a given task. This rate may also be taken, inferentially, to indicate the rate at which a subject is able to store information in its permanent repertoire. Given this interpretation, the facilitative effect of strychnine has been interpreted as enhancement of consolidation of the memory trace [6, 7].

Reprinted from *Science, 145:* 1331–33 (1964) with permission of the author and the publisher. Copyright 1964 by the American Association for the Advancement of Science.

The results of the experiment reported here offer further support for the hypothesis that injections of strychnine given after training sessions facilitate consolidation of the memory trace. The results indicate that such injections facilitate the learning of a three-choice discrimination and discrimination reversal, and facilitate the solution of an oddity problem.

Twelve male Long-Evans hooded-rats, 110 to 120 days old, were first given 7 days (10 trials per day) of preliminary training in the discrimination apparatus. Only one of the three doors allowed access to the goal-box. The subjects were placed in the starting compartment and then the starting door was opened. Thirty seconds after the door was opened the subjects were given a 4-ma shock through a grid floor. After 2 days of this training, all of the subjects responded quickly to the opening of the starting door and required little or no shock before they reached the goal-box. Incorrect responses resulted in a 4-ma shock to the forepaws immediately in front of the incorrect doors. The position of the correct door was varied randomly. On days 1 and 2, the door leading to the goal-box was open, and the remaining doors were locked and covered with medium gray paper. On days 3 through 7 all of the doors were covered with gray. The door leading to the goal-box was progressively lowered. By day 6 all of the subjects had learned to avoid shock by finding the door which led to the goal-box. The interval between daily trials was 2 minutes on day 1 and was progressively decreased to 30 seconds by day 6. This interval remained unchanged throughout the remainder of the experiment. No injections were given during preliminary training.

On day 8 the subjects were divided equally into experimental and control groups and were given ten trials a day in the following stages. During the first stage, half of the subjects in each group were trained in the same discrimination apparatus, in which a black door was the correct door and two white doors were incorrect. The remaining subjects were trained to a correct white door and two incorrect black doors. Upon reaching a criterion of 19 errorless trials out of a total of 20 trials, the second stage, discrimination reversal, was introduced, the subjects of both groups being shifted to the reverse set of doors (correct door opposite in brightness to that to which the rat had already been trained) and trained to the same criterion.

Upon reaching the criterion on the reversal task, the six stimulus sets (according to brightness and position) were combined and presented randomly to the subjects twice a day. To solve the oddity problem, the subject had to choose the odd, correct door—that is, the position and absolute brightness of the correct door did not serve as a consistent cue for reaching the goal-box. Only the odd door was consistently correct. Each subject was given 12 such trials daily until 300 trials had been completed.

Thirty seconds after each daily block of trials, the experimental subjects were given an intraperitoneal injection of a 0.20 mg/ml solution of strychnine sulfate for each kilogram of body weight. This

Table 1.

Total Number of Errors Made by Experimental Subjects (Injected with Strychnine) and Control Subjects (Injected with Saline) before Reaching Criterion during the First and Second Stages of Discrimination Training

Subject	Strych-nine	Subject	Saline
Stage 1. Brightness Discrimination			
1	13	7	33
2	30	8	44
3	16	9	25
4	1	10	0
5	4	11	6
6	0	12	5
Stage 2. Discrimination Reversal			
1	49	7	50
2	40	8	64
3	44	9	80
4	24	10	54
5	32	11	84
6	26	12	68

dosage was equivalent to 20 percent of the 50 percent convulsive dose and 12 percent of the 50 percent lethal dose. The control subjects were injected with a corresponding volume of physiological saline. A plus or minus score was recorded for each trial depending upon whether the subject's initial response was to the correct or to the two incorrect doors.

During the first stage of discrimination training, subjects given injections of strychnine made significantly fewer errors before they reached the criterion than subjects given saline ($p < .01$, Mann-

Whitney test). Similarly, the subjects injected with strychnine made fewer errors than the controls during the second, reversal, stage ($p <$ .001, Mann-Whitney test; see Table 1). It should be noted, however, that during the first stage there was a strong preference for black. Both experimental and control subjects which were trained to a black-correct door made significantly fewer errors before they reached the criterion ($p < .001$, Mann-Whitney test; see subjects 4, 5, 6, 10, 11, and 12 in Table 1).

During trials on the oddity problem, the number of correct responses made by subjects in the two groups (see Figure 1) were pooled into ten

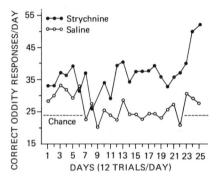

Figure 1. Total number of correct responses on the oddity trials made by rats injected with strychnine and by the control rats over 300 trials. Abscissa: 25 daily blocks of 12 trials each

blocks consisting of 30 trials each for the purpose of statistical analysis. An analysis of variance over blocks of trials showed that the subjects injected with strychnine made significantly ($p < .005$, F- test or variance ratio value) more correct responses than the control animals. The two groups differed at the beginning of oddity training and then made progressively fewer correct responses until, by day 8, the performance of both groups had deteriorated to chance level. This finding was related to the fact that all of the subjects, at the beginning of training on the oddity problem, tended to use the response which was correct during the reversal phase of training. Thus, it would appear that the strychnine subjects began solving the oddity problem by trial 8.

To determine whether the rate of changes over trial-blocks, made by the two groups, was different, the treatment by trial-blocks interaction was partitioned into the first through fifth orthogonal components. Of these components only the linear was significant ($p < .005$, F-test). This analysis showed that the linear function for the group injected with strychnine was positive—that is, these subjects made increasingly more correct responses. The control subjects, on the other hand, tended to perform at chance level ($p = .33$).

The finding that post-trial injections of strychnine sulfate facilitate the learning of a simple discrimination task and a discrimination reversal task is consistent with previous studies of drug effects upon discrimination learning [8] and supports the hypothesis that strychnine facilitates consolidation of the memory trace.

The finding that strychnine facilitated the solution of a simple oddity problem was also consistent with the hypothesis given above. However, since the oddity problem has been shown to be extremely difficult, the present findings would suggest that the rat's difficulty in solving such problems results from a memory storage process which is either slow or inefficient. Since oddity training was discontinued before the control subjects showed improvement in performance, the question remains as to whether strychnine enhanced the rate of memory storage or the learning capacity of the subjects. Earlier writers [9] have suggested that individual differences in learning capacity are dependent upon differences in rate of memory storage. Further, previous work suggests that the rate of efficiency of memory storage decreases as a function of the difficulty of the task to be learned [10]. In the present situation, then, it might be supposed that strychnine increased the rate or efficiency of memory storage so that the storage rate exceeded the rate required to solve the difficult oddity problem. The question of rate or capacity, then, is reduced to the same term. This interpretation would require empirical demonstration since it is only inferred from earlier experiments [9, 10].

It is important to note that the subjects were injected *after* each daily block of trials. Therefore, the subjects were not influenced by the drug while in the apparatus. Thus, the injections should have influenced only the postulated consolidation process [6, 7], not motivation, perception, or other performance variables.

references and notes

1. H. Harlow, in *Comparative Psychology,* C. P. Stone, Ed. (Prentice-Hall, New Jersey, 1960), p. 183; K. Smith, *ibid.,* p. 316.
2. K. Lashley, *J. Gen. Psychol. 18,* 123 (1938); E. Rose, *Univ. Calif. Berkeley Publ. Psychol. 6,* 189 (1939).
3. J. Wodinsky and M. Bitterman, *Am. J. Psychol. 66,* 137 (1953).
4. M. Rosenzweig, D. Krech, E. Bennett, *Psychol. Bull. 57,* 476 (1960).

5. R. Tryon, *Yearbook Natl. Soc. Study Education 39*, 111 (1940).

6. J. McGaugh, C. Thomson, W. Westbrook, W. Hudspeth, *Psychopharmacologia 3*, 352 (1962).

7. J. McGaugh, W. Westbrook, G. Burt, *J. Comp. Physiol. Psychol. 54*, 502 (1961).

8. J. McGaugh and C. Thomson, *Psychopharmacologia 3*, 166 (1962); L. Petrinovich, *ibid. 4*, 103 (1963).

9. C. Thomson, J. McGaugh, C. Smith, W. Hudspeth, W. Westbrook, *Can. J. Psychol. 15*, 69 (1961).

10. R. Thompson, *J. Exptl. Psychol. 55*, 496 (1958).

11. Supported by research fellowship MH-16876 to W. J. Hudspeth, and in part by research grant M-5207 to O. T. Law from the National Institute of Mental Health. I thank Eli Lilly and Co. for supplying the drug.

5
Gene and Embryo Changers

Now a quick change to things internal from things external.

—Ludwig Van Beethoven

In the years 1959 to 1961 a series of tragic events occurred which, after the cause became known, made millions of people shockingly aware of the profound effect that seemingly harmless chemicals can have on living tissue. Unprecedented numbers of malformed infants were born with a hitherto rare syndrome described as *phocomelia*.[1] Some of the children were horribly deformed. After carefully detailed investigations by a few concerned medical men, the finger of guilt pointed to a popular European drug called *thalidomide*, used as a tranquilizer and sleeping pill.

Thalidomide was a sedative drug so mild that it had become a standby over-the-counter sleeping tablet for the young and the old and was thought to be particularly beneficial for pregnant women. Unfortunately, the drug caused disastrous results in infants if the mother had taken it in early pregnancy. Almost all the deformities were associated with the use of the drug during the first few weeks of the formation of the embryo. In humans within 42 days of conception, tiny arms and legs are visible on the fetus, then about an inch long. It is during and shortly before this critical period that the damage can most easily occur.

Discovered by a Swiss pharmaceutical manufacturer, thalidomide

---

[1] *Phoke* (*Gk*) = *seal; melos* (*Gk*) = *limb.*

was thought to be so safe that it could be purchased without prescription in West Germany; it was, however; dispensed only by prescription in several other countries. Thalidomide was never sold in the United States. It was in the process of being cleared by the Food and Drug Administration when an alert staff physician, Dr. Frances Kelsey, learned of some of its adverse side effects from the results of European investigations. When pregnant women learned of the physicians' reports, near panic ensued. One young mother in the United States who had obtained the drug while in Germany gained notoriety by traveling to Sweden for an abortion that would have been illegal anywhere in her own country at the time. The embryo, so it was reported, was deformed.

The way in which chemicals such as thalidomide act on tissue to thwart nature in fulfilling the growth of structure and form is not known. Such chemicals are said to be *teratogenic*.[2] Thalidomide produces no observable effect on the hereditary material to indicate inheritable defects. Substances that do bring about changes in the carriers of heredity within the cells may have even more profound effects. They are called *mutagenic*. What mutagenesis is and how it can happen is partly explained by the nature of the hereditary stuff that lies deep within the cells.

Within the nucleus of nearly every kind of living cell is the genetic material that appears at certain stages of cell division in the form of distinct bodies called *chromosomes*.[3] Chromosomes have long been thought of as consisting of subunits called *genes*, a term used to define the vehicles for inheritable characteristics of the living organism. Since the chromosomes are present in body cells in pairs, the genes also exist in pairs, and each gene is responsible for a specific characteristic. For example, in the fruit fly, if both members of a gene pair for body color are alike, the fly will be gray or black depending on whether both members of the gene pair are for gray or both are for black. If one member of the gene pair is for gray body and the opposing gene is for black body, the fly will be gray; therefore, the gene for gray body is said to be *dominant*. There are many variations of this scheme for gene control of inherited characteristics.

The basic principles of the concept of inheritance were proposed in 1866 by the Austrian Monk, Gregor Mendel; since then, knowledge of

---

[2] *Teras (Gk) = monster; gen (Gk) = produced.*
[3] *"Chromosome" = "colored body," so called because of the readiness with which the chromosomal material takes up stains.*

the nature of the gene has expanded enormously. It is now known that genes consist essentially of macromolecules of nucleic acids, in most organisms DNA (deoxyribonucleic acid), and that this substance is the embodiment of the genetic code. One of the functions of the DNA macromolecule is the transmission of the code to cellular structures called *ribosomes,* which supervise the orderly arrangement of amino acids in the synthesis of proteins. The transmission of signals to the ribosomes is via *messenger* RNA (ribonucleic acid), a substance closely related to DNA. In the process of reproduction, DNA normally is duplicated exactly, passing the code to the progeny as well as to each daughter cell of the individuals.

DNA, then, is the ultimate basis for the species; it is responsible for the dual function of regulating the individual organism according to rigidly programmed biochemical components and processes and, secondly, of maintaining the physical and chemical makeup of the organism, through reproduction, in the same form among the progeny.

Actually DNA is not always completely accurate in transmitting the code of life to the progeny of the organism. For practical purposes the scheme of inheritance may seem reliable enough, but in the process of duplicating itself the DNA macromolecule makes occasional mistakes in one or more of its portions. These imperfections, however small, modify the code in ways that result in drastic, if not lethal, alterations in the organism or in its progeny. Such changes in the chemistry of the genetic code or in the structure of the chromosomes are called *mutations.* They occur in the formation of the sperm and ova, based on animal experimentation, at the rate of at least 1 out of 100,000. Inasmuch as man, it is estimated, has at least 10,000 genes in his cellular makeup, the chance that at least one of the genes in a sex cell is highly deleterious or lethal is 1 out of 10.

Mutations often appear to occur spontaneously, but they are known to have several underlying causes. As early as 1927 it was recognized that mutations are brought about by some forms of radiation. In that year Hermann Muller, later awarded the Nobel prize, showed that x-rays cause genetic changes. Mutations can also be induced by ultraviolet rays, ionizing radiation, particles from radioactive chemicals, and certain compounds called *mutagenic chemicals.* Chemicals that produce cellular changes similar to those caused by x-rays are said to be *radiomimetic.*

A wide variety of chemicals and drugs are capable of inducing mutations, chromosomal aberrations, inhibition of cell division, or related effects. Such diverse chemical structures as phenols and similar hydrocarbons, mustard gas, urethane, allyl isothiocyanate, formaldehyde, benzene, nitrous acid, maleic hydrazide, hydroxylamine, and such common substances as antibiotics may have drastic effects on chromosome behavior. There are also many substances that interrupt nuclear and cell division. Such *mitotic poisons* include the alkaloid colchicine, acenaphthene, halogenated benzenes, and a number of other natural and synthetic chemical compounds. Many of the substances to which we are routinely exposed probably have these properties in mild degree. Caffeine causes aberrations on human chromosomes in a test tube. Though effect on humans from normal consumption of beverages has not been shown, large doses of caffeine cause genetic changes in the living fruit fly, *Drosophila*. Not all agents have clear cut mutogenic effects. The drug LSD, for example, has been associated with chromosome breakage in human cells, but this is still under scientific debate. Even the common household aspirin has been associated with chromosome breaks in human tissue culture.

The geneticist George Beadle who, with Edward Tatum, was to receive the Nobel prize in 1958, developed evidence that each gene is associated with a particular enzyme. Their work gave rise to the "one gene, one enzyme" theory. Inasmuch as an enzyme is a substance within the organism that brings about a specific cellular reaction, or in some cases a group of reactions, any change in the gene makeup, such as a chemical change in the genetic code of the DNA, has the effect of altering the signal-calling mechanism.

Most mutations are catastrophic to the organism. In those few cases where the mutation results in a change beneficial to the organism, the progeny may thrive better than their less fortunate brethren and possibly in time result in a new race or even a new species.

The Chemical Production of Mutations

C. Auerbach

Twenty years ago, *Science* published an article with the above title [1]. A few years earlier, the first potent chemical mutagens had been discovered, and this discovery started a vigorous and astonishingly successful search for more substances with mutagenic ability. The hopes which my colleagues and I set on the new field of chemical mutation research were expressed as follows. "If, as we assume, a mutation is a chemical process, then knowledge of the reagents capable of initiating this process should throw light not only on the reaction itself but also on the nature of the gene, the other partner in the reaction. Moreover, it could be hoped that among chemical mutagens there might be some with particular affinities for individual genes. Detection of such substances not only would be of high theoretical interest but would open up the long sought-for way to the production of directed mutations." It is interesting to look back and see how far these hopes of 20 years ago have been fulfilled.

reactions between mutagens and genes

The chemical nature of the gene has not been elucidated by research on mutation but in entirely different ways. On the contrary, mutation research now starts from the presumption that "the gene, the other partner in the reaction" consists of DNA, or—in some viruses—of RNA. The DNA molecule is a duplex structure, consisting of two sugar-phosphate strands which are helically wound round each other and which carry attached sequences of the four nucleotide bases adenine, guanine, thymine, and cytosine. The two strands are held together by hydrogen bonds between opposite bases; since, for steric reasons, the purine adenine is always opposite the pyrimidine thymine and the purine guanine is opposite the pyrimidine cytosine, the whole structure is internally complementary. At replication, the two strands separate, and each constructs a new complementary strand. The genetic information is coded by the sequence of bases, and, if this has been changed by mutation, the same principle of complementarity that governed replication of the original sequence now leads to perpetuation of the mutated one. It appears that this structure of the genetic material is common to all living species, from viruses to man. Among viruses there are some exceptions, but they have retained the principles of coding by base sequence and of replication by complementarity. In some viruses, DNA is single-stranded when it is not engaged in replication, and in some it has been replaced by RNA. The RNA molecule is single-stranded except at replication; three of its nucleotide bases are the same as those in DNA, but thymine has been replaced by uracil. When speculating about the action of mutagens, we no longer ask whether they react with DNA, but how they react with it. We shall see that, as these questions were answered for a series of mutagens, specificities of reaction appeared at the level of nucleotides and nucleotide sequences and furnished valuable clues for the deciphering of the genetic code. Thus, chemical mutagens have, after all, proved important analytical tools for the study of the genetic material, but at a level of chemical structure that was still quite unsuspected 20 years ago.

Knowledge of the structure of DNA furnishes a framework for the classification of mutations. The least drastic alteration—which, however, may have drastic consequences for the organism—is replacement of one nucleotide base by another. The most frequently observed base changes are "transitions," in which a purine has been replaced by another purine (adenine by guanine or vice versa) or a pyrimidine by a pyrimidine (thymine by cytosine or vice versa). Much rarer are "transversions," in which a purine has been replaced by a pyrimidine or vice versa. Since the genetic code is read in triplets of bases, each triplet coding for one amino acid, mutations due to base changes—whether transitions or transversions—usually result in a protein in which one amino acid has been replaced by another. In which way this will affect the organism depends on the type of amino acid change and on the position in the protein in which it occurred. Occasionally, a base change results in a so-called "nonsense triplet" which, instead of coding for an amino acid, codes for premature termination of the growing polypeptide chain, so that only incomplete protein molecules can be formed. These mutations lead to complete loss of gene function. A mutant gene that arose through a base change may be reversed by another base change that restores the original code. Such mutations are called "reverse" mutations; they restore a gene function that has become altered or abolished by the first mutation. Since reverse mutations require a very precise chemical change, they are very rare even after mutagenic treatment and can be studied profitably only in material that permits work on very large numbers, such as bacteria or bacteriophages.

A different class of mutations is due to deletions of one or more bases from the sequence of a gene. Since the code is read in base triplets from one end of the gene to the other, deletions of even one base will alter every triplet from the missing base to the end of the gene, and this in turn will alter every one of the corresponding amino acids. Insertion of an extra base has the same effect. Such mutations are often called "reading frame shifts"; they result in loss of gene function. They cannot be reversed by base changes, but, if a deletion and an insertion occur sufficiently close together, the original reading frame will be restored after the second change. If the portion between the two changes is relatively unimportant, this may result in a sufficiently normal protein to pass as a reversion.

Changes in genetic information that take place within the confines of a gene and affect the action of this gene only are called "gene mutations." On a grosser scale, we have to consider changes that affect the order of the genes on the chromosomes. In this article, I shall use the term "chromosome" for all linear structures that carry hereditary information in any organism whatsoever. This terminology is simple and suffices for our purposes, but it obscures the fact that in all organisms beyond the evolutionary level of bacteria the chromosomes are complex structures, containing not only DNA—often several replicas of it—but also proteins and RNA. The role of this complexity in the production of mutations is likely to be important, but hardly anything is known about it. Within the chromosome, there may be deletions of whole genes or sequences of genes. This can happen when a chromosome is broken into several fragments, one of which gets lost when the broken ends rejoin. Rejoining of chromosome fragments in the wrong order may also result in other types of "chromosome rearrangement," for example, a "translocation" in which two broken chromosomes have exchanged pieces. Some of these chromosome rearrangements resemble gene mutations in their effects on the organism and in their mode of hereditary transmission.

the discovery of chemical mutagens

The first agent shown to produce mutations was x-irradiation, but the search for chemical mutagens had started already before this discovery and was continued after it. Although some of the substances tested in the 1930's, for example, iodide and coppersulphate, seemed to have weakly mutagenic effects on the fly *Drosophila*, no clear positive results were obtained before the early years of World War II when, independently, the mutagenic action of mustard gas was discovered in Edinburgh and that of urethane was found in Germany. These first successes provided a strong stimulus for the testing of more substances, many of which proved mutagenic. By now, we know a large number of chemical mutagens, belonging to a variety of chemical classes. Very different principles have been used in the selection of chemicals for testing. Some of the most powerful mutagens were discovered on the basis of what we now know to be the wrong concept of the gene. Mutation research offers good cautionary examples against the belief that a successful experiment necessarily proves the hypothesis that inspired it. In the following, I shall briefly review the most important classes of mutagenic chemicals.

alkylating agents

This class contains some of the most potent mutagens, including mustard gas. The rationale for testing mustard gas was the pharmacological similarity between mustard-gas burns and x-ray burns, coupled with the knowledge that x-rays cause damage to chromosomes and genes. While this speculation was fully vindicated by the results, pharmacological observations are not always a reliable guide to the detection of chemical mutagens. This became clear very early when lewisite, like mustard gas, a potent vesicant war gas, proved quite ineffective in mutation tests. All the same, tests of pharmacologically active substances for mutagenicity have retained their value as part of the program for protecting man and his domestic animals and plants against genetic damage. Occasionally, this may lead to the discovery of a new group of strong mutagens. This happened with the pyrrolozidine alkaloids (for example, heliotrine) which were tested because they produce liver damage in sheep that ingest them in ragwort. The antibiotic streptonigrin has produced mutations in fungi and chromosome breaks and rearrangements in cells of plants and mammals. In mutation tests on *Drosophila*, streptomycin and the insecticide DDT were ineffective, and carcinogenic hydrocarbons gave, at best, doubtful results. It must be kept in mind, however, that negative results of mutation tests can rarely be considered as final. A chemical that fails to yield mutations in a particular type of experiment may be mutagenic under different conditions or for a different organism or cell type. Examples for this will be found in this article.

Chemically, mustard gas is dichloroethyl sulphide $S(CH_2CH_2Cl)_2$; the related and equally mutagenic nitrogen mustard "NH2" has the formula $CH_3N(CH_2CH_2Cl)_2$. These and other "mustards" owe their biological activity to their chloroethyl groups; they act by alkylating biologically important macromolecules. In addition to mustards, many other compounds, in particular epoxides, ethylene imines, and alkylmethanesulphonates, have alkylating abilities, and many of them are mutagenic. Indeed, the correlation between alkylating and mutagenic abilities is so strong that a tendency has arisen to attribute alkylating reactions to mutagens whose mode of action is not yet understood, such as a number of nitrosocompounds and the pyrrolizidine alkaloids mentioned above.

In vitro, alkylation affects preferentially the guanine in DNA, and this appears to be so also in vivo, although in a bacteriophage with single-stranded DNA all four bases were attacked [2]. Alkylation of guanine is thought to produce mutations mainly through the tendency of alkylated guanine to pair erroneously with thymine instead of cytosine. At the next replication, thymine will pair correctly with adenine, and the final result will be a transition from a guanine-cytosine to an adenine-thymine pair at the site of mutation. It has also been suggested that mutations may arise through the relative ease with which alkylated guanine detaches from the DNA backbone, leaving an "apurinic gap," which might be filled by a wrong base. This could lead to transversions as well as transitions, but so far there has been no clear evidence for the production of transversions by alkylation. The assumption that alkylation usually changes guanine-cytosine into adenine-thymine but only rarely adenine-thymine into guanine-cytosine agrees well with the fact that alkylating agents are not usually able to revert the mutations that they themselves have produced, while other mutagens—able to change adenine-thymine into guanine-cytosine (see below)—may do so.

In addition to gene mutations, alkylating agents also produce deletions and other types of chromosome rearrangement. Indeed, their genetical effects are so strikingly similar to those of x-rays that the term "radiomimetic substances" is often applied to them. Differences, however, also exist, and these are of special interest for an analysis of the mutation process. Two major differences from x-rays were found early and seem to be characteristic of all alkylating agents, possibly of most chemical mutagens. One is a relative shortage of chromosome rearrangement compared with gene mutations. This is found for all alkylating agents, but its magnitude varies from a moderately high number of rearrangements after treatment with ethylene imines to their almost complete absence after treatment with diethylsulphate. For mustard gas it has been shown that the shortage of rearrangements is not due to a shortage of chromosome breaks but to an inhibition of the process by which the broken ends rejoin into new arrangements. How far this factor contributes to the shortage of rearrangements after treatment with other alkylating agents has not been established.

The inhibition of reunion between chromosome fragments is mainly a consequence of the second and more fundamental peculiarity of alkylating agents and, possibly, of most other chemical mutagens. This is a tendency for injuries to the genetic material not to result directly in chromosome breakage and mutation but to remain latent over a period that may extend over many cell cycles. Since the formation of a chromosome rearrangement requires the simultaneous presence in the same cell of two chromosome breaks, while single unjoined breaks usually result in cell death, a potential rearrangement will be lost every time when the two breaks that might have given rise to it open in different cell cycles.

Although the phenomenon of delayed chromosome breakage and mutation was first observed and studied in *Drosophila*, it can be illustrated more easily by an example from experiments on fission yeast, *Schizosaccharomyces pombe*, in which mutations from red to white colony color can be scored. When cells of the red strain are exposed to the alkylating agent ethylmethanesulphonate and subsequently plated out, the majority grow again into red colonies, but a minority of mutated ones grow into white colonies. In addition, there are "mosaic" colonies that are partly white, partly red. In the early days of mutation research, this observation alone would have suggested that some mutations to white must have arisen with a delay of at least one division. This argument has become invalid with our realization of the duplex nature of DNA. If a chemical change affects only one strand of DNA—and the majority are likely to do so—the first division should result in one mutated and one nonmutated cell, and these should grow into a mosaic colony. Decisive proof for the delayed occurrence of mutations after treatment with ethylmethanesulphonate was obtained when cells from mosaic colonies were respread. As would be expected, the majority grew into either wholly red or wholly white colonies, but in most experiments some grew again into mosaics, and these, in turn, yielded some mosaics when respread. Moreover, although the mutations to white involved a number of different genes, in any particular line of mosaics it was always the same gene that gave rise to delayed mutations. The simplest way of describing these observations, and similar ones obtained in other systems and with other mutagens, is to say that treatment with alkylating agents, in addition to producing mutations immediately, may cause instabilities of individual genes that continue to give rise to mutations. Moreover, since in these lines each mosaic must have started with an instability, and since several cells from the same mosaic may again grow into mosaics, the instability must be able to replicate as such. No satisfactory explanation of these instabilities has so far been put forward. Their nature, in particular their ability to replicate in the unstable state, is difficult to fit into a molecular explanation at the level of DNA unless, as has been suggested very recently, an apurinic gap may replicate as such [3]. Probably, different types of instability arise in different ways; this applies in particular to instabilities for gene mutations on the one hand, delayed chromosome breakage on the other.

Many alkylating mutagens are carcinostatic, and some have been found to be carcinogenic. This triad of effects is produced also by other agents, notably urethane and x-rays. The correlation between carcinogenicity and mutagenicity is obscure; it has been used in support of the somatic mutation theory of cancer. The carcinostatic action of mutagens is doubtless connected with their ability to break chromosomes; for chromosome breakage preferentially kills dividing cells such as are present in malignant tissue. Among alkylating agents, only those with two or more functional (for example, chloroethyl) groups are carcino-static, while related ones with but one functional group are not. Yet many such agents not only produce high frequencies of gene mutations but are also efficient chromosome breakers. A clue to this discrepancy between oncological and genetical observations may be found in recent experiments on *Drosophila* in which pairs of closely related monofunc-tional and polyfunctional epoxides and ethylene imines were compared [4]. When treated spermatozoa were utilized on the day following treatment, the ratios between chromosome rearrangements and gene mutations caused by mono- and polyfunctional members of the same pair were the same. This, however, was drastically changed when the treated spermatozoa were first stored for six or more days in the seminal receptacles of untreated females. During storage, the frequency of chromosome breaks and rearrangements, but not that of mutations, increased up to 15-fold after treatment with the polyfunctional com-pounds, while it did not change at all after treatment with the mono-functional ones. The superiority of polyfunctional compounds in can-cer therapy may, therefore, be related to the fact that treatment allows the full effect of storage to manifest itself.

urethane

Like x-rays and many alkylating agents, urethane is mutagenic, carci-nostatic, and carcinogenic. In flowering plants, as well as in *Droso-phila*, it produces chromosome breaks and rearrangements; in *Droso-phila*, the breaks produced by urethane resemble breaks caused by x-rays, at least to the extent that fragments produced by the two treatments given in succession combine as freely with each other as do fragments produced by only one of them. In *Drosophila*, urethane also produced gene mutations which appeared to be unconnected with chro-mosome breakage. Urethane is, however, a very "spotty" mutagen, acting strongly in some organisms and not at all in others. The fungus *Neurospora* was entirely recalcitrant to its action, even when the whole of the genome was tested for mutations and deletions by a special technique [5]. Possibly, this organism specificity of urethane as muta-gen is related to its even more striking organism specificity as a carcinogen. It produces lung cancers in some rodent species but not in others; the active principle in this case appears to be a metabolite of urethane which is produced in mice but not in guinea pigs [6].

phenols

These are similarly "spotty" in their mutagenic effects. A number of phenols, for example, pyrogallol and hydroquinone, produced chromosome fragmentations in plants, although few rearrangements were formed. In *Drosophila*, exposure of the explanted and subsequently reimplanted larval ovary to phenol produced high frequencies of mutations (or small deletions) in some experiments and none in others, and, in spite of prolonged and determined efforts, the conditions for successful application could not be elucidated. These results have gained new significance through the finding of an increased frequency of chromosome rearrangements in lymphocytes of men that had been exposed to ambient benzene [7].

formaldehyde

When formaldehyde is mixed into the food of *Drosophila*, it may act as a strong mutagen. The conditions for its action are, however, more stringent than for any other mutagen. Although, as shown by labeling experiments, formaldehyde penetrates into all germ cells of larvae and adults, mutations occur exclusively during one part of the cell cycle of one germ cell stage in one developmental phase of one sex, namely in early larval spermatocytes. Moreover, the frequency of mutations depends on the nutritional status of the larvae: any conditions that slow down development, including an excessive dose of formaldehyde, decrease the frequency of mutations, and under very poor growth conditions no mutations at all are recovered. On synthetic media, adenosine riboside is an indispensable adjuvant; whether it is involved in the production of a secondary product with mutagenic ability or whether it aids in the release of free formaldehyde from a reversibly bound form or acts in some other way could not so far be decided. Studies on the distribution of mutations along the chromosome have led to the conclusion that mutations are produced during the time of DNA replication and occur in close neighborhood to the point of replication. Casein that has been treated with formaldehyde is also mutagenic; this has raised some doubt about the advisability of feeding breeding pigs skim milk sterilized with formalin. Cytologically, formaldehyde produces few gross chromosome rearrangements but many small deletions and repeats, that is, duplications of small chromosome regions in tandem or reverse. Since duplications are generally assumed to have played an important part in evolution, it is of interest to see that they can be produced by a compound that is closely related to normal metabolic processes.

organic peroxides and irradiated medium

Formaldehyde can also produce mutations when applied in aqueous solution to microorganisms or *Drosophila* spermatozoa. Applied in this way it is a very weak mutagen whose effectiveness, however, can be greatly enhanced by the addition of hydrogen peroxide, which by itself is hardly mutagenic. This suggests that a mutagenically active peroxide is formed and that small amounts of this substance can arise through reaction of formaldehyde with metabolically produced hydrogen peroxide. Indeed, the addition compound of formaldehyde and hydrogen peroxide, as well as other organic peroxides, are fairly good mutagens. They form a link with radiation mutagenesis, for peroxides have been made responsible for the mutagenic action of bacterial medium that has been exposed to heavy irradiation with ultraviolet light or ionizing radiation. In recent years, the sterilization of human food with very heavy x-ray doses has given concern about the possible introduction of mutagens into human consumption. Plant chromosomes can, indeed, be broken by heavily irradiated fruit juices or sugar solutions or by growing of the plants on irradiated potato medium [8]. Mutation tests on *Drosophila*, on the other hand, have given negative results in some investigations and slightly, though significantly, positive ones in others [9]. The bearing of these findings on human affairs is doubtful. Experiments on mice might give clearer evidence, although even extrapolation from mice to man is hazardous when one is dealing with slight genetical effects of chemicals that have been introduced to the germ cells by way of the food.

inorganic salts

A number of inorganic salts produce chromosome breaks and rearrangements in plant cells and mutations in bacteria. In particular, manganese chloride is an excellent mutagen for some bacterial strains, but its action depends strongly on ancillary conditions such as the presence of other salts before treatment. In fungi, attempts to produce mutations with $MnCl_2$ have been unsuccessful. It seems likely that the genetical effects of inorganic salts are not due to direct reactions with DNA, but to the creation of cellular conditions that favor the occurrence of "spontaneous" mutations and chromosome breaks.

purine derivatives

Certain alkylating agents, as well as formaldehyde, were first tested because of their known reaction with proteins. This was natural at a time when most geneticists believed that the specificity of the gene resided in its protein moiety. Yet even then, it was thought possible that reaction with the DNA moiety might produce mutations, and a number of purines and pyrimidines were tested for mutagenicity. While the results with pyrimidines were negative, various purines were found to produce chromosome breaks in plants and mutations in fungi and bacteria. Special interest was aroused by the mutagenic action of caffeine because of the large amounts of it that civilized man consumes in tea or coffee. Tests on mice that had been given the highest tolerated dose of caffeine in their drinking water gave no evidence for the production of either chromosome breakage or mutation, but chromosome breaks, although no rearrangements, were found in human cell cultures that had been exposed to solutions of caffeine [10]. Experiments on *Drosophila* gave contradictory results, but the latest evidence indicates that feeding or injection of caffeine has a weak mutagenic effect [11]. As in the case of food sterilized with radiation, the application to human affairs is doubtful and hazardous. An interesting feature of the experiments on bacteria was the finding that adenosine riboside, which, as mentioned above, is required for the mutagenic action of formaldehyde, abolished that of caffeine and related purines. Moreover, it greatly reduced the frequency of spontaneously occurring mutations, suggesting that a proportion of them is due to ingested or metabolically produced mutagenic purines. The frequency of radiation-induced mutations was not reduced by adenosine riboside or related "antimutagens."

substances tested because of their reactivity with DNA

base analogs

With the recognition of DNA as the essential genetic material, the search for mutagens became directed towards substances that are known to react with DNA or may be presumed to do so. The first of these to be tested were analogs of the purine and pyrimidine bases in DNA. It was thought that these analogs, by being mistakenly incorporated into DNA, might misdirect the subsequent incorporation of the natural bases at the time of replication, leading to transitions from adenine-thymine to guanine-cytosine or from guanine-cytosine to adenine-thymine. Indeed, the pyrimidine 5-bromouracil which, under appropriate conditions, may replace most of the thymine in the DNA of bacteria and viruses, proved to be an excellent mutagen; so, however, did the adenine analog 2-aminopurine of which only traces are incorporated. Thus, although incorporation into DNA almost certainly is a prerequisite for the mutagenic action of base analogs, their mutagenic efficiency does not necessarily depend on the chemically detectable degree of incorporation. Since then, evidence has been obtained for assuming that 5-bromouracil, when incorporated instead of thymine, is only weakly mutagenic, presumably because its pairing preference for adenine is almost as high as that of thymine. However, in the rare and chemically not yet detected instances in which it is incorporated instead of cytosine, this same strong pairing preference for adenine leads to the eventual replacement of a guanine-cytosine pair by an adenine-thymine pair. It is in agreement with this assumption—and, in fact, has been used in formulating it—that mutations which are easily reversed by alkylating agents are also easily reversed by 5-bromouracil. 2-Aminopurine, on the contrary, preferentially reverts mutations that do not respond to alkylating agents, including those produced by them. This is taken as evidence that 2-aminopurine usually acts by incorporating instead of adenine, pairing erroneously with cytosine, and finally changing an adenine-thymine pair into a guanine-cytosine pair. Base analogs have also proved mutagenic in some fungi, and they are able to break chromosomes in human cell cultures. The use of one of them, iododeoxyuridine, for the treatment of herpes lesions in the cornea has caused some concern for possible genetical consequences on the patient; but the chance that this strictly localized treatment will allow appreciable amounts to penetrate to the gonads seems negligible.

acridines

These have long been known to react with nucleic acids, and instances of chromosome breakage and mutation by substances such as acridine orange or proflavine have been reported repeatedly in the past. In most of these experiments, however, visible light had not been excluded, and the effects might have been due to the so-called photodynamic action of the dyes, that is, their ability to sensitize other molecules to the action of visible light. A different and more interesting mechanism of mutagenesis by acridines was suggested by the finding that in vitro acridine molecules intercalate between the nucleotides of DNA. If this should happen also in vivo, replication of the affected strand would be disturbed, and this, it was thought, might lead to the insertion or deletion of a base in the normal sequence. In other words, mutations produced by acridines should be reading-frame shifts and should be characterized by three properties: (i) complete absence of gene function, (ii) lack of reversibility by agents producing only base changes and (iii) ability of being at least partially reversed by other reading-frame shifts of the complementary type that had occurred close enough to the first one to give a functional protein. Experiments with bacteriophage confirmed all these predictions: acridine-induced mutations resulted in completely inactive genes; they could not be reversed by base analogs, which are assumed to cause mutations exclusively by transitions; they could be reversed, or partially so, by additional acridine mutations in their neighborhood. The final proof for the hypothesis was brought by amino acid analysis of the enzyme lysozyme in a certain type of bacteriophage [12]. The enzyme was completely absent from two strains with acridine-induced mutations, and was partially active in a strain combining these two mutations. As predicted, the enzyme in the doubly mutant strain had a short stretch of faulty amino acids between the sites of the two mutations but was normal beyond it. Moreover, the faulty amino acids were of just the types expected from a reading frame shift applied to the original base sequence. Acridines, sometimes in the form of a so-called "acridine mustard" with a mustard as well as an acridine moiety, have produced mutations also in fungi and *Drosophila*. There is evidence that these mutations, too, are due to reading-frame shifts.

nitrous acid and hydroxylamine

Nitrous acid was tested many years ago because of its known reactions with proteins. These experiments gave suggestive results, but they were not followed up. More recently, new experiments were stimulated by the fact that nitrous acid in vitro deaminates three of the bases of DNA and RNA: adenine, guanine, and cytosine. Deamination of adenine produces hypoxanthine, whose pairing properties resemble those of guanine, so that the process in vivo might lead to a transition from adenine to guanine (in double-stranded DNA from adenine-thymine to guanine-cytosine). Deamination of guanine yields xanthine, whose pairing properties resemble those of guanine, so that no mutational change is expected. Finally, deamination of cytosine yields uracil. In RNA, this change results in an immediate change of code; in DNA it might be expected to do so after replication, because uracil tends to pair with adenine rather than with guanine. Genetic experiments, first on tobacco mosaic virus (containing RNA), then on bacteria and fungi, showed that nitrous acid is an excellent mutagen, provided the *p*H is kept low. The results with tobacco mosaic virus were of special importance because of their contribution to the decoding of the nucleotide base triplets. Coding triplets were derived from the correlation between the chemically predicted base changes and the observed amino acid changes in the mutant proteins, and they agreed remarkably well with those derived in other ways. In addition to base changes, nitrous acid can produce deletions; this may be related to its ability to form crosslinks between the strands of DNA. Nitrous acid was the first agent to cause mutations when applied to free nucleic acid in vitro, either to the RNA of tobacco mosaic virus or to the DNA of bacteria. The induced mutations could be detected because RNA, like the virus from which it has been isolated, infects tobacco leaves, while bacterial DNA can enter other bacterial cells and become integrated into their chromosomes by a process called transformation.

Hydroxylamine, too, can produce mutations in free bacterial DNA. In vitro, it reacts preferentially with cytosine. The *p*H dependence of this reaction parallels that of mutation frequency in extracellularly treated bacteriophage, suggesting that mutations are produced exclusively by reaction with cytosine, presumably followed by a transition from guanine-cytosine to adenine-thymine. This high chemical specificity has made hydroxylamine into a standard mutagen for deriving the chemical specificities of others. Thus, the fact that 5-bromouracil tends to revert the same mutations that are also reverted by hydroxylamine, while 2-aminopurine rarely does so, is the mainstay for the assumption that the former preferentially changes guanine-cytosine into adenine-thymine; the latter, changes adenine-thymine into guanine-cytosine. It is, however, important to realize that this simple picture is valid only for bacteriophage treated outside the bacterial cell. Applied to phage inside its host cell, hydroxylamine produces mutations by acting on all four bases [2]. This should be taken as a warning against the frequently made assumption that the genes of cellular organisms, which are unavoidably treated inside their "host cell," will necessarily undergo the same reactions with mutagens as does DNA treated in the test tube or bacteriophage treated outside its host.

directed mutation and the mutation process

What has become of the hope that chemical mutagens might be a tool for producing directed mutations by reacting selectively with certain genes? Since the vast majority of randomly produced mutations are harmful, means for directing mutation into desirable channels would be of immense importance for "mutation breeding." At a time when we conceived of genes as complex nucleoprotein molecules with highly specific overall composition and structure, the hope of finding selectively acting chemicals did not seem unreasonable. Nowadays, when we conceive of genes as linear sequences made up of the same four nucleotides, it seems a forlorn hope. It is true that, in the nucleotide bases, mutations do not occur at random but tend to attack preferential sites, whose positions within a given gene depend on the mutagen. The nature of these "hot spots" is obscure. They cannot be due to specific reactions between a given chemical and one out of four nucleotides, every one of which occurs many times within the gene. They have been tentatively attributed to the effect of neighboring nucleotides on the chemical reactivity of a given base. Since, however, the same short nucleotide sequence that produces a hot spot in one gene is likely to recur in many or most other genes, the phenomenon of hot spots, however interesting in its own right, holds out no promise for the production of directed mutations.

Does this mean that we have to give up all hope of achieving at least a modicum of control over the direction of mutation. I do not think it does. This defeatist conclusion could be drawn only if numbers and types of mutation were determined wholly by the reaction between DNA and mutagen, and this is most certainly not so. It is true that a change in the information carried by DNA is a necessary condition for mutation, but it is not a sufficient one. It is preceded as well as followed by secondary steps, and these act as so many sieves determining whether a change in DNA will take place and whether, once it has taken place, it will give rise to an observable mutation, that is, to a population of cells with a new type of genetic information. It is at the level of these sieves that specificities may be expected, and have already been found [13].

The sieves that precede the reaction between mutagen and DNA are concerned with the chemical changes that a mutagen may undergo before reaching the gene, and with the accessibility of the gene. They are influenced by strain, cell type, and metabolic state and probably depend on the degree of coiling of chromosomes and chromosome regions and on the amount and type of the chromosomal components other than DNA. A possibility that has been considered but not yet adequately tested is that active genes are more accessible to certain mutagens than repressed ones. If this were true, it would offer a means of selecting genes for mutagen attack. There is also the more remote possibility that one might maneuver a mutagenic group, say a chloroethyl or ethylene imine group, into close neighborhood of repressed genes by attaching it to a repressor substance. This should give a complementary response pattern to the above, and the pattern should be similar if similar mutagenic groups were attached to the same type of repressor substance.

The sieves following the reaction between mutagen and gene determine which of the changes in DNA will eventually appear as observable mutations. The first sieve is repair which, in one form or another, seems capable of reversing chemical changes in DNA after treatment with most or all mutagens. Repair processes are presently under intensive study [14]. They involve enzymes, and their efficiency depends on the time available between the production of the chemical change and the next replication of DNA. The latter factor certainly is influenced by mutagenic treatment, the former probably is so in many cases. This is one of several ways in which a mutagen may act as a screening agent for the potential mutations that it has itself induced. There has as yet been no systematic search for repair processes that are specific to certain genes; research on *Neurospora* and bacteria suggests that they may exist.

Once the mutational change in DNA has become stabilized it has to be transcribed by messenger RNA. This particular sieve may be clogged by substances like fluorouracil, which specifically inhibit the manifestation of certain mutational changes [15]. Then follows a series of sieves concerned with translation; they include all processes by which a mutated cell is formed under the influence of the new messenger RNA. When the mutation leads to the formation of a new enzyme or other protein, ribosomes and transfer RNA are involved; other steps have to be carried through for the formation of a new type of transfer, or ribosomal, RNA. Again, many factors including the mutagen itself may affect the action of these sieves, and some may do so specifically. Thus, streptomycin and neomycin specifically prevent the manifestation of certain types of mutation by misdirecting translation on the ribosomes [16]. Finally, the mutated cell has to grow into a population of mutant cells. In mutation experiments on microorganisms, this last sieve has often to be passed in competition with a vast majority of nonmutant cells. Moreover, in the most frequently used type of experiment, the screening for mutations that render the mutant cells resistant to conditions by which the nonmutant ones are killed, there is a race between death and the completion of the mutation process, and all sieves have to be passed within a strict time limit.

For many years, the remarkable successes in the molecular analysis of mutagenesis at the DNA level have channeled most mutation research into this line of approach, and a study of mutation as biological rather than chemical process has hardly begun. There are, however, already a fair number of cases which point to the importance of cellular events for making or marring potential mutations. In some of them, the observed effects were directed ones in the sense that the proportion between different types of mutation could be profoundly altered by conditions such as temperature, pH, visible light, plating medium, type and dose of mutagen, treatment before or after with mutagenic or nonmutagenic chemicals, or the introduction of new genes into the genetic background of those to be screened for mutation [17]. In my opinion, it is along these lines that progress toward a direction of mutation is to be expected. Moreover, this approach will help us to understand one of the most interesting biological processes, by which a change in the information carried in DNA leads to the emergence of a population of cells with altered hereditary properties.

summary

Since the discovery of the first potent mutagens over 20 years ago, progress in mutation research has been rapid. Many new mutagens, belonging to a variety of chemical classes, have been discovered, and for some of them the reaction with DNA in vitro has been established. It seems that the findings of these chemical investigations usually also apply to viruses which are treated outside the cell. This has made chemical mutagens into an important tool for the analysis of the genetic code. When DNA is treated inside the cell, its reactions would not be expected to be always identical with those observed in vitro; in one case they have, indeed, been found to be different.

A chemical change in DNA is a necessary but not a sufficient condition for the production of an observable mutation. Intercalated between this primary change and the emergence of a population of cells with a new hereditary property is a whole series of cellular events, including a variety of repair mechanisms, transcription and translation of the new information, and growth of the mutant cell into a mutant population, often in the face of severe competition from nonmutant cells. These events act as so many sieves that screen out a proportion of potential mutations for realization. The study of mutation as cellular process has hardly begun, but it already shows the importance of these cellular events for the numbers and types of mutation produced. In addition to its theoretical interest, this approach is the only one likely to lead to the production of directed mutations for "mutation breeding."

references

1. C. Auerbach, J. M. Robson, J. G. Carr, *Science 105*, 243 (1947).

2. I. Tessman, R. K. Poddar, S. Kumar, *J. Mol. Biol. 9*, 352 (1964); I. Tessman, H. Ishiwa, S. Kumar, *Science 148*, 507 (1965).

3. J. D. Karkas and E. Chargaff, *Proc. Nat. Acad. Sci. U.S. 56*, 1241 (1966).

4. W. A. F. Watson, *Z. Vererbungsl. 95*, 374 (1964); *Mutation Res. 3*, 455 (1966).

5. C. Auerbach, *Microbial Genet. Bull. 17*, 5 (1960).

6. S. Rogers, *J. Nat. Cancer Inst. 15*, 1675 (1955).

7. I. M. Tough and W. M. Court Brown, *Lancet 1965-II*, 684 (1965).

8. M. S. Swaminathan, V. L. Chopra, S. Bhaskaran, *Radiat. Res. 16*, 182 (1962); V. L. Chopra, A. T. Natarajan, M. S. Swaminathan, *Radiat. Bot. 3*, 1 (1963); V. L. Chopra and M. S. Swaminathan, *Naturwissenschaften 50*, 374 (1963); F. C. Steward, R. D. Holsten, M. Sugii, *Nature 213*, 178 (1967).

9. V. L. Chopra, *Nature 208*, 699 (1965); O. S. Reddi, G. M. Reddy, J. J. Rao, D. N. Ebenezer, M. S. Rao, *ibid.*, p. 702; R. R. Rinehart and F. J. Ratty, *Genetics 52*, 1119 (1965).

10. W. Ostertag, E. Duisberg, M. Stürmann, *Mutation Res. 2*, 293 (1965); W. Ostertag, *ibid. 3*, 249 (1966).

11. W. Ostertag and J. Haake, *Z. Vererbungsl. 98*, 299 (1966).

12. E. Terzaghi, Y. Okada, G. Streisinger, J. Emrich, M. Inouye, A. Tsugita, *Proc. Nat. Acad. Sci. U.S. 56*, 500 (1966).

13. C. Auerbach, *Soviet Genet. 2*, 1 (1966).

14. E. M. Witkin, *Science 152*, 1345 (1966).

15. S. P. Champe and S. Benzer, *Proc. Nat. Acad. Sci. U.S. 48*, 532 (1962).

16. J. Davies, W. Gilbert and L. Gorini, *ibid. 51*, 883 (1964); L. Gorini and E. Kataja, *ibid.*, p. 487.

17. V. L. Chopra, *Mutation Res. 4*, 382 (1967); C. Auerbach and D. Ramsay, *ibid.*, p. 508; B. J. Kilbey, *Mol. Gen. Genet. 100*, 159–165 (1967).

bibliography

C. Auerbach, *Biol. Rev. 24*, 355 (1949).

———, *Radiat. Res. 9*, 33 (1958).

———, in *Nat. Acad. Sci.-Nat. Res. Council Publ. 891* (1961), p. 120.

E. Freese, in *Molecular Genetics*, J. H. Taylor, Ed. (Academic Press, London, 1963), Part 1, pp. 207–269.

E. Freese and E. B. Freese, *Radiat. Res. Suppl. 6*, 97 (1966).

B. A. Kihlman, *Actions of Chemicals on Dividing Cells* (Prentice-Hall, Englewood Cliffs, N.J., 1996).

D. R. Krieg, in *Progress in Nucleic Acid Research*, J. N. Davidson and W. E. Cohn, Eds. (Academic Press, New York, 1963), vol. 2, pp. 125–168.

A. Loveless, *Genetic and Allied Effects of Alkylating Agents* (Butterworth, London, 1966).

Caffeine May Damage Genes by Inhibiting DNA Polymerase

Public health authorities and the food industry sooner or later may be faced with having to answer this unsettling question: Does caffeine damage genes? Some scientists think it does. They believe that caffeine (1,3,7-trimethylxanthine) inhibits the mechanism by which a cell's deoxyribonucleic acid (DNA) normally repairs itself after chemical injury.

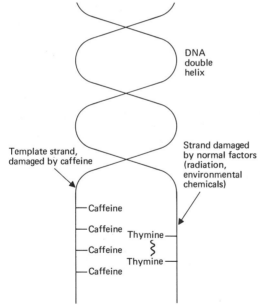

Caffeine may interfere with normal DNA repair by combining with adenine sites on strand opposite thymine dimers. Thus, even with thymines broken in preparation for repair, resynthesis could not occur because of template interference by caffeine.

The latest case against caffeine comes from the laboratory of Dr. Marvin S. Legator of the Food and Drug Administration's Washing-

Reprinted from *Chemical & Engineering News:* 19 (November 20, 1967) with permission of the publisher.

ton laboratories. June B. Wragg, a biochemist working under Dr. Legator, said at a Cell Biology Society meeting . . . that caffeine inhibits activity of the enzyme DNA polymerase. She said concentrations of caffeine greater than 200 micrograms per milliliter produced the effect immediately during in vitro experiments. In vivo (on cells taken from human lung tissue) inhibition began after 24 hours.

DNA polymerase, and perhaps a series of similar isoenzymes, is part of the enzyme system that routinely repairs DNA when it's damaged by various chemical and physical "insults." These might range from ultraviolet radiation to carcinogenic alkylating agents like aflatoxin.

Scientists working in this field have known of caffeine's cellular effects since 1951 when Evelyn Wilkin of the Downstate Medical Center, Brooklyn, N.Y., showed that caffeine inhibits the repair of UV-caused lesions on bacterial DNA. This initial, UV damage takes the form of dimerization reactions between adjacent thymine molecules on a single strand of the double-stranded DNA. In repair, one enzyme breaks the dimer, another strips off the residue, a third rebuilds the section guided by the coding on the opposite DNA strand, and a fourth seals the new chemical patch. The repair enzyme is probably DNA polymerase, since it is directly responsible for multiple linkage of DNA's four bases.

Mrs. Wragg's work is the first direct enzymic tie-in between caffeine and the repair mechanism. The experiments consisted of adding caffeine to cells and cell-free systems treated beforehand with actinomycin c or aflatoxin B_1, both injurious to DNA. The polymerase activity was measured by uptake of tritiated thymidine (a DNA base) and by synthesis of new DNA. Inhibition began above 200 micrograms per milliliter and reached 50% at 10 times that concentration.

What is the mechanism of caffeine's attack? One speculation (see sketch) has caffeine combining with DNA on the strand complementary to the injured strand. This would prevent the section it reacted with from acting as template for repair synthesis.

Drosophila melanogaster Treated with LSD: Absence of Mutation and Chromosome Breakage

Dale Grace
Elof Axel Carlson
Philip Goodman

Chromosome breakage, apparently induced by lysergic acid diethylamide, LSD-25, in human leukocytes was reported, in vitro, by Cohen *et al.* [1] and, in vivo, by Irwin and Egozcue [2]. In these two reports there was no consistent relation of LSD concentration to breakage frequency. This was unusual because chemical mutagens in *Drosophila* do show a proportionality between concentration and mutation frequency [3]. The frequency of breaks among the controls in the leukocytes studied by Cohen (34/925) is significantly lower than that obtained from Irwin's study (211/1800).

The unusual features of the dose-frequency response by the LSD-treated cells in Cohen's report prompted us to design a series of experiments on *Drosophila melanogaster* to test for chromosome breakage and mutation. The choice of *Drosophila* was based on our experience in studying mutagenesis with a variety of chemical mutagens: monofunctional quinacrine mustard (ICR-170) [4–6], nitrosomethylurea (NMU) [7], and ethyl methanesulfonate (EMS) [3]. Fruit flies were the first organisms used to detect mutations induced by ionizing radiation [8] and by chemical mutagens [9]. In none of our tests did

Reprinted from *Science, 161:* 694–96 (1968) with permission of the authors and the publisher. Copyright 1968 by the American Association for the Advancement of Science.

we find any evidence that LSD was associated with chromosome break-age or mutations. Our tests were designed to assay the sensitivity to LSD for all stages of the male meiotic cycle.

We assayed for mutations with three techniques: the sc^{s1} B InS w^a sc^8 (Basc) sex-linked lethal test, which detects lethal mutations by an absence of a class of X chromosomes [10]; the yf doubly attached-X (yf: =) sex-linked visible test, which detects any induced, visible mutation in the X chromosomes of the sons [11]; and a specific visible test, *ed dp cl*, using a well-studied complex locus, dumpy, which detects all induced alleles of that specific locus [4, 12]. In addition to the three tests for mutation, we employed a *bw; st* translocation test for breakage [11].

LSD was injected into males at three different concentrations: 1, 100, and 500 μg per milliliter of a tartrate (8.7 μg/ml) solution (for the 100-μg solution the tartrate was already present in the capsules; for the 1-μg and 500-μg concentrations, a stock solution was prepared with the same solution of tartrate—8.7 μg/ml). The injection techniques were identical to those used for analysis of dumpy mutations and sex-linked lethals. The males were transferred by an aspirator to new virgin females every 3 days, the procedure thereby establishing a minimum of five broods. These provided a test of postmeiotic (0 to 7 days), meiotic (8 to 10 days), and premeiotic (11 or more days) stages of spermatogenesis [13]. This brooding analysis is particularly useful in the detection of mutations requiring one or more replications for incorporation of a mutagen; the postmeiotic cells might not be reactive to the agent, but the premeiotic broods could provide the assay for such late-arising mutations. The range of concentrations was based on the tissue-culture studies of Cohen [1] (0.001 μg/ml to 10 μg/ml) and the studies in vivo of Irwin [2] (200 μg to 500 μg of LSD per mean dose per subject). Our 100 μg/ml and 500 μg/ml series represent a much higher tissue saturation in *Drosophila* than in human tissue because sufficient LSD solution was injected to distend the abdomens of the flies. This would be equivalent to intraperitoneal injections of about 1 liter of the LSD concentration in each human subject. A concentration of 500 μg of LSD per milliliter is approximately that used for ICR-170 studies (0.5 to 1.0 mg/ml) which would induce approximately 10 percent of sex-linked lethals and 0.5 percent of dumpy mutations. Controls were injected with the stock tartrate solutions.

In all four series the males were Oregon R wild type (+). These males, 24 to 48 hours old, were injected abdominally with fine glass needles prepared from Pasteur pipettes heated over a microburner [4]. Although flies may express some of the fluid injected at the site of puncture, tests with vital dyes showed clearly that the tissues of the fly are perfused rapidly after injection [14].

In the sex-linked lethal tests (Table 1), among 4786 progeny of the LSD series, a total of seven lethals and semilethals were found. There were two lethals among 3168 tested X chromosomes in the controls.

Table 1.

Mutational and Breakage Events among F₁ Progeny of Untreated and LSD-Injected *Drosophila melanogaster* Males, at Intervals Indicated

Types	Mutations and Breakages (No.)						Total	Frequency
	1-3 Days	4-6 Days	7-9 Days	10-12 Days	13-15 Days	16-18 Days		
yf: = (Control)								
Minutes	0	1	1	1	2		5	0.6
F₁ Abnormal Phenotypes	9	20	9	5	4		47	5.9
F₂ Transmitted Mutants	0	0	0	0	0		0	0.0
Normal F₁ Males	1176	2875	1297	516	810		7944	
yf: = (1 µg/ml)								
Minutes	0	0	3	0	0		3	0.8
F₁ Abnormal Phenotypes	4	0	6	0	11		11	2.8
F₂ Transmitted Mutants	0	0	0	0	0		0	0.0
Normal F₁ Males	898	396	1349	221	530		3894	
yf: = (100 µg/ml)								
Minutes	1	2	1		1		5	0.8
F₁ Abnormal Phenotypes	9	7	8		6		30	4.7
F₂ Transmitted Mutants	1	0	0		0		1	0.2
Normal F₁ Males	1706	1780	1990		946		6422	
yf: = (500 µg/ml)								
Minutes	1	3	1	0	1		6	1.3
F₁ Abnormal Phenotypes	5	10	5	2	1		23	5.0
F₂ Transmitted Phenotypes	0	0	0	0	0		0	
Normal F₁ Males	1269	1166	605	1924	268		4602	

Table 1. (Continued)

Types	1-3 Days	4-6 Days	7-9 Days	10-12 Days	13-15 Days	16-18 Days	Total	Fre- quency
			ed dp cl (500 µg/ml)					
Mosaic F₁ dp								
Phenotypes	2	2	1	2	0		7	0.2
Complete F₁ dp								
Phenotypes	1	1	0	0	0		2	0.06
Normal F₁	8853	11205	4453	7428	3118		35157	
			Basc (Control)					
Lethals	0	1	0	1	0		2	0.6
Semilethals	0	0	0	0	0		0	0.0
Nonlethals	674	723	669	604	498		3168	
			Basc (1 µg)					
Lethals	0	1	0		0		1	0.6
Semilethals	1	0	0		0		1	0.6
Nonlethals	415	480	395		344		1634	
			Basc (100 µg)					
Lethals	0	0	0		0		0	0.0
Semilethals	2	0	1		0		3	1.7
Nonlethals	496	494	435		367		1792	
			Basc (500 µg)					
Lethals	2	0	0		0		2	1.5
Semilethals	0	0	0		0		0	0.0
Nonlethals	410	343	342		265		1360	
			bw; st (1 µg)					
Translocations	0	0	0				0	0
Nontranslocations	376	314	442				1132	
			bw; st (100 µg)					
Translocations	0	0	0				0	0
Nontranslocations	475	468	353				1296	
			bw; st (500 µg)					
Translocations	0	0	0		0	0	0	0
Nontranslocations	461	417	414		273	212	1777	

The frequency of spontaneous mutation previously found for this Oregon R stock in our laboratory was 0.2 percent [5].

In the sex-linked visible test, all aberrant male phenotypes were recorded and tested with yf: = females. Only one mutant phenotype, a Minute bristle (M, about 50 different loci) disturbance associated with smaller body size and pale body color, was transmitted with high frequency. These Minute mutations usually arose as complete rather than mosaic or fractional phenotypes. The frequencies were 5/7944 for the control series; and 14/14,918 among the total LSD series. None of these LSD values differs significantly from that obtained in the control. Because the Minute mutant is a dominant, the appearance of F_1 Minutes tells nothing about the chromosome which bears it or the sex from which it arose. This can be determined, however, from the F_2 progeny when Minute F_1 males are mated to yf: $=$ females. If the Minute is autosomal (not sex-linked), at least half of the F_2 males will show normal bristles. Minutes are usually recessive lethal and it was thus expected and found that all of the transmitted male Minutes from the F_1 were autosomal. Among all of the other phenotypes (mostly fractional and mosaic wing mutations) only one mutant, in the 100-μg series, transmitted. This was a male with a trident or pentagon pattern on the thorax, which proved to be a recessive sex-linked mutant. The frequency of aberrant phenotypes among the F_1 males was: 47/7944 for this control; and 64/14,918 among the total LSD series. The lower frequency of aberrant phenotypes among the LSD series is not significant. The transmission of only one sex-linked mutant among the 18,296 F_1 males examined is not unexpected. Schalet [15] reported a frequency of about 1/90,000 or 1.1×10^{-5} as the average spontaneous mutation frequency for any one of 13 specific sex-linked mutants he studied.

For the dumpy series, only an injection of 500 μg of LSD per milliliter was used in this experiment. Among the F_1 progeny there were nine dumpy phenotypes and 35,157 non-dumpy phenotypes. Control frequencies from the same Oregon R stock had been obtained by Carlson (6/31,154), Southin (8/27,426), and Jenkins (3/13,789) for a total spontaneous mutation frequency of 17/72,369 [3, 6, 12]. Thus, in the LSD series in which 500 μg/ml were given, there was no difference from control expectations. By contrast, injections of EMS, NMU, or ICR-170 would have yielded frequencies of about 1 percent dumpy phenotypes in the F_1 [7, 12].

A very high percentage of the Minute mutations arose as complete, rather than mosaic, phenotypes (17 complete and 2 mosaics). By contrast, most of the dumpy mutations were mosaics (two complete and seven mosaic phenotypes). None of the nine dumpy mutants transmitted the dumpy phenotype to the F_2 progeny. Most of the fertile Minutes (11/16) transmitted to the F_2 generation. Schalet reported most spontaneously arising sex-linked visible mutations to be mosaic in origin, a characteristic also found for spontaneous dumpy mutants. Most of the Minute mutations arising spontaneously probably are derived from nondisjunction of the fourth chromosome [16] rather than from small deletions of chromatin in the larger autosomes. In radiation experiments, Minute mutations are frequently associated with small deletions of the chromatin [17].

The translocation test for breakage was negative for all of the LSD series—no translocations were found among a total of 4205 progeny tests. Spontaneous translocations are rare, their frequency being less than 10^{-4} [18]. The absence of translocations places LSD in a class quite distinct from ionizing radiation which would have yielded 14.4 percent translocations in the *bw; st* test at a dose of 4000 roentgens [19]; atmospheric mustard gas bubbled through water would have given 0.4 percent translocations in the *bw; st* test [20].

The absence of induced mutations (sex-linked or autosomal, visible or lethal) and the absence of induced chromosome breakage in *Drosophila* by LSD suggests that LSD, if it is a mutagen or radiomimetic agent in human chromosomes, is not a very powerful one. It is more probable, in view of reports that do not confirm leukocyte breakage [21] and from our results, that LSD induces neither mutations nor chromosome breaks in man. The initial report of positive results with LSD in human leukocytes or among LSD-users, we believe, was based on small samples of individuals and on inadequate controls [22].

The difficulties of proving an agent nonmutagenic are more severe than for obtaining positive results. It is unlikely but theoretically possible that LSD is enzymatically degraded in *Drosophila* but not in mammals. Alternatively, it might be argued that LSD can induce very low frequencies of mutations or breaks which are slightly above control rates. Our tests are not extensive enough to detect such low level mutagenesis, but they do rule out any effect above a doubling of the spontaneous mutation frequency. To assay for such low-level effects, it would be more appropriate to test LSD with microbial systems (*Neurospora, Aspergillus, Saccharomyces,* bacteria) where populations of 10^7 or more treated cells have been assayed by selective techniques for antibiotic resistance, nutritional mutants, or reverse mutations [11].

It is our belief that the most satisfactory screening method for a definitive analysis of the genetic effects of LSD or other chemicals should be a three-step procedure: (i) mutagenesis tests with microbial organisms; (ii) mutagenesis and breakage tests with *Drosophila*; and (iii) cytological tests for breakage in small mammals (rats, hamsters, and so forth) whose genetic lineage can be rigorously controlled. The universality of the basic components of metabolism and the universality of the genetic coding machinery [23] make it unlikely that a dangerous mutagen would be missed by the three-step procedure we recommend.

This procedure is similar to that recommended by Kaufmann ᵢ Schuler for pharmaceutical products [24]. Because of the possible ᵢ proven genetic and teratogenic hazards associated with certain pharmaceuticals, antibiotics, preservatives, additives, and other chemical agents [25] we believe that the screening procedure we described should be used before these substances are made available to the public.

Our experiments in *Drosophila* do not substantiate the conclusion that LSD had any pronounced effect on genes and chromosomes. We recognize that high doses of LSD (varying from 100 μg to several thousand micrograms) induce strong psychological reactions in humans [26]. For this reason we do not wish our results at the genetic level to be used as a justification for nonmedical use of LSD as a mind-altering chemical. We strongly recommend that the social debate on the uses and abuses of LSD be based on what is actually known, from rigorously controlled experiments, rather than from conjecture, insufficient sample size, isolated case histories lacking rigorous controls, and subjective individual experience.

references and notes

1. M. Cohen, M. J. Marinello, N. Back, *Science 155*, 1417 (1967).

2. S. Irwin and J. Egozcue, *ibid. 157*, 313 (1967).

3. J. B. Jenkins, *Mutation Res. 4*, 90 (1967).

4. E. A. Carlson and I. I. Oster, *Genetics 47*, 561 (1962).

5. E. A. Carlson and J. L. Southin, *ibid. 48*, 663 (1963).

6. J. L. Southin, *Mutation Res. 3*, 54 (1966).

7. H. O. Corwin, thesis, University of California, Los Angeles (University Microfilms, Ann Arbor, Mich., 1966).

8. H. J. Muller, *Zeitschr. Indukt. Abstamm. Vererb. Suppl. I* (1928), p. 234.

9. C. Auerbach, *Proc. Roy. Soc. Edinburgh 62*(2), 211 (1945).

10. ———, *Mutation*, Part 1, *Methods* (Oliver and Boyd, Edinburgh, 1962); T. Alderson, *Nature 207*, 164 (1965); O. G. Fahmy and M. J. Fahmy, *ibid. 180*, 31 (1957); E. A. Carlson, *J. Theor. Biol. 6*, 432 (1964); J. L. Epler, *Genetics 54*, 31 (1966).

11. W. J. Burdette, Ed., *Methodology in Basic Genetics* (Holden-Day, San Francisco, 1963).

12. E. A. Carlson, *Genetics 44*, 347 (1959); J. B. Jenkins, *ibid. 47*, 783 (1967).

13. A. C. Chandley and A. J. Bateman, *Nature 193*, 299 (1962).

14. The efficiency of this injection technique depends primarily on the quality of the needle used. In these experiments only those flies which visibly retained the injected solution, and were not otherwise injured, were used.

15. A. P. Schalet, thesis, Indiana University, Bloomington (University Microfilms, Ann Arbor, Mich., 1960).

16. C. B. Bridges, *Proc. Nat. Acad. Sci. U.S. 7*, 186 (1921).

163

nd r

res, J. Schultz, *Carnegie Inst. Wash. Year Book 32*, 298

Acad. Sci. U.S. 14, 714 (1928).

. Oster, *Mutation Res. 1*, 437 (1964).

C. Auerbach, *Z. Vererb. 91*, 253 (1960).

d D. V. Siva Sankar, *Science 159*, 749 (1968); W. D. Loughman, gent, D. M. Israelstam, *ibid. 158*, 508 (1967).

per control would have taken into account the subject's history of all ags taken and health records including diseases contracted and general health condition. Experimental and control subjects should be closely matched.

23. R. E. Marshall, C. T. Caskey, M. Nirenberg, *Science 155*, 820 (1967).

24. B. N. Kaufmann and D. Schuler, *Genetic and Chromosomal Changes Produced by Drugs in Pharmacological Techniques in Drug Evaluation*, P. E. Siegler and J. H. Moyer, III, Eds. (Year Book, Chicago, 1967), vol. 2.

25. W. Ostertag, E. Duisberg, M. Sturmann, *Mutation Res. 2*, 293 (1965); J. M. Krogh, *Acta Med. Scand. 177*, 783 (1965); R. C. Nowell, *Exp. Cell Res. 33*, 286 (1964); M. W. Shaw and M. M. Cohen, *Genetics 51*, 181 (1965).

26. J. T. Ungerleider, D. D. Fisher, M. Fuller, *J. Amer. Med. Ass. 197*, 389 (1966); D. B. Louria, in *LSD, Man and Society*, R. C. Debold and R. C. Leaf, Eds. (Wesleyan Univ. Press, Middletown, Conn., 1967).

27. We thank Patricia Girard for technical assistance and Patricia Mukai for clerical assistance. Supported by NSF GB 6595 to E.A.C. The LSD was supplied by the NIMH under drug No. IND 4102. The LSD for the 1-μg and 500-μg tests was Sandoz batch No. 53032; for the 100-μg tests, it was Sandoz batch 65002.

6

The Rebellious Cell:
Cancer's Causes and
Cures

Last scene of all
That ends this strange eventful history
Is second childishness and mere oblivion.
—JAQUES, IN *As You Like It*.

Cancer is an ancient affliction. It has been a disorder of plants and animals of all kinds since before recorded history. Although the disease has always been of common occurrence in man, its incidence in humans has increased sharply within recent times. The explanation is simple. Cancer is an affliction of aging tissue. It kills more of the well-fed, well-clothed, well-housed, medically attended, and sanitary people because they live longer. In short, cancer is a disease of civilization.

Cancer will strike nearly one-fourth of all Americans now living. Yet despite a massive effort to unravel the mystery of the cancerous cell, the one predominant cause of the affliction, and hence its cure, remains as elusive as ever. Fragments of the process have been worked out and some of the pieces fitted together. But even as progress is made, the problem continues to defy the best efforts to give clearly defined answers and remains one of the most puzzling, frustrating, and expensive endeavors in the medical, chemical, and biological sciences.

The condition of tissue described as cancerous is one in which the cells have gone on a rampage. There is often an early latent period after which the cells typically grow and divide uncontrollably until their onslaught causes the death of the organism. The rebellious cell, apparently overcoming the body's regularity, reverts as if in a fit of anarchy to a more primitive and embryonic type—savagely independent and free of the restraints imposed by the society of cells that make

etabolic signals have somehow gone awry and
obey the instructions given by the normal
anism of the organism. The cells are said to be
vidence indicates that they no longer carry the
ae of normal somatic[1] cells but, instead, possess "wrong
as of DNA or perhaps extraneous material within their
nich send out distorted signals. Cells have no intelligence of
own; born and bred to act as a team, they must respond slavishly
o the instructions of DNA. Whatever the code, it is obediently transmitted to all of the cells of the cancer colony, thereby perpetuating
their riotous behavior and ultimately resulting in their proliferation
beyond control.

The biological concept then, of the causation of cells gone berserk, is
based on the evidence that the cells are victimized by virus nucleic acids
or by mutations of one kind or another that render them no longer
subject to the normal controls of the body. Moreover, daughter cells
are similarly out of step with the normal functioning of the organism.
As in the mutational theory of cancer, the related virus theory holds
that the signal-calling mechanism of the nuclear DNA is thrown out
of gear, in this case by the invasion of a virus, since it is known that
viruses themselves are composed only of protein and nucleic acid. Frequently, only the nucleic acid is needed to induce an infection in a
recipient cell. The presence of the invading nucleic acid accounts for
the confusion in the instructions given out by the cell headquarters.
Some types of cancer in animals, such as the Rous fowl sarcoma and
the rabbit papilloma, are known to be caused by viruses that can be
transmitted like other pathogens from one animal to another. Yet the
virus theory cannot explain, on the basis of present knowledge, the
causes of cancer generally. For example, it has long been known that
forms of cancer are caused by x-rays and by mutagenic chemicals.

The first real success in identifying a causative agent for cancer
occurred in 1775 in England. Sir Percival Pott, an alert London
surgeon, was intrigued by the high frequency of scrotal cancer among
chimney sweeps. Dr. Pott noted the accumulation of soot in the region
of the crotch and other crevices of the skin and recommended frequent
bathing. That cancer can have other occupational associations was
earlier brought in evidence by Agricola's writing of lung cancer affecting miners in the fifteenth century as well as by more recent revelations
of cancer in industry.

---

[1] *Soma (Gk) = body.*

One hundred and forty years after Dr. Pott's observations, two Japanese doctors, Yamagiwa and Ichikawa followed up the lead in 1915 by painting coal tar on rabbit's ears. The coal tar caused cancer. The final step in the coal tar episode came from work in the period 1920–30 when the British scientists Cook, Hewett, and Heiger isolated the prime causative agent, a substance identified as 3,4-benzopyrene.

Since then more than a hundred carcinogenic chemicals[2] have been identified. Some of them are of common occurrence. The coal tar killer benzopyrene is found in minute quantities in tobacco smoke, charcoal-broiled steaks, and automobile exhaust. "Butter yellow," an azo dye, caused liver cancer in laboratory animals. (A sidelight of this revelation was that the investigator, Riojun Kinosito of Osaka University, fed the animals polished rice, deficient in riboflavin (vitamin B_2), which triggered the dye, apparently by replacement of the vitamin in the metabolism of the animals.) Certain common dyes also were found to cause bladder cancer in factory workers. In an effort to trace the causes of cervical cancer, investigators found herpes virus under the prepuce of uncircumcised men.

Many people remember the "cranberry scare" of 1959 when the U.S. Department of Health, Education, and Welfare frightened millions of Americans just before Thanksgiving Day with an announcement that Oregon cranberries had been sprayed with a weed-killing carcinogen, aminotriazole.

Present-day nonoccupational hazards to which everyone may be exposed in varying degrees are cigaret smoking, x-rays, combustion exhaust, and possibly other chemicals, including drugs, hormone imbalance, and even food contaminants.

Strong medicine is needed in the chemotherapy of cancer. It is not surprising that the chemicals that are most effective in suppressing the misbehaving cells are themselves potent mutagens or mitotic poisons. The effect of such compounds is liable to be most drastic on dividing cells. Some of the chemicals have been adapted to the experimental chemosterilization of insects, since it is on the rapidly dividing cells of the gonads in the formation of the sperm and ova that such chemicals can be targeted. The extreme toxicity of most of the cancer drugs seriously limits their utility, and until safe and highly effective materials are discovered, cancer will remain among the most hotly pursued of man's enemies.

---

[2] *Carcinogenic = cancer causing.*

The Challenge to Man of the Neoplastic Cell

Peyton Rous

Tumors destroy man in a unique and appalling way, as flesh of his own flesh, which has somehow been rendered proliferative, rampant, predatory, and ungovernable. They are the most concrete and formidable of human maladies, yet despite more than 70 years of experimental study they remain the least understood. This is the more remarkable because they can be evoked at will for scrutiny by any one of a myriad chemical and physical means which are left behind as the tumors grow. These had acted merely as *initiators*. Few situations are more exasperating to the inquirer than to watch a tiny nodule form on a rabbit's skin at a spot from which the chemical agent inducing it has long since been gone, and to follow the nodule as it grows, and only too often becomes a destructive, epidermal cancer. What can be the reason for these happenings?

Every tumor is made up of cells that have been so singularly changed as no longer to obey the fundamental law whereby the cellular constituents of an organism exist in harmony and act together to maintain it. Instead the changed cells multiply at its expense and inflict damage which can be mortal. We term the lawless cells neoplastic because they form new tissue, and the growth itself a neoplasm; but on looking into medical dictionaries, hoping for more information, we are told, in effect, that *neoplastic* means "of or pertaining to a neoplasm," and turning to *neoplasm* learn that it is "a growth which consists of neoplastic cells." Ignorance could scarcely be more stark.

The chemical and physical initiators are ordinarily called *carcinogens*; but this is a misleading term because they not only induce the malignant epithelial growths known as carcinomas but other neoplasms

Reprinted from *Science, 157:* 24–28 (1967) with permission of the author, the publisher, and the Nobel Foundation.

of widely various kinds. In the present paper the less-used term *onco-gens* will be employed, meaning thereby capable of producing a tumor. It hews precisely to the fact.

Some may exclaim on reading what comes next that it consists mostly of truisms. This does not make these the less vital to my theme.

Tumors occur in vertebrates of so many kinds that it would not be surprising if neoplastic changes took place in them all. Normal cells of any sort capable of multiplying in response to ordinary stimuli are liable to become neoplastic if acted upon by an initiator. It follows that the growths they form are almost incredibly multifarious, and this not only because of their widely various, cellular sources but because tumors of several kinds may derive from a single one. Nevertheless the changed cells are all alike in the basic respect that they disobey the law of organism. Obviously, what has to be understood is not the tumor but the neoplastic state of its cells. These are all animated by some principle exploiting their capabilities. In this respect the problem they present is a coherent entity.

The range in effectiveness of neoplastic changes in tumors is exceedingly great. Often the obvious alterations undergone by neoplastic cells are so slight that they look scarcely different from the normal and function in a similar way, retaining the task of storing fat for example. Yet even such cells, when forming tumors, possess an abnormal power to multiply, however slowly they divide. They are euphemistically termed "benign." The cells of some not only retain the normal ability to form hormones needed by the body but may produce these in such quantity as to disturb it greatly; and the hormones themselves are sometimes changed to a pathological extent.

In proportion as neoplastic cells diverge from the normal they ordinarily function less well. As time goes on their ability to multiply usually increases, and often they undergo such alterations in their state as to render them lawless and a threat to life. For the tumors they then produce we again use a humanistic term, "malignant." The changes for the worse undergone by the cells are not gradual but are the result of discontinuous steps according to their magnitude, sometimes several of them following one another at intervals; and they may take place in differing directions with result in heterogeneous growths. With each change in this *decensus averni*—"*progression*" as I've ventured to term it—the cells leave behind more of the specialized features which have distinguished them when normal, until at last they may have wholly lost all of their normal aspect, becoming so completely "anaplastic" that one cannot tell their source. As the consecutive changes go on they tend to lose their adherence to one another, and not infrequently they become a disorderly mob, penetrating the adjacent normal tissue in groups or individually, and destroying it. They frequently enter blood vessels or lymph channels and, coming loose within, are borne along on their fluid to lodge in distant organs and there form secondary tumors of the same sort, "metastases." Sometimes it's every cell for itself! Not infrequently a primary neoplastic change resulting in malignancy makes the affected cells so fatally ill that they would form no tumors did not their rate of division exceed that of their death. Here one is inclined to ask whether drastic neoplastic changes may not sometimes kill cells at once.

Many of the chemical and physical initiators already mentioned must be brought to bear for quite a time before their oncogenic effect becomes perceptible. Often those of different kinds, when applied successively, have cumulative action. Since neoplastic change manifests itself by tumor formation as a culminating event the assumption is generally made that it occurs abruptly; but facts speak decisively against this view. Epidermal carcinomas of the penis almost never occur if circumcision has been done at birth, whereas if delayed until adolescence in persons of the same race, penile cancers not infrequently arise when the man grows old, for no reason that is perceptible then. Evidently in these instances some initiating oncogen must have acted upon the epidermal cells prior to circumcision, though not sufficiently to bring about neoplastic changes at that time, but only what can be termed a *pre-neoplastic condition* which has persisted in the cells' descendants and has come to completion, or been brought to it at last by some imperceptible, initiating factor. Similar longtime culminating events have been observed in my laboratory during study of rabbit skin exposed many months previously to an initiating oncogen without any growth occurring in the interval.

Tests have shown that single, living cells, taken from notably vigorous tumors and transferred to other inbred animals of the same stock, will give rise to growths of the same sort; yet the traits of neoplastic cells cannot easily be discerned by studying them singly. When many are proliferating together in tumors though, much can be learnt about them.

An exceedingly important trait of most neoplastic cells is their unnatural excitability which sometimes renders them extremely active on what seems slight encouragement. Infection with inflammatory bacteria often has this effect. Indeed merely the healing of a hole a centimeter across, punched through a rabbit's ear that had been swabbed on its smooth, inner surface with an oncogenic tar some weeks before, may cause several tumors to start forth from the epidermal sheet which is extending in to close the hole, although elsewhere on the tarred ear none has arisen. Some of the growths thus elicited actually behave as if malignant, their cells invading and replacing those of the new connective tissue underlying them, and building up into what appears to be a genuine tumor. But this activity only lasts as long as they are exposed to reparative stimulation. When this ceases, on closure of the hole, the growths gradually disappear, leaving an epidermal layer which looks normal microscopically but is not, as shown by recurrence of the spurious malignancy when a new hole is punched inside the boundaries of the old. The hidden cells rendered neoplastic by the tar had not been altered one whit; they had been merely exploited by the stimulus of healing. Many initiating chemicals possess the power to act in a similar way on the cells that they have caused to undergo neoplastic change, but they do so only during the period of their application. *Promotion*, as Dr. Friedewald and I termed it, can have a great deal to do with the behavior of tumors.

Neoplastic cells never get well if they are self-assertive, meaning thereby capable of forming a tumor without any extraneous help such as promotion. The great majority are of this kind, as made plain by their success on transplantation. Those that have got worse by steps never retrace these. Were this not the case one would find at autopsy now and then residual nodules composed of cells to all appearance normal, marking the place where once there was a tumor. Neoplasms occasionally get smaller for one intercurrent reason or another, and often they are forced to disappear when subjected to strong irradiation. Yet in both instances the cells languish and die as the same neoplastic elements that they previously were. They never revert to the normal but are potentially immortal by way of their progeny if transferred to compatible new hosts before they have killed the old. Not a few rat and mouse tumors have been maintained in this way for study throughout more than 50 years.

A striking trait of actively multiplying, neoplastic cells is their ability to evoke from the adjacent tissue the blood vessels and structural support needed for the production and maintenance of the growths they are capable of forming. In proportion to the rate at which these latter enlarge, their demands of this sort become peremptory, unless indeed their cells have become capable of actively invading and replacing the normal tissue next to them, and hence are capable of "living off the country." One can perceive how crucial help of this kind is for most growths by scattering, amidst the subcutaneous tissue of a mouse, tiny fragments of a murine, mammary carcinoma, containing several mingled neoplastic components of widely differing capabilities. This can be done by rapidly injecting a suspension of the fragments in salt solution under the dorsal skin, together with sufficient air to split the underlying connective tissue horizontally, thus "plating out" the tiny bits of tissue on its broad expanse, much as bacteria are purposely scattered for colony formation on an expanse of nutritive agar. Many of the fragments thus implanted soon give rise to tumors because their cells call forth blood vessels and stroma swiftly from the tissue on which they lie, whereas others do no more than survive because their cells are devoid of these evocative powers. It is as if the normal tissue were acting as a school for iniquity and rapidly promoting its worst scholars.

However slowly neoplastic cells divide they must of course obtain additional food if they are to multiply; and however "benign" the growing tumors, their demands can be peremptory. During old times in China, when surgery was seldom done, benign tumors sometimes reached a prodigious size, whereas the body serving them emaciated because of their first claim upon its food. One can witness the same course of events after implanting a small piece of a benign, mouse tumor at a subcutaneous spot in another mouse, where it can grow big without damaging the adjacent tissue. The resulting growth gets huge while the body wastes.

With the sole exception of the tumor cells initiated and actuated by hormones and viruses—which have yet to be discussed—neoplastic cells neither give off any telltale substance indicative of their presence nor elicit any specific reaction from the body, whereby they can be certainly discerned, nor do they form any injurious substance characteristic of themselves, even while flourishing in great number or undergoing necrosis. True, the body often reacts against them while they are small, as it does against grafts of incompatible normal tissue, destroying them; yet so rarely do established tumors disappear that such happenings seem miraculous. The generality of them, while growing, do away so completely with the initial resistance the body offers to strange cells that even grafts from animals of alien species may succeed. Pig skin has been known to flourish when transplanted to the skin of volunteers having inoperable, lymphoid cancers.

Confronted with the dire challenge offered by neoplastic cells the physician does what he can. Fortunately he is sometimes aided now, and to a lifesaving extent, through the discoveries of Dr. Huggins, an experimental oncologist though a practicing surgeon, who has shown that the existence of not a few cancers in the human body, namely those of the prostatic gland, are initiated, actuated, and promoted by hormones formed within the patient's body; and that many of them can be made to disappear by bringing a female sex hormone, or a closely related, chemical agent to bear upon them. Their cells, like those of other regressing neoplasms, never get well. They die.

The medical consultant who has found a tumor makes the tacit assumption, based on the experience of his innumerable predecessors, that the presence of this growth does not ordinarily imply any significant liability in the same individual to others of differing sorts, unless indeed his patient has tissues ultrasensitive to initiating agents through inheritance, as in the case of those unfortunates who are albinos or who are subject to intestinal popyposis, both of which render the affected tissues abnormally susceptible to oncogenic changes. The physician's attitude in this relation signifies how dependent most neoplastic changes are on intercurrent, episodic initiation.

What can be the nature of the generality of neoplastic changes, the reasons for their persistence, their irreversibility, and the discontinuous, step-like alterations that they frequently undergo? A favorite explanation has been that oncogens cause alterations in the genes of the ordinary cells of the body, as distinct from the generative, somatic mutations as these are termed. But numerous facts, when taken together, decisively exclude this supposition [1].

The number of viruses realized to cause disease has become great during the last half century, but relatively few have any connection with the production of neoplasms. Yet it should be said at once that what these few have been found to do has surpassed imagination.

Two Danes, Ellermann and Bang, reported the first tumor virus in 1908 [2]. It caused leukemia in chickens, and they made six successive passages of it from fowl to fowl, producing the same disease each time. They studied it until 1923, meanwhile reporting upon a second virus causing a chicken leukemia of a differing sort. Yet though their work was convincing it was written off because of the leukemias were not then realized to be neoplastic diseases; nor indeed did this happen until after 1930.

In 1910 I described a malignant, chicken sarcoma which could be propagated by transplanting its cells, these multiplying in their new hosts and forming tumors of the same sort. In other ways the growth showed itself to be a neoplasm of classical type yet, as reported in 1911, its cells yielded a causative virus. Numerous workers had already tried to get extraneous causes from transplanted mouse and rat tumors, but the transferred cells had held their secret close. Hence the findings with the sarcoma were met with downright disbelief, though soon several other, morphologically different, "spontaneous," chicken tumors were propagated by transplantation, and from each a virus was got causing growths of precisely its kind. Not until after some 15 years of disputation amongst oncologists were the findings with chickens deemed valid, and then the growths were relegated to a category distinct from that of mammals because from these no viruses could be obtained. Only in 1925, through the efforts of a British worker, W. E. Gye, was much attention given them by scientists.

The virus causing the chicken sarcoma studied first, now generally termed the RSV, has been maintained for more than 55 years and it is still busily investigated in many countries. Throughout most of this time it would engender growths only in chickens and closely related fowls; but of late several extraneous, non-neoplastic viruses have become associated with it, during its passage in unusual avian hosts and through their action as adjuvants its scope has been so enlarged that now not a few mammals, including monkeys, have been found to develop tumors as result of inoculation with it.

After working out the complex relationships existing between the original RSV, the cells it affects, and their hosts, I tried for several years to get causative viruses from the transplantable tumors of rodents, but with the same failure as previous investigators, and hence I quit the neoplastic problem for others in pathology yielding positive results. Not for years did a virus opportunity come my way again. But in 1933 Richard Shope of the Rockefeller Institute (a worker already renowned for discovering animal diseases with human implications) reported on a virus causing the giant warts often present on the skin of wild "cottontail" rabbits in the southwestern U.S.A. This virus, on inoculation, proved effective only in rabbits; and it produced far more vigorous warts on animals of domestic breeds than on its native host, the cottontail. When describing the growths of both species Shope remarked that they might be true tumors. He knew of my fruitless search for a mammalian tumor virus, and he and I had long been friends. Hence he asked me to determine the character of the warts, asserting that he knew nothing about tumors and already had more than he could do, what with possessing four new viruses responsible for animal diseases of other sorts. Thus it came about that I experimented as his deputy throughout many later years. Now and again he reported on the peculiarities of the papilloma virus as such, but never did he concern himself with its relationship to tumors until after the work in my laboratory had come to a close. He died—and of cancer—less than a year ago. One of his last papers, written while ill, ranks as a classic [3]. It is concerned with "the many sly and devious ways that viruses may behave in causing tumors"; and he stressed, as example, an extraordinary finding reported by him early, namely that the papilloma virus can rarely be recovered from the prodigiously active growths it yields in domestic rabbits, although immunological tests show it to be present and it can regularly be got in quantity from those of cottontails.

Experimentation carried out in my laboratory, together with Beard, Kidd, Friedewald, and MacKenzie, showed the "warts" produced by the virus to be genuine tumors, benign epidermal papillomas in which the virus persists although eliciting an antibody capable of neutralizing it on direct exposure. The same anomalous state of affairs had previously been found to exist in chickens carrying the first tumor that had yielded a virus, and collateral experiments had disclosed the fact that the phagocytic cells of normal blood can protect ingested bacteria from antibodies present in the surrounding medium as long as they themselves remain alive, and will even shield ingested red cells of a foreign species from a markedly hemolytic serum. Later work with Hudack and McMaster showed that rabbit fibroblasts separated from one another with trypsin, and placed in a suspension containing vaccina virus would, on becoming infected with this, protect it from a strong antibody placed in the surrounding fluid, but only while they were living.

These findings enable one to understand why the Shope papilloma virus flourishes in the proliferating cells of cottontail growths despite the strong antibody that it engenders, and why it never causes the adjacent normal cells to become neoplastic but instead produces tumors which grow by intrinsic cell multiplication, *aus sich heraus*, to use the German phrase, as do the neoplasms of unknown cause.

After some months carcinomas arose from most of the actively proliferating virus papillomas of both cottontail and domestic rabbits, owing to further changes in their cells which resembled those that take place now and again in benign papillomas initiated in rabbits by chemical agents and actuated in some way unknown. Yet the two changes were unlike in certain distinctive, cytological respects; and when the papilloma virus was injected into the blood stream of domestic rabbits carrying papillomas due to chemical initiation it localized in these and urged them on, rendering them much more vigorous, and altering the cells of some in such wise that they became mongrel growths exhibiting merged features referable to both agents. It also rendered others carcinomatous forthwith. Furthermore when fragments of the epidermal carcinomas, arising from papillomas induced by oncogenic hydrocarbons in cottontail rabbits, were exposed to the Shope virus *in vitro* and reimplanted in the animals from which they had just been procured, their cells, on proliferating anew, exhibited the mongrel aspect indicative of viral influence, and their malignancy was also greatly enhanced.

Later tests showed that after the brief application of a powerfully oncogenic hydrocarbon to the lightly scarified skin of domestic rabbits, into which the papilloma virus had just been rubbed, the "warts" that arose looked and behaved like those induced as controls elsewhere on the same scarified skin; and yet they underwent carcinomatous changes much sooner than these latter did. The inference seemed justified that the hydrocarbon had acted on the same cellular mechanism as the papilloma virus.

Some of the carcinomas arising from the papillomas of domestic rabbits were serially transplanted, and one that soon became anaplastic and exceedingly malignant has now been maintained for 28 years by transfer from rabbit to rabbit. Never has it yielded a virus of any sort, and tests of the blood of its early, successive hosts showed that the antigen inducing an antibody against the papilloma virus was gradually disappearing. Now it has been gone for many years. This cancer, known as the V2, is studied in many laboratories today because, like the generality of those in mammals, that are due to other causes, it yields no sign of what actuates it. Obviously the Shope virus had been merely an initiator when producing the V2, though some antigenic remnant of it had persisted for a while. In this relation a remarkable recent discovery by the Kleins of the Royal Caroline Institute of Sweden deserves mention, namely that certain polycylic hydrocarbons initiating mouse tumors put a specific, antigenic mark on these growths, which persists despite their repeated transplantation.

Nature sometimes seems possessed of a sardonic humor. In the 1930's a group of American geneticists, long concerned with the incidence of "spontaneous" tumors in rodents, undertook to determine how a pronounced liability of female mice of certain strains to develop mammary carcinomas as they grow old is inherited; and through breeding tests they came upon the astounding fact that this liability reaches the young from their mothers. How could this be? Was it passed on through the ovum, the placenta, or what? A member of their group soon afterwards made a revealing test. He arranged for some of the young of the strain under study to be suckled from birth by mice of a breed in which the cancers did not occur; and the mice thus wet-nursed never had any! His later work showed that the liability to these cancers had been due to a virus passed on to the young in their very first milk. This virus lay latent within them until they matured, and then it caused orderly, benign tumors in the breasts of females; and from these growths carcinomas derived by step-like changes like those described some pages back. To this day no virus directly responsible for the cancers has been got from these, but only the "milk virus" producing the benign growths. The problem of the actuating cause of the cancers remains unsolved like that of the V2 carcinoma of rabbits [see 4]. In both instances the virus causing the benign tumor has been no more than an initiator of the malignant growths deriving from them.

In 1953 Gross [5] discovered a neoplastic virus that has greatly widened knowledge. He obtained it from a carcinoma arising spontaneously in the parotid gland of a mouse, and on inoculation into other mice it proved capable of producing tumors of more than 20 kinds, and some in rats, rabbits, guinea pigs, hamsters, and ferrets as well. Because of these widely various neoplastic effects it has been aptly termed the polyoma virus. The growths it induces can be maintained indefinitely by transplantation, and nearly always the virus disappears from them as time goes on; yet the activity of the tumor does not lessen. Obviously in such instances its role is no more than that of an initiator, comparable in such respect to the chemical and physical oncogens. Very occasionally though, it is an actuating agent as well, persisting and multiplying in a parotid cancer like the one originally providing it; and from this favorable growth it can be recovered anew and started again on its polyomatous career. Under natural conditions the virus maintains itself as an infectious agent widely prevalent in mice, but causing only a trivial, scarcely perceptible illness of non-neoplastic sort, save in those rare instances in which it produces a neoplasm.

No virus has as yet been found that indubitably actuates tumors in man. Yet this is not to say that viruses play no part in initiating them occasionally. Now and again a human cancer arises where a virus has persistently wreaked other cellular injury. The virus causing "fever blisters" repeatedly next to the mouths of persons notably susceptible to its action provides an instance in point, cancer sometimes arising after a while from the epidermal tissue long kept in a disturbed state. One sees the same course of events occasionally on skin where the severe virus causing herpes zoster ("shingles") has left tissue permanently damaged. Yet these instances tell no more, as concerns causation, than do the cancers that now and then arise on the skin of old people where this was burned in youth. Sunlight provides yet other examples, cancer arising from skin that it has kept inflamed instead of tanned. In all these instances the tumors have been merely initiated. No virus actuating any of them has been found.

Of late many gifted investigators have sought new neoplastic viruses with the aid of technics recently devised, and not a few have been disclosed in rodents. Certain adenoviruses of man fail to cause any tumors in their human hosts, yet do this in small mammals to which they are foreign. Some viruses of both chickens and mammals, which cause no tumors when acting alone, do it when they are inoculated together. The possibilities in both these directions are boundless, opening vistas of complexity. Yet they will not be dealt with today because a far greater problem presses, namely that of man's mortality from cancer. About one person in six is now killed by neoplastic cells. Can nothing be done to combat them?

During the present century we have learnt enough to undertake this task. First there was the observation that the tumors of mammals closely resemble our own. Then they were maintained by transplantation for study. Next came the realization that what one discovers by experimenting with rodent tumors throws light on what happens in man. And then in 1918 came the epoch-making discovery by Yamigiwa and Ichikawa that tarring rabbit skin will cause tumors to arise. This opened an era of rewarding search for other chemical agents—and physical as well—which are oncogenic. It is an era so far from done as to have been the main theme a few months ago of the International Cancer Congress held in Japan, a theme chosen with urgent reason since some of man's habits, many of the occupations through which he earns his living, and the mischances taking place in his own body can prove fatal through the growths they induce unless something is done to ward them off. All such oncogens are initiating in character, and some can be dangerous promoters too, if the exposure to them is long.

The wider and closer one looks the more clearly does one see that chemical and physical agents start off nearly all human tumors, and that these latter are occupational diseases resulting from the exceedingly hazardous occupation of living out a life in this world. Despite strong admonitions and active preventive steps—many are now taken in civilized lands—deaths from cancer have not as yet been markedly lessened.

What can be the character of the alterations which render a cell and its progeny permanently neoplastic, and so self-assertive in behavior as to kill? On these matters we have only the meager information provided by the neoplastic viruses of animals. Innumerable attempts have been made to obtain evidence of the action of similar agents in human tumors, and recently to discern them with the electron microscope. Yet such attempts have drawn blanks save in a few highly dubious instances.

In the enormity of our ignorance we have now resorted to "try-and-see" tactics on a large scale, attempting to destroy the tumors of animals, because of what success with these may mean for man. In all the larger, civilized countries efforts with this aim are made, and they are amply supported, in some instances, with governmental funds. Already more than half a million chemicals and materials of biological origin have been tested in the U.S. Several institutions exist for this special purpose, and there is much cooperation by manufacturing concerns. The most encouraging results thus far have been those provided by Dr. Huggins, whose rescues of patients with prostatic cancer have been prodigious. The leukemias of children have been overcome by chemotherapy in some instances, and the singular, highly malignant lymphomas occurring in African children and known as Burkitt's disease. Yet the successes have been episodic thus far. Save in the case of the relatively small, though slowly increasing, number of viruses, no inkling has been obtained of what happens when a cell becomes neoplastic, nor of how its power is passed on when it divides. Man must and *will* find out.

references and notes

1. P. Rous, "Surmise and fact on the nature of cancer," *Nature 183,* 1357 (1959).
2. C. Ellermann and O. Bang, *Zentralbl. Bakteriol. Paresitenk. 4,* 595 (1908).
3. R. Shope, "Evolutionary episodes in the concept of viral oncogenesis," *Perspect. Biol. Med. 9,* 258 (1966).
4. Despite protracted search aided by the electron microscope, no sign of any tumor virus has ever been found in human milk, and family histories definitely rule it out.
5. L. Gross, *Oncogenic Viruses* (Pergamon Press, Oxford, England, 1961).

The Health Consequences of Smoking

smoking and cancer: conclusions of the surgeon general's 1964 report

lung cancer

1. Cigarette smoking is causally related to lung cancer in men; the magnitude of the effect of cigarette smoking far outweighs all other factors. The data for women, though less extensive, point in the same direction.

2. The risk of developing lung cancer increases with duration of smoking and the number of cigarettes smoked per day, and is diminished by discontinuing smoking.

3. The risk of developing cancer of the lung for the combined group of pipe smokers, cigar smokers, and pipe and cigar smokers is greater than for nonsmokers, but much less than for cigarette smokers. The data are insufficient to warrant a conclusion for each group individually.

oral cancer

1. The causal relationship of the smoking of pipes to the development of cancer of the lip appears to be established.

2. Although there are suggestions of relationships between cancer of other specific sites of the oral cavity and the several forms of tobacco use, their causal implications cannot at present be stated.

Excerpts reprinted from *The Health Consequences of Smoking*, Public Health Service Publication No. 1696: 1–199 (1967).

laryngeal cancer

Evaluation of the evidence leads to the judgment that cigarette smoking is a significant factor in the causation of laryngeal cancer in the male.

esophageal cancer

The evidence on the tobacco-esophageal cancer relationship supports the belief that an association exists. However, the data are not adequate to decide whether the relationship is causal.

cancer of urinary bladder

Available data suggest an association between cigarette smoking and urinary bladder cancer in the male but are not sufficient to support judgment on the causal significance of this association.

stomach cancer

No relationship has been established between tobacco use and stomach cancer.

Additional chemical, experimental, pathological, and epidemiological evidence has been reported that substantiates the conclusions of the Surgeon General's 1964 Report concerning the various sites of cancer that were shown to be associated with or caused by smoking.

lung cancer

Deaths from lung cancer in the United States are continuing to rise rapidly. Epidemiological evidence concerning cigarette smoking and lung cancer has confirmed positive relationships with increasing numbers of cigarettes smoked, with increasing duration, and with decreasing age of initiation of the habit. Male cigarette smokers of less than one pack a day have mortality ratios as high as 10 and smokers of more than one pack a day have mortality ratios as high as 30.

There is a much smaller increase of the lung cancer death rates associated with pipe and/or cigar smoking than with cigarette smoking.

Additional evidence provides specific information on the increased mortality ratios of female cigarette smokers. These have significantly elevated mortality ratios ranging as high as 5 for the groups with greatest exposure. Lung cancer rates appear to be somewhat lower for women who have never smoked regularly than for men who have never smoked regularly. The mortality rates for women who smoke, although significantly higher than for nonsmokers, are lower than for men who smoke. How much of this is due to lower exposure to cigarettes and how much to other factors cannot be determined from the data available.

Ex-cigarette smokers are shown to have significantly lower death rates compared with those who continue to smoke. As discussed under the general topic of cessation earlier in this report, the finding of reduced lung cancer rates in the population of British physicians [1–3] over a period of time in which the proportion of cigarette smokers was dropping significantly can be interpreted as similar to a controlled cessation experiment and provides critical confirmation of the judgment that cigarette smoking is the major cause of lung cancer and that sharp reductions can occur in the risk from lung cancer with the cessation of smoking.

Additional information is available concerning the presence of known or suspected carcinogens in tobacco smoke. It has been reported that the "tar" and nicotine content of cigarette smoke[1] tends to reflect the tumorigenicity of this smoke, and that a reduction of the "tar" and nicotine content is accompanied by a reduction in the tumorigenicity. Research is needed to identify and separate the tumor-initiating and tumor-promoting agents in tobacco smoke and to elucidate their interactions in the pathogenesis of cancer. Similarly, while additional data are available concerning experimental carcinogenesis, it is not yet certain that the typical characteristics of human squamous-cell lung cancer, with invasion and metastasis, have been experimentally produced by tobacco smoke in animals. It should be noted that this may never be achieved not only because it may not be possible to duplicate man's smoking action for anatomic and physiologic reasons but also because of species' differences in cellular response.

There is evidence that certain other exposures, for example, occupational exposures to asbestos and uranium ore may interact with the cigarette effect to produce an enhancement of the tumor-producing effect. There is also information to indicate that the occurrence of

---

[1] *The phrase " 'tar' and nicotine" is used here as a general indicator of total particulate matter in cigarette smoke.*

second primary lung cancers in smokers may be more frequent than previously indicated.

oral cancer

Substantial mortality ratios are found for cancers of the buccal cavity and pharynx. Mortality ratios for cancer of the pharynx are especially high. There is some evidence implicating alcohol and/or dietary deficiencies in some of these sites. With the exception of the pipe-lip cancer relations there are too few cases related to the individual parts of the buccal cavity to evaluate each independently, and data are inadequate on the interaction of smoking with other factors. Although all forms of smoking have high mortality ratios with these sites, mortality ratios for those smoking cigarettes appear to be somewhat higher than for those smoking pipes and cigars, especially in the case of cancer of the pharynx.

laryngeal cancer

Continued evidence from the prospective studies supports the existence of a high laryngeal cancer mortality ratio for pipe and cigar smokers as well as for cigarette smokers. Data on the smoking habits of patients treated for buccal cancer subsequent to their therapy suggests that continuing to smoke after therapy may increase the likelihood of an independent laryngeal cancer. The epidemiological evidence supports the previous conclusion that cigarette smoking is a significant factor in the causation of cancer of the larynx.

esophageal cancer

Additional data from the prospective studies confirm the high mortality ratio previously found for smokers of all forms of tobacco. Autopsy studies of smokers compared with nonsmokers specifically observing pathological changes in esophageal tissue have been reported from both smokers and nonsmokers who died from causes other than esophageal cancer. The findings were similar to the abnormalities generally accepted as representing premalignant tissue changes of the epithelium of the respiratory tract; that is, epithelial cells with atypical nuclei were found far more frequently in cigarette smokers than in nonsmokers. Tissue sections with basal cell hyperplasia were also found more frequently in cigarette smokers and, as with the atypical nuclei, these findings increased with amount of cigarette smoking. Additional data to evaluate the relative importance of smoking and alcohol, independently and jointly, would help clarify the significance of these findings.

urinary bladder cancer

The Dorn [4] and the Hammond [5] studies both show mortality ratios over 2.0 for smokers of over 20 cigarettes a day, but the Doll-Hill study [1, 2], based on only 38 deaths, shows no apparent relationship. Two retrospective studies have shown significantly higher proportions of smokers among patients than among controls. Small scale metabolic studies suggest that cigarette smoking may block the normal metabolism of tryptophan, which would lead to the accumulation of carcinogenic metabolites in the urine. Further studies to verify this finding and studies analyzing changes in the bladder tissue of smokers as compared with nonsmokers would be helpful in arriving at a judgment of the significance of the elevated death rates found in smokers in the largest of the prospective studies.

stomach and pancreatic cancer

Epidemiological evidence does not show a significant relationship between smoking and stomach cancer. An association between cigarette smoking and pancreatic cancer is implied, but the significance of this association is not clear at the present time.

highlights of current information

lung cancer

1. Additional epidemiological, pathological, and experimental data not only confirm the conclusions of the Surgeon General's 1964 Report regarding lung cancer in men but strengthen the causal relationship of smoking to lung cancer in women.

2. Cessation of cigarette smoking sharply reduces the risk of dying from lung cancer relative to the risk of those who continue.

3. Although additional experimental studies substantiate previous

experimental data, additional research is needed to specify the tumor-initiating and tumor-promoting agents in tobacco smoke and to elucidate the basic mechanisms of the pathogenesis of lung cancer.

laryngeal cancer

The conclusion of the Surgeon General's 1961 Report that cigarette smoking is a significant factor in the causation of laryngeal cancer in the male is supported by additional epidemiological evidence.

other cancers

Additional evidence supports the conclusions of the Surgeon General's 1964 Report and indicates a strong association between various forms of smoking and cancers of the buccal cavity, pharynx, and esophagus. In the absence of further information concerning the interaction of smoking with other factors known or suspected as causative agents, further conclusions cannot be made at this time, although a causative relationship seems likely.

Additional epidemiological, clinical, and experimental data strengthen the association between cigarette smoking and cancer of the urinary bladder, but the presently available data are insufficient to infer that the relationship is causal.

other conditions and areas of research: conclusions of the surgeon general's 1964 report

peptic ulcer

Epidemiological studies indicate an association between cigarette smoking and peptic ulcer which is greater for gastric than for duodenal ulcer.

tobacco amblyopia

Tobacco amblyopia (dimness of vision unexplained by an organic lesion) has been related to pipe and cigar smoking by clinical impressions. The association has not been substantiated by epidemiological or experimental studies.

cirrhosis of the liver

Increased mortality of smokers from cirrhosis of the liver has been shown in the prospective studies. The data are not sufficient to support a direct or casual association.

maternal smoking and infant birth weight

Women who smoke cigarettes during pregnancy tend to have babies of lower birth weight. Information is lacking on the mechanism by which this decrease in birth weight is produced. It is not known whether this decrease in birth weight has any influence on the biological fitness of the newborn.

psychosocial aspects

The overwhelming evidence points to the conclusion that smoking—its beginning, habituation, and occasional discontinuation—is to a large extent psychologically and socially determined. This does not rule out physiological factors, especially in respect to habituation, nor the existence of predisposing constitutional or heredity factors.

current information, 1967

By and large the contributions to knowledge in this area of varied considerations have been meager, although a number of investigations on one or another aspect of the problem of smoking and varied health consequences have been undertaken.

peptic ulcer

The relationship between cigarette smoking and death rates from peptic ulcer, especially gastric ulcer, is confirmed. In addition, morbidity data suggest a similar realtionship exists with the prevalence of reported disease from this cause.

tobacco amblyopia

Tobacco amblyopia is now believed to be a manifestation of nutritional amblyopia, which is aggravated by the inhalation of tobacco smoke.

Various vitamin B factor deficiencies may be involved and there is evidence to suggest that chronic low vitamin B_{12} levels may potentiate the toxic effects of cyanide in tobacco smoke.

cirrhosis of the liver

Increased mortality of smokers from cirrhosis of the liver is found in the prospective studies. This has generally been thought to be largely secondary to an association between smoking and heavy consumption of alcohol. Published data are inadequate to test this interpretation.

maternal smoking and infant birth weight

Further studies have confirmed the fact that women who smoke during pregnancy tend to have babies of lower birth weight, but data are lacking to determine either the mechanism or the significance of this finding.

psychosocial aspects

There has been a sharp increase in the attention devoted to behavioral research since the Surgeon General's Report. A number of new concepts have been developed and more sophisticated multivariate approaches are being used. However, because of the recency of these studies very little in the way of findings has been published on which firm conclusions may be based.

references

1. R. Doll and A. B. Hill, "Mortality in relation to smoking: 10 years' observations of British doctors (Part 1)," *British Medical Journal (London)* *1*(5395): 1399–1410, May 30, 1964.
2. R. Doll and A. B. Hill, "Mortality in relation to smoking: 10 years' observations of British doctors (Concluded)," *British Medical Journal (London)* *1*(5396): 1460–1467, June 6, 1964.
3. R. Doll and A. B. Hill, "Mortality of British doctors in relation to smoking: observations on coronary thrombosis," in W. Haenszel, editor, *Epidemiological Approaches to the Study of Cancer and Other Chronic Diseases*, Bethesda, U.S. Public Health Service, National Cancer Institute monograph No. 19, January 1966. Pp. 205–268.

4. H. A. Kahn, "The Dorn study of smoking and mortality among U.S. veterans: report on 8½ years of observation," in W. Haenszel, editor, *Epidemiological Approaches to the Study of Cancer and Other Diseases,* Bethesda, U.S. Public Health Service, National Cancer Institute monograph No. 19, January 1966. Pp. 1–125.

5. E. C. Hammond, "Smoking in relation to the death rates of 1 million men and women," in W. Haenszel, editor, *Epidemiological Approaches to the Study of Cancer and Other Diseases,* Bethesda, U.S. Public Health Service, National Cancer Institute monograph No. 19, January 1966. Pp. 127–204.

Drugs vs. Cancer

the role of drugs

Cancer takes a death toll of almost 300,000 Americans each year. If present rates continue, about 50 million Americans now living will eventually develop cancer. Even the best treatment by conventional methods—surgery and radiation—does not help certain cancer patients. For example, those with acute leukemia, or advanced cancer that has spread throughout the body, usually do not respond to such treatment.

Within the last 25 years, methods of treating disseminated cancer by chemotherapy (drug therapy) have slowly been evolving. Vast sums have been spent by government and private organizations to hasten the discovery of effective chemotherapy for all forms of cancer. Some useful drugs have been developed. Better ones are being sought.

This [article] describes the present status of cancer chemotherapy, its clinical and research problems, and leads that scientists are pursuing in the search for effective drug treatments.

cancer drugs now available

More than two dozen cancer drugs have already earned a place in the hospital pharmacy and on the druggist's shelf. Despite their limitations, these chemical compounds provide helpful treatment for many forms of cancer that are unresponsive to surgery and radiation. In some cases drugs offer temporary relief from symptoms, prolonging life and easing pain and discomfort. In other cases they provide long-term chemical control.

The drugs now in use against various forms of cancer are listed by class in the chart that follows.

Reprinted from *Drugs vs. Cancer,* National Cancer Institute Research Report No. 3, Public Health Service Publication No. 1652: 1–17 (revised 1968) with permission of the publisher.

Drugs Used Against Cancer

Drugs Used Against Cancer	Other Names	Acute Granulocytic Leukemia	Acute Lymphocytic Leukemia	Chronic Granulocytic Leukemia	Chronic Lymphocytic Leukemia	Adrenal Cancer	Breast Cancer	Choriocarcinoma	Colon Cancer	Endometrial Cancer	Hodgkin's Disease	Lung Cancer	Lymphosarcoma	Multiple Myeloma	Neuroblastoma	Ovarian Cancer	Prostatic Cancer	Retinoblastoma	Rhabdomyosarcoma	Stomach Cancer	Testicular Cancer	Wilms' Tumor
Alkylating Agents:																						
Busulfan	Myleran			X																		
Chlorambucil	Leukeran				X		X				X	X	X			X					X	
Cyclophosphamide	Endoxan, Cytoxan		X		X		X				X	X	X	X	X	X		X	X			X
Nitrogen Mustard	HN2, Mustargen						X				X	X	X			X						
Phenylalanine Mustard	L-Sarcolysin, Melphalan, Alkeran						X							X		X						
Thio-TEPA	TSPA						X									X		X			X	
Triethylene Melamine	TEM										X		X	X				X				
Antimetabolites:																						
Methotrexate	Amethopterin		X				X	X				X									X	
5-Fluorouracil	5-FU						X		X			X				X				X		
6-Mercaptopurine	6-MP, Purinethol	X	X	X				X														
Hormonal Agents:																						
Adrenal Cortical Compounds:	Hormonal Agents Are Known by a Variety of Trade Names.																					
Cortisone			X		X		X				X		X									
Hydrocortisone			X		X		X				X		X									
Prednisolone			X		X		X				X		X	X								
Prednisone			X		X		X				X		X	X								
Androgens:																						
Fluoxymesterone							X															
Testosterone Propionate							X															
Estrogens:																						
Diethylstilbestrol							X										X					
Ethinyl Estradiol							X										X					
Other:																						
ACTH			X				X															
Progesterone										X												
Miscellaneous:																						
Actinomycin D	Dactinomycin, Cosmegen, Meractinomycin							X							X				X		X	X
Methyl Hydrazine Derivative	MIH, Natulan, Procarbazine	X									X	X	X									
Methylglyoxal Bis (Guanylhydrazone)	Methyl-GAG	X		X																		
o,p'-DDD						X																
Vinblastine Sulfate	Velban						X	X			X		X								X	
Vincristine Sulfate	Oncovin		X				X				X		X		X				X			X

Thirty years ago all of these drugs were unknown or unrecognized as agents active against cancer. The first advance came in 1941. In that year Drs. Charles Huggins and Clarence V. Hodges of the University of Chicago reported that the female sex hormone, estrogen, was useful in the treatment of prostatic cancer in men.

World War II accelerated a medical research effort that continues to this day. The discovery of nitrogen mustard's effectiveness as a cancer drug was the product of a wartime investigation of chemical warfare agents. Drs. Alfred Gilman and Frederick S. Philips, working with the Chemical Warfare Service, described its therapeutic potential. Drs. L. S. Goodman, Leon O. Jacobson, Cornelius P. Rhoads, David A. Karnofsky, and others defined its role in the treatment of various forms of cancer.

In 1948 the first of the "antimetabolites," an antivitamin called aminopterin, was reported by Dr. Sidney Farber and his associates at the Children's Medical Center, Boston, to be useful in treating leukemia. In the following year the effectiveness of a related drug, methotrexate, was reported by the same investigator. Since then the stockpile of drugs has grown each year.

The availability of cancer drugs is now generally known, and their use is widespread. Of the drugs shown on the chart, methotrexate has proven strikingly useful, particularly against a rare uterine cancer known as choriocarcinoma. Before methotrexate's effectiveness was discovered, five of every six women with this or a related kind of cancer, even when treated early with surgery, died within a year. Then, in 1961, Dr. Roy Hertz and his associates at the National Cancer Institute reported on 63 patients treated with methotrexate, and noted that 44 percent were freed from all evidence of cancer. More recently, in 1965, Dr. Griff T. Ross and associates at the National Cancer Institute reported on 50 patients given methotrexate and the antibiotic actinomycin D. Seventy-four percent of this group experienced a complete disappearance of their disease, and some have been without symptoms for more than 5 years.

Very few of the cancer drugs produce such dramatic, long-term results. Nor have other forms of cancer been as responsive to drug therapy as choriocarcinoma. Usually the drugs can be taken only in limited doses, since they produce undesirable or injurious side effects. And drugs frequently seem to lose effectiveness after a period of time.

Despite problems, chemotherapists are making significant gains against several forms of cancer. A general indication of progress is the sixfold increase during the last decade in the number of acute leukemia patients who live 2 years or longer. Children with Wilms' tumor (a cancer of the kidney) and those with neuroblastoma (cancer of the cells of the nervous system) also have greater life expectancy, and in some no evidence of the disease remains.

Further progress in chemotherapy research will, it is hoped, provide far more efficient new drugs and point to new ways of using known drugs with peak effectiveness.

how the drugs work

The target of a cancer drug is a cancer cell—a cell of the human body so altered that it reproduces abnormally, and sometimes at a rapid rate, in an uncontrolled pattern of growth. Such a cell is often described as a "mutant" cell. Many scientists believe that it has an error in the chemical instructions that control its reproduction.

Each time a cancer cell reproduces, its daughter cells are also mutants, with the same unrestrained growth pattern. As they multiply, they crowd out their normal neighbors, invading and damaging normal tissues and organs. One or more cancer cells may metastasize; that is, become detached from the primary tumor and travel in the bloodstream or lymph channels to another part of the body, where they start a new colony of cancer cells.

The task of cancer drugs is to selectively seek out cancer cells and destroy them outright or interfere with their ability to divide or reproduce.

How does a drug interfere with cell division? Scientists believe that many cancer drugs inhibit the cancer cell at the same site where the cancerous change is thought to occur: at the core of the cell, within the nucleus, in the chemicals that contain the cell's genetic machinery—the nucleic acids called DNA and RNA.

Scientists believe that the cancerous change is induced in the cell's nucleic acid by a chemical, radiation, or a virus, or by some combination of these factors. Medical scientists are attempting to employ the same factors to block growth of cancer cells.

The chemicals being used, cancer drugs, act in a variety of ways to block cell growth. The following is a description of the various drug types and the ways in which they are believed to exert their effects on cancer cells.

alkylating agents

This group of quick-acting, highly reactive compounds includes nitrogen mustard and other close relatives of the wartime poison gases. Often referred to as "cell poisons," these agents are rich in electrons when they are in solution. For this reason they combine rapidly with many of the constituents of a cell. Many scientists believe that the alkylating agents exert their anticancer effects by a direct chemical interaction with the DNA of the cell.

In addition to nitrogen mustard, among the best known alkylating agents are cyclophosphamide (Endoxan, Cytoxan), chlorambucil (Leukeran), triethylene thiophosphoramide (thio-TEPA), and dimethanesulfonoxybutane (Myleran). They act primarily on tissues that are being quickly replaced, such as bone marrow and cells lining the intestine. They are used primarily in the treatment of Hodgkin's disease, lymphosarcoma, the chronic leukemias, and in some cancers of the lung, ovary, and breast.

antimetabolites

These drugs structurally resemble metabolites, the nutrients a cell needs for growth. Antimetabolites mimic normal nutrients so closely that they are taken up by the cell through mistaken identity. Once inside the cell they interfere competitively with the production of nucleic acids and thereby prevent cell growth.

Among the antimetabolites are antagonists of purines and pyrimidines, essential components of the cell's nucleic acids. The drugs 6-mercaptopurine and 5-fluorouracil are examples, respectively, of the antipurines and antipyrimidines. 6-Mercaptopurine was developed by Drs. Gertrude B. Elion, Elizabeth Burgi, and George H. Hitchings of the Wellcome Research Laboratories; 5-fluorouracil was synthesized in the laboratory by Dr. Charles Heidelberger and his associates at the University of Wisconsin.

One of the most widely used antimetabolites is amethopterin (methotrexate), synthesized in 1948 by Dr. Doris R. Seeger and associates at the American Cyanamid Co. By inhibiting the enzyme folic acid reductase, methotrexate acts as an antagonist to a needed B vitamin, folic acid. This in turn interferes with both purine and pyrimidine synthesis.

The antimetabolites are useful in leukemia and in several types of solid tumors (see chart).

hormones

Unlike the previously described drug types, which tend to act on all rapidly growing cells, natural and synthetic hormones tend to accelerate or suppress the growth of specific cells, tissues, and target organs. They are thought to derive their effectiveness by altering or reversing a hormonal imbalance in the body that encouraged the cancer cells to thrive.

The female hormone estrogen, for example, helps to suppress the growth of disseminated cancer of the prostate. Conversely, male hormones or androgens cause temporary regression of disease in 20 percent of breast cancer patients, and are especially helpful in premenopausal women.

Among the other hormonal types, corticosteroids such as cortisone and prednisone seem to suppress the growth of white blood cells known as lymphocytes. For this reason these drugs are frequently useful in acute lymphocytic leukemia, which is characterized by an abundance of abnormal lymphocytes.

Scientists are uncertain as to the exact chemical mechanism by which hormones influence the growth of cells. However, evidence is accumulating that here, too, nucleic acid may be implicated. Drs. P. Karlson and Ulrich Clever at the Max-Planck Institute of Munich have demonstrated through experiments with insects that a hormone controls certain phases of insect growth by controlling its production of the nucleic acid RNA. Studies of hydrocortisone in rat cells by Dr. Gordon M. Tomkins and associates at the National Institute of Arthritis and Metabolic Diseases also suggest hormonal stimulation of RNA production.

miscellaneous drugs

Antibiotics. Notable in this group is actinomycin D, a drug believed to achieve its effectiveness by locking itself onto a base of the DNA molecule, thereby blocking cell growth. Actinomycin D has proved useful in the treatment of Wilms' tumor, a rare cancer of the kidney in children.

Plant alkaloids. Several compounds, derived from extracts of the common periwinkle plant, seem to act through interference with a phase of cell division. Best known are vinblastine sulfate and vincristine sulfate, the latter of which is useful in treating acute lymphocytic leukemia. Both are effective in certain lymphomas.

Other types. A drug used in treating cancer of the adrenal gland, o,p'-DDD, is closely related chemically to the insecticide DDT. It seems to have a selective destructive effect on adrenal cells. Methylglyoxal bis (guanylhydrazone), often called Methyl-GAG, is a synthetic chemical with activity against acute myelocytic leukemia, the type of acute leukemia occurring mostly in adults. Its mechanism of action, as yet undetermined, seems unique.

problems and possible solutions

Most cancer drugs are limited in their usefulness primarily by two factors: (1) toxicity—damage to normal cells and tissues as well as cancer cells and tissues; and (2) decreased effectiveness—gradual loss of drug effectiveness due to host resistance, a phenomenon that may also signal acceleration or reactivation of the disease process.

toxicity

The cancer drug prescription reflects a delicate balancing of a drug's effectiveness against its toxicity. Physicians attempt to prescribe "the maximum tolerated dose" to provide the greatest anticancer effect with the least damage to normal cells. Most frequently injured are cells that grow most rapidly; for example, those of the oral and gastrointestinal mucosa and the bone marrow. When the drug administered is a hormone, toxicity is sometimes manifested as changes in secondary sex characteristics, such as voice and facial hair. Other drugs may temporarily produce nausea, loss of appetite, loss of hair, hypertension, or diabetes. These side effects are usually reversed when drug treatment is halted.

Chemotherapists working in the clinic can usually anticipate a drug's toxicity from data gathered in animal tests. Rats, dogs, and monkeys are ordinarily reliable indicators of the human response to potential new drugs. Initial clinical trials of a drug begin at one-tenth the dose level tolerated by the larger laboratory animals. The final dosage formula is measured in milligrams of drug per kilogram of body

weight, or even more efficiently, by milligrams of drug per square meter
of body surface.

Besides carefully regulating dose, medical scientists have devised
other means of minimizing toxicity. One of the most ingenious of these
is called "regional perfusion," a technique developed in 1957 by Drs.
Robert F. Ryan, Edward T. Krementz, Oscar Creech, Jr., and colleagues at Tulane University. By this method drugs circulate in a
closed circuit through the bloodstream of the cancer-affected region,
while a tourniquet prevents the drug from reaching and damaging
sensitive organs beyond the cancerous area. The drug is injected
through an artery to the cancerous area, is withdrawn from a vein by
special tubes, and then recirculated through artery and vein by means
of a pump oxygenator. Regional perfusion is especially suited to treating certain cancers of the arms and legs.

Infusion methods, by which a drug is dripped slowly into a patient's
bloodstream and travels throughout his entire circulatory system, have
also been modified to focus drug effects on cancerous areas; for example, cancers of the head and neck. Another adaptation has been developed by Dr. Robert D. Sullivan at Lahey Clinic for treating cancer of
the liver. In this system, a plastic tube carries a continuous supply of
drug directly to the cancer at a uniform rate regulated by an infusion
pump. The tiny pump and a week's supply of the prescribed drug
(together the size of a cigarette package) may be strapped to the chest
of a nonhospitalized patient for round-the-clock treatment.

Another means of minimizing toxicity is the administration of an
"antagonist," the chemical opposite number, so to speak, of a cancer
drug. Studies led by Drs. H. E. Sauberlich, Harry P. Broquist, Abra-
ham Goldin, and Joseph H. Burchenal at several institutions disclosed
the ability of citrovorum factor, a natural metabolite obtained from
liver extracts, to reverse the toxic effects of the antimetabolites, aminopterin and methotrexate, when given before or at the same time as
the drugs. Drug antagonists are often given in conjunction with the
infusion of a cancer drug.

Drug toxicity to bone marrow frequently results in the depletion of
important blood elements, particularly in patients with acute leukemia,
causing serious hemorrhage and lowering the patient's resistance to
infection. Medical experts are developing remarkable new techniques to
help control these life-threatening problems. To prevent hemorrhage,
transfusions of platelets, the blood element that induces clotting, are
being given at several medical centers. Such transfusions may soon

become part of the essential therapy in leukemia and other forms of cancer when hemorrhage is a problem.

In the control of fatal infections, transfusions or granulocytes, the white blood cells that fight bacterial and fungal infections, may prove useful if obtainable in adequate quantities. Practical means for obtaining, preserving, and transfusing granulocytes are being developed at the National Cancer Institute and elsewhere.

An anti-infection measure now being evaluated among patients receiving intensive chemotherapy is the use of protective care units that offer a relatively germ-free environment. Although still regarded as experimental, isolation chambers of plastic or glass have been built for the hospitalization of patients for several weeks while they receive massive doses of cancer drugs. Room-size hospital areas kept sterile by laminar airflow currents are also under investigation.

decreased effectiveness

In addition to toxicity, another major limitation of cancer chemotherapy is host resistance to a drug—a gradual waning of a drug's ability to halt cancer growth. For example, a patient may respond well initially to a drug and all or almost all evidence of cancer may disappear. This "remission" of disease may last for weeks, months, sometimes years. Then the symptoms recur and the cancer resumes its malignant pattern of growth.

Such a situation may indicate that the cancer cells have undergone mutation, and are now able to survive, and even grow rapidly, in the presence of the once destructive drug. Dr. Dorris J. Hutchison and her coworkers at the Sloan-Kettering Institute for Cancer Research have conducted experiments with cells grown in the laboratory which suggest that drug-resistant cell lines do develop.

On the other hand, failure of the drug to continue its destructive effect on cancer cells may indicate that the cancer cell population has multiplied to a size where it is no longer controlled by a drug dose that the patient can tolerate.

To overcome the problem, whether due to mutated cancer cells or to a cancer cell population too large to be effectively controlled by drugs, chemotherapists now are striving for 100 percent kill of cancer cells in the early stages of treatment. Using mouse leukemias as an experimental system, Dr. Howard E. Skipper of the Southern Research Institute has proposed a mathematical model based on the rate of leukemic cell growth and the rate of destruction of cells by cancer drugs. His observations in the mouse have shown that intensive drug therapy, or administration of massive drug doses in a short time period, is able to eradicate the leukemic cell population.

Utilizing Skipper's hypothesis, Drs. Emil J. Freireich, Myron Karon, and Emil Frei III at the National Cancer Institute developed a four-drug regimen for treating acute leukemia in children. The drugs employed were vincristine, methotrexate, 6-mercaptopurine, and prednisone. Preliminary studies in 16 children were encouraging. As of January 1968, two of the 16 children are surviving, $4\frac{1}{2}$ and 5 years after diagnosis of leukemia.

In a more recent study conducted at the National Cancer Institute, 35 children with acute leukemia were treated intermittently for 14 months with larger doses of vincristine, methotrexate, 6-mercaptopurine, and prednisolone. Dr. Edward L. Henderson and associates reported that the patients' initial remissions averaged over 13 months. Moreover, most of those who relapsed were brought into a second remission by treatment with the same four drugs, indicating that resistance to the drugs usually did not occur. As of January 1968, the median survival time of the 35 children is about 3 years after diagnosis of their disease. Evaluation of the treatment is continuing.

other problems

Some scientists believe that recurrence of cancer following remission may be due to other factors. For instance, leukemia recurrence might be due to reinfection by a leukemia-causing agent, perhaps a virus, as yet unidentified. Other scientists attribute such a recurrence to the fact that a percentage of leukemic cells often lodge inside the protective membranes of the brain and central nervous system, untouched by drug treatment. Such hidden cells continue to multiply and then gradually reappear in the general circulation, signaling re-emergence of the disease.

Several techniques are in use to overcome this latter obstacle to effective drug therapy. One is the injection of drugs directly into the cerebrospinal fluid as reported by Dr. G. Sansone of the University of Geneva and Dr. James A. Whiteside and associates at the Memorial Sloan-Kettering Cancer Center. Another is the administration of drugs directly into the cavities of the brain by means of implanted plastic tubing, a method developed by Dr. Ayub K. Ommaya of the National

Institute of Neurological Diseases and Blindness. These techniques are also under study for possible usefulness in the treatment of brain tumors, as well as leukemia. Another approach is the development of drugs such as BCNU whose chemical structure and special solubility enable them to pass into the cerebrospinal fluid through the barrier of the brain's sheath.

research toward more effective drug therapy

Cancer, as noted earlier, is a disease primarily of cells. Only as it develops does it become a disease of tissues, and organs, and sometimes entire regions of the body. The details of the cancerous change and its multiplication are hidden submicroscopically in the cell itself.

A major research effort is being made to discover the facts of life in the human cell: the details of its reproduction or cell-division process; its rate of growth; its genetic inheritance, transmitted through the DNA molecule; its nutritional requirements and the means by which food and drug materials pass through the cell membrane; finally, all of the chemical building blocks that make the cell a biological whole.

The scientist in cancer research is also interested in defining biochemical differences between the cancer cell and the normal cell. It is known, for example, that most cancer cells have larger nuclei and contain more DNA than normal cells. Dr. Julian L. Ambrus of the Roswell Park Memorial Institute has reported that the DNA in the cancer cell has a lower molecular weight and a more rigid configuration than DNA from corresponding normal tissues. However, qualitative chemical differences have thus far eluded scientists. When chemically identifiable distinctions are recognized, chemists may then be able to design drugs that will damage cancer cells without injuring normal cells.

development of new drugs

An intensive effort is being made by the National Cancer Institute, the drug industry, universities, medical centers, and private research organizations to develop new drugs for cancer. Many of the studies are supported by funds from the National Cancer Institute and major elements of the drug search are coordinated by National Cancer Institute scientists and their advisers.

In hundreds of laboratories across the nation and the world, scientists are creating new chemical compounds, studying plant specimens, and extracting antibiotics from natural fermentation products and soil samples. At the same time, many of the country's top chemists are searching for ways to improve the activity of the known drugs. That is, they are trying to design new compounds related to the known drugs, but with innovations in structure that enhance drug activity.

Some drugs have been discovered empirically, in the routine testing of thousands of new compounds for their effect on animal tumors. Others are designed with certain structures on the basis of scientific information previously obtained.

To identify active drugs empirically, scientists use a "screen" of animal tumors that are useful in predicting the material's activity against human cancer. The Cancer Chemotherapy National Service Center of the National Cancer Institute has demonstrated that, of about 20 useful test systems, two animal tumors are most effective in predicting the clinical usefulness of drugs. These are L-1210, a leukemia in the mouse, and Walker 256 I.M., a carcinosarcoma injected intramuscularly in the rat. If a drug shows anticancer activity in this screening process, tests to determine its toxicity are conducted in normal, larger animals such as dogs and monkeys. If these tests indicate that the drug can be used safely in patients, more specific details of toxicity and dosage are worked out before the material is referred to investigators for clinical evaluation.

In contrast to drugs detected by a screening procedure are those developed by a rational approach to chemotherapy. In the latter group is 5-fluorouracil (5-FU), synthesized first by Dr. Charles Heidelberger and colleagues at the University of Wisconsin. Heidelberger theorized that the substitution of an atom of fluorine in place of a hydrogen atom in the 5 position of the nucleic acid base uracil would interfere with the production of a base needed for DNA. Thus, he reasoned, cells taking up this false metabolite would be unable to divide. Tests of the effect of 5-FU on animal tumors proved the accuracy of his hypothesis. The drug, an antimetabolite, is used in metastatic cancers of the large bowel, stomach, and breast.

In addition to developing antimetabolites, hormonal agents, and other drugs of known types, cancer scientists are pressing forward an effort to develop entirely new kinds of drug treatment. Two approaches are worth mentioning:

The first is an effort to develop or isolate immunochemical agents, substances to bolster a patient's natural immunity, so that, in combination with conventional cancer drugs, the immunity-stimulating agents might enable the patient to overcome the disease. As early as 1900 concepts of immunotherapy, such as Paul Ehrlich's, were proposed. Many scientists since that time (Pillemer, Southam, Fogh, Szent-Gyorgyi) have advanced the proposition that the normal body manufactures a substance or substances inimical to cancer growth. Isolation and characterization of such inhibitory substances are being attempted in many laboratories. (A related effort to develop a vaccine continues, but this is a preventive rather than a treatment approach, so the effort is not described here.)

Another approach is an effort to develop drugs with antiviral activity, desirable in the event that some forms of human cancer should prove to be caused by viruses. A naturally occurring antiviral substance called interferon was reported in 1957 by Drs. Alick Isaacs and Jean Lindenmann of the British National Institute for Medical Research. It is being widely studied but its practical usefulness has not yet been developed. Iododeoxyuridine (IUDR), a close chemical relative of 5-FU, appears lethal to certain viruses but unfortunately has not proven itself useful against human cancer. A promising new antiviral substance called cytosine arabinoside is undergoing preliminary testing and may have some application in cancer of the lung and testis, malignant melanoma, lymphoma, and acute leukemia.

better use of known drugs

For the past few years, chemotherapists have been learning new ways to use cancer drugs with greater benefit to cancer patients. Various routes of administering drugs have proved useful in different disease situations, and different doses and schedules of administration have heightened the effectiveness of certain drugs. It has been demonstrated, for example, that some drugs are more effective when given orally; others, when injected or dripped into the bloodstream intravenously or intra-arterially; and still others, when given intramuscularly. Small daily doses may be the best method of administering one drug; with others, such as methotrexate used in acute leukemia, a larger dose given at longer intervals may be not only more than twice as effective in producing remissions but also less toxic. Drug combinations have often proved more beneficial than single drug therapy. And in some instances combinations of drugs with surgery and/or radiation may be the preferred treatment.

To determine the most effective means of using cancer drugs, intensive pharmacologic studies are being undertaken at many centers. Pharmacologists are attempting to determine the chemical fate of cancer drugs after they are absorbed in the body, the optimum concentration to reach the cancer cell, and the period the drug must remain there to achieve selective damage. Chemotherapists at the National Cancer Institute are making a full-scale investigation of the ways various drugs are metabolized or converted to the body's use, and their absorption, excretion, and distribution in body fluids. The kinetics of the cells themselves are being explored in an effort to develop drug administration schedules that take advantage of characteristic differences in the cell division cycle of cancer cells and normal cells. Cells are relatively invulnerable to certain cancer drugs during the resting phase. Thus, because of differences in cell cycle, massive doses of drugs administered in a series of strategically timed "pulses" could damage the cancer cells repeatedly and irreversibly while the normal cells would survive.

clinical evaluation

All of the various treatment methods are being analyzed in detail and evaluated for usefulness against different forms of cancer. Information on methods of treating cancer patients at more than 250 hospitals in the United States and Canada is being collected at a central statistical office of the National Cancer Institute. Hundreds of thousands of clinical reports by physicians are being analyzed in an effort to identify the best methods available today to treat the various forms and stages of cancer.

looking ahead

Medical scientists are making no rash promises about cancer drugs. There is no panacea on the horizon. Since cancer is a disease of cells—and the body's cells differ greatly from organ to organ—a variety of drugs may be essential to provide the sought-after chemical cure.

Twenty-five years of intensive drug research has taught the cancer scientists much: the need for thorough experimentation in animals, painstaking recordkeeping, controlled experiments, and close observation of patients. They know the unpredictability of the cancer patient's response, the frequent onsets of toxic side effects, along with the ever-present but remote possibility of a spontaneous, unexplained remission of disease.

They have also learned the need for a rationale in the search for new drugs. They seek drug mechanisms that will exploit the body's physiologic phenomena. They want chemical formulas designed to interact with chemical constituents of cancer cells. They have learned the need for basic information about cell life, information that will illuminate the biologic, physical, and chemical nature of life itself.

These mysteries are at the core of the chemotherapy research effort. They are being explored by some of the nation's great scientists. A farsighted Congress is providing funds for the effort. Laboratories sparkle with excellent equipment. Opportunities for the training of young scientists abound.

The scientists do not promise miracles. But rigorously trained, generous of their time and effort, they are working hard to develop the new drugs and the new treatment methods that are the hope of those gravely ill with cancer.

7

Nature's Cures and Killers

You know all is very well without knowing how it
is so.
—BERNARD LE BOVIER DE FONTENELLE

When the plasmas of living molecules emerged from the bubbling slime
of the young Earth, they encountered an incredibly hostile environment. The poisonous fog of the planet—hydrogen, methane, cyanide,
ammonia—would be instantly lethal to most forms of present-day life.
Though the environment has changed, so have living things, and a
talent for adaptation to unfriendly conditions is still the key to success
for any living organism.

Animals, plants, fungi, bacteria, and cells are continually exposed to
an immense variety of deleterious substances in their surroundings.
About fifteen of the chemical elements are essential for life. Zinc, iron,
copper, and manganese, among the so-called micronutrients, are needed
in barely trace amounts by living organisms. Cobalt, iodine, and selenium are required by higher animals, boron and vanadium by higher
plants. Yet some of the trace elements are highly toxic when present in
the environment of the organism in only slightly higher concentration
than the minimum requirement. For example, arsenic, which commonly
causes acute poisoning, is abundantly present in seafood. Cobalt, a
component of vitamin B_{12} and essential for the nutrition of ruminants
and man, is sometimes present in such abundance in soils that it may
result in feed poisonous to cattle. Selenium, another trace nutrient,
occurs in the soils of rangelands in sections of North and South Dakota
in quantities that impart poisonous characteristics to cereals grown on

the land. Boron, essential to plants, is highly injurious when present in high concentrations in the soil. Fluorine, essential for healthy teeth, is sometimes present in natural water in amounts that cause mottling and abnormalities of the teeth. Thus, whether an element is beneficial or injurious often depends on its abundance and the degree to which the animal or plant is capable of using or rejecting it.

Animals and plants commonly manufacture within their systems substances that drastically affect the metabolism of other organisms that may haplessly come in contact with them. The oldest medicines in the arsenal of the physician are plant remedies, many of which nature intended to be toxic to trespassers. In minute amounts, digitalis, the foxglove toxin of *Digitalis purpurea*, affects the heart. Belladonna, or deadly nightshade, *Atropa*[1] *belladonna*,[2] which has throughout its structure the alkaloid atropine, blocks the action of the neuromuscular hormone, acetylcholine,[3] thereby depressing the parasympathetic nervous system. During the Renaissance women used a belladonna preparation in their eyes to dilate the pupils, which was considered to be an indication of vivacity and beauty.

Atropine is currently useful not only as a medicine but also as an antidote to counteract so-called nerve gas poison, which, when unhampered, characteristically puts the enzyme acetylcholinesterase out of action.

Many other plants possess useful toxic substances. Nicotine is present in tobacco leaves and stems in amounts from 2 to 8 percent. The poison is readily extractable with water and is useful as an insecticide. Nearly all household aerosol sprays contain the extract of pyrethrum flowers, which produce substances called pyrethrins, lethal to insects but nearly nontoxic to humans. Rotenone is used to kill insects and "trash" fish. The paralytic toxicant was discovered by South American natives, who used it for catching fish. They shredded the roots of the rotenone-bearing *Derris* or *Lonchocarpus* and beat them against the sides of their canoes; collecting the catch afterward was literally easier than shooting fish in a barrel.

Narcotics are classic examples of nature's toxins. The seed capsule

---

[1] Atropos (Gk): of the three Fates, the one that cut the thread of life.

[2] Bella donna (Ital.) = beautiful lady.

[3] *Acetylcholine serves to stimulate nerve impulses, especially of the parasympathetic nervous system. In order to avoid overstimulation, the tissues must get rid of the hormone, which they do by bathing the synapses (nerve junctions) with an enzyme, acetylcholinesterase, which immediately destroys the hormone.*

of the opium poppy *Papaver somniferum* yields 22 alkaloids, among them the life- or death-dealing morphine, codeine, and heroin. Milder natural toxins are caffeine of the coffee bean, theobromine of the cacao bean, and the identical stimulants of the tea leaf.

Quinine, the malaria drug, from the bark of the South American cinchona tree, *Cinchona officinalis;* curare, the arrow poison extracted from the plant *Chondodendron tomentosum* by the Indians of the Amazon, now used medicinally to bring about muscular relaxation; strychnine, the violent poison from the seeds of *Strychnos nux-vomica,* used medicinally and to kill rodents, are a few examples of the many poisonous substances that have been put to beneficial use by man.

Animals have done their share in producing substances inimical to other forms of life. Snake venom, secreted by modified salivary glands, serves primarily as a means of procuring food and secondarily as a defense. Poisons of various kinds of snakes act differently. The venoms of many poisonous snakes appear to act as nerve poisons (neurotoxic), with an effect on the optic nerve resulting in blindness and respiratory paralysis. Other effects may be prostration, staggering, cold sweats, vomiting, a feeble and rapid pulse, dilation of the pupils of the eye, and mild mental confusion. Some venoms also affect the circulatory system and are said to be hemolytic. If rapidly introduced into the bloodstream they may cause extensive clotting, which later subsides from flowing of the blood into the tissue spaces and breakdown of the red blood corpuscles. Cobra venom is said to block the functioning of the nerve centers of the cerebrospinal system. Snakes themselves are not immune to venom, as they can poison each other, even other individuals of the same species.

The red tide contains the poisonous secretion of the single cell dinoflagellate *Gonyaulax,* which inhabits the ocean in such abundance that in certain seasons the algal bloom discolors the surface and at night causes a brilliant display of phosphorescence in waves or in the wake of a ship. The tiny creature's poisonous substance ultimately comes to rest in mussels, which feed on the organisms. The poison remains in the flesh of the mussels for many months and renders it unfit for human food.

Toxins occur in nature in such diverse forms as the poisons of the scorpion and the spider, the mild bufotoxin secreted by the skin of the frog, the painful tetrodotoxin of the puffer fish, and the highly dangerous aflatoxin of the fungus *Aspergillus flavus* which grows on stale beans and peanuts.

Nature has given to man, most bounteously, toxins in the form of antibiotics, the life-saving substances derived from micro-organisms. The first antibiotic was discovered by the British microbiologist Alexander Fleming who noted that staphyloccoccus bacteria could not grow in the immediate vicinity of the common bread mold *Penicillium notatum*. The discovery lay unnoticed for 10 years. Eventually, as a result of the interest and further research by the Britisher Howard Flory and the German-born Ernst Chain, the wonderdrug penicillin was developed. Fleming, Flory, and Chain shared the Nobel prize in medicine and physiology in 1945.

A series of antibiotics followed penicillin. Knowledge that these substances are merely nature's toxins put to work should cause us concern over their indiscriminate use. Penicillin shock is nature's way of showing that her creations are not to be treated lightly. Besides, many pathogenic organisms, including staphyloccus pus-formers and those causing venereal diseases (the gonococcus of gonorrhea and the spirochete of syphilis), have developed resistant strains that are difficult to subdue with the once-reliable antibiotics. Chloramphenicol, originally obtained from the soil bacterium *Streptomyces venezualeae*, is reported to be useful in the treatment of typhoid fever but may cause a serious blood disease, aplastic anemia, and death.

Despite the multitude of malevolent forces, life continues. Animals, plants, and bacteria would quickly succumb to the injurious substances in the environment or be consumed by the poisons of their adversaries if it were not for the fact that each possesses built-in mechanisms for detoxication. The metabolic routes for detoxication are numerous and complex. When the processes proceed to a successful conclusion, they are nature's way of providing adaptations in their cellular functions for survival of the organism despite the unfriendly chemistry of the environment.

Natural Food Poisons

A. D. Campbell

Plants, animals, and micro-organisms can be sources of naturally occurring toxic substances which may remain in foodstuffs unless adequate precautions are taken to eliminate them. Many of the naturally occurring toxic components of food have received comparatively little attention, but acute (short term) and chronic (long term) toxicity have been recognized as results of man and animals eating foods contaminated with these substances.

Generally, through a trial-and-error process, man has been able to place plants and animals into safe and unsafe food categories. This trial-and-error process has been useful in eliminating those which produce acute toxicity; the results are usually sudden illness or death. However, the manifestations of chronic toxicity of some of these substances are not readily associated with the source; symptoms may occur after a considerable lapse of time. More sophisticated research studies are usually necessary to find the cause-and-effect relationships for chronic toxicity.

Plants may contain toxic substances, such as protein digestion inhibitors, toxic proteins (for example, those found in castor beans), estrogenic substances, substances containing cyanides, solanine substances (for example, toxins from potato sprouts), and a number of other toxic materials.

In some instances, the toxicant is at such a low level that it does not present a health problem when eaten; the estrogenic substances of soybeans are examples. In other instances, the toxicant can be inactivated by heating the foodstuff before it is eaten. For example, the protein digestion inhibitor of soybeans and the cyanide substances in lima beans are inactivated as toxicants by heating.

Reprinted from *FDA Papers*: 23–27 (September 1967) with permission of the author and the publisher.

The toxic portions of some plants are usually removed and discarded. Those found in the skin and sprouts of potatoes which have been exposed to sunlight are thus avoided. Stalks of rhubarb are eaten and the toxic leaves are discarded.

Harvesting at the proper stage of maturity is a means of avoiding other plant toxicants. For example, unripened grapefruit contain a toxic substance which is not present in mature fruit. The use of selective breeding by the plant geneticist is another means of eliminating toxic substances from some plants. Gossypol, a toxic pigment of cottonseed, has been successfully bred out of cotton by this technique.

Some animals or animal products which are normally suitable as food can contain toxic substances under unusual circumstances. Oysters, clams, and other shellfish have been shown to contain a toxic substance known as "the paralytic shellfish poison" when they grow under adverse conditions. The puffer fish, considered a delicacy by some, contains a highly toxic substance in its skin and sex organs. Toxic animal metabolites (substances produced by the life processes) are known to contaminate some animal products when some toxic substances from molds are eaten by the animals. Detection by analytical means and discarding the contaminated lots may be the only means of avoiding them.

Micro-organisms (molds, yeasts, and bacteria) are known to produce toxic metabolites called microbial toxins. In considering microbial toxins the scientist is not concerned with the infectious nature of the micro-organism but with the toxic metabolites produced when the micro-organisms grow on foodstuffs. Examples of this class of toxic materials are the botulinum and staphylococcus toxins produced by bacteria. Less familiar are the mycotoxins produced by molds, such as the aflatoxins, the ochratoxins, and the estrogenic substances.

Mycotoxins have undoubtedly been with man since the beginning. However, they were not recognized as health problems until relatively recent years. The current emphasis in this field was stimulated in 1961 when a large number of turkeys died in England. British researchers investigated the "Turkey X" disease and found that the causative toxic material was a peanut meal coming from Brazil. They further related the toxic principle to the mold *Aspergillus flavus* and coined the word aflatoxin.

It is now known that the aflatoxins are produced by a number of molds, in addition to *Aspergillus flavus*. These are very potent toxins for some animals and the sensitivity varies over a considerable range for different species. Rainbow trout are the most sensitive animals that have been found so far. It is interesting to note that brown trout are relatively resistant compared to rainbows.

Ducklings are also quite sensitive, whereas sheep are the most resistant animals that have been studied. Primates are also sensitive to aflatoxins; however, nothing as yet is known about the toxicity to man. In addition to the acute toxicity of the aflatoxins, they have been found to be carcinogens for some animals.

It is not uncommon for the mycologist to isolate molds from cereal grains and other foodstuffs. Individual kernels are often found to be damaged by molds, but these are usually removed in the normal cleaning and processing of the grains. Only some molds produce toxic metabolites and only some strains of specific species produce toxic metabolites.

Many micro-organisms produce metabolites which have beneficial uses for man. The leavening effect of yeast in baked products is well known. Carbon dioxide (a metabolite of growing yeast) is entrapped in the dough or batter and produces the leavening effect. Other examples of useful microbial metabolites are the antibiotics and certain enzymes produced by yeasts, molds, and bacteria which find useful places in the processing and manufacture of food.

Sometimes the microbial metabolite can have both a good and a bad effect when fed to animals. The estrogenic substance produced by *Gibberella zeae* is of this nature. When this substance is administered to some farm animals at the proper dosage level, an enhanced growth rate is observed, and thus, it has a potential economic advantage to the farmer. However, when this substance is administered at higher levels, it can be troublesome in that it can cause abortion or prevent conception in breeding stock.

The Food and Drug Administration recognized the potential mycotoxin problem after Britain's encounter with the "Turkey X" disease. Scientists in the Division of Food Chemistry were immediately assigned to a research project to identify the problem. Moldy agricultural commodities were analyzed and in some cases aflatoxin was detected. This suggested that a potential problem might exist in this country. Research was initiated to develop reliable analytical methods for surveillance and control purposes.

Problems of this type require a multidisciplinary scientific approach, because the specific talents of the microbiologist, the chemist, and the pharmacologist are closely interrelated.

Scientists in FDA's Divisions of Microbiology and Pharmacology joined the investigation. The microbiologists obtained aflatoxin-producing strains of mold and grew them in the laboratories to produce aflatoxins for further work by the chemists. The chemists developed techniques for the isolation and purification of the aflatoxins for chemical characterization and identification. These isolated aflatoxins were also used by the pharmacologists to investigate their toxicity and to develop sensitive toxicity methods.

At the same time, the chemists were devising more rapid and reliable analytical methods for the detection of aflatoxins in suspect agricultural commodities. The original methods required two and a half days for completion. The Division of Food Chemistry developed a rapid method which required only three and a half hours so a chemist could analyze eight or more samples in a day.

A small quantity of partially purified aflatoxins was supplied to a research team at the Massachusetts Institute of Technology for chemical structure research. They separated four aflatoxins and established their chemical structures. This valuable information was of great assistance to the chemists in their development of reliable chemical confirmation tests. The pharmacologists developed a reliable and sensitive chick embryo toxicity test.

While this phase of the research was going on, the FDA was in contact with members of the food industry, the U.S. Department of Agriculture, university research groups, and independent laboratories. Technical information was pooled and exchanged, expediting the collection and dissemination of technical data and information. This minimized duplication of efforts by the various groups and promoted a coordinated research effort on the problem.

As methodology was developing, technical personnel from industry, Government agencies, and universities were trained in the FDA laboratories on the most up-to-date techniques.

There has been a continued exchange of information between Britain, Canada, Holland, and other foreign countries from the start of this problem. In March of 1963, an international symposium was held at MIT on the subject of mycotoxins in foodstuffs. This provided an excellent opportunity to bring together investigators from all parts of the world to present scientific information and discuss this problem. The Food and Drug Administration, the National Institutes of Health, the U.S. Department of Agriculture, and a number of international organizations were participants. A subcommittee was established under the auspices of the International Union of Pure and Applied Chemistry

Testing brazil nuts for mycotoxins (l to r): grinding nuts;

to coordinate international efforts on the development of analytical methodology for the mycotoxins; a member of the Food and Drug Administration has been chairman of the subcommittee since its inception. Committees were formed in the Association of Official Analytical Chemists and the Association of Oil Chemists to further coordinate efforts in methods development. Members of the Food and Drug Administration have served on both of these committees.

A number of symposia dealing with mycotoxins have been held at scientific meetings, such as the Association of Official Analytical Chemists, Institute of Food Technologists, American Chemical Society,

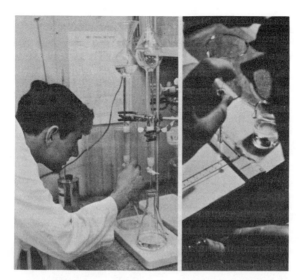

purification of crude extract; preparing thin-layer chromotography plates to detect mycotoxins.

American Society of Microbiologists, and others in this country. Several of these have been of an international nature with recognized experts in the field of mycotoxins from many countries as participants. Professor Uritani of Nagoya University, Japan, world-renowned for his work in mycotoxins, was a guest speaker at the 1966 Annual Meeting of the Association of Official Analytical Chemists. A number of private meetings have been held with representatives of the food industry, U.S. Department of Agriculture research personnel, and Food and Drug Administration personnel in which current research was discussed and future research programs planned.

As a result of FDA's early efforts and through the cooperation of industry and the U.S. Department of Agriculture, contaminated peanuts have been diverted from food channels by a sound program for the prevention of aflatoxin-contaminated peanuts entering food channels.

Each lot of peanuts as it comes from the farm is examined and the lots likely to be contaminated with aflatoxins are analyzed. If the contamination is found too high, the lot of peanuts is used only for the production of peanut oil, because the refining process eliminates all traces of aflatoxins. If the peanut meal byproduct from this process is contaminated, it is used only for fertilizer. Processing of peanuts includes shelling, sorting, and cleaning; these processing steps are helpful in eliminating aflatoxin contamination. Aflatoxins analyses are carried out at further steps of processing, manufacturing, and on the finished consumer products. This cooperative effort between Government and industry assures the wholesomeness of peanut products for sale to consumers.

The aflatoxin problem has not been confined to peanuts. An industry group concerned with the importation of brazil nuts into the United States was recently formed to deal with the aflatoxin problem in this commodity. This group was provided with technical information and assistance by the Food and Drug Administration and the U.S. Department of Agriculture. Laboratory equipment for the analysis of the aflatoxins was purchased and taken to Brazil to expedite the efforts to prevent the shipment of aflatoxin-contaminated brazil nuts into this country. The group was successful in encouraging the Brazilian Government to establish a laboratory which will analyze exports of brazil nuts and certify the absence of aflatoxin. This is another excellent example of the fine cooperation which has existed in attempts to cope with this problem in a manner which protects the consuming public.

Protection of the public health, of course, is the incentive for the Food and Drug Administration to initiate and coordinate such an effort. In the case of aflatoxin in peanuts, it was possible to protect the public through combined research and self-regulation efforts. However, it was necessary from the beginning for FDA to recognize that peanut products would have to be handled like any other food adulterated because of contamination by fungal infestation, or by toxins elaborated by fungal organisms. For that reason, it was necessary to develop reliable biological and chemical tests to provide proof of adulteration for regulatory purposes.

For practical reasons, these tests should be specific, simple, rapid, and yet be sufficiently sensitive and accurate to measure small but significant quantities of deleterious substances. As already indicated, sensitive and reliable chemical methods, chemical confirmatory tests and toxicity tests suitable for regulatory purposes, have been developed.

FDA does not assert that any one of these methods meets all ideals of accuracy, precision, sensitivity, and specificity. Nevertheless, when considered as a battery of tests, they give consistent and reliable information.

Current analytical methods are capable of detecting and confirming the presence of aflatoxins in a range well below 50 parts per billion of product. At present, there is no pharmacological data indicating a safe level of aflatoxin in man. Since they are carcinogens for some animals, no tolerance can be set for these substances. Any demonstrable concentration of aflatoxin is proof of excessive contamination with fungal toxins.

A new dimension in the potential for a health hazard from aflatoxin has appeared. It has recently been reported by Oregon State University researchers that an interaction exists between the cyclopropenoic fatty acids and aflatoxins when fed to rainbow trout. The cyclopropenoic fatty acids are normally present in cottonseed oil. They do not produce liver tumors in the trout when fed alone; however, when they

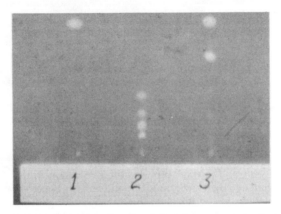

Developed thin-layer chromotography plates showing estrogenic factor (left), aflatoxins, and ochratoxin.

are fed along with the aflatoxins, tumors are produced in the trout at much lower levels than when the aflatoxins are fed alone.

This important finding illustrates the potential of interrelationship between naturally occurring food poisons and suggests the possibility of other food constituents having an effect upon the sensitivity of animals to the aflatoxins and other naturally occurring toxins.

The development of a screening method which will detect the three recognized classes of mycotoxins (aflatoxins, ochratoxins, and the estrogenic factor of *Gibberella zeae*) in foodstuffs is nearing completion in our laboratories. This will provide a timesaving means for screening of foodstuffs for the presence of some of the mycotoxins. Validation studies are presently being conducted. When these studies are complete,

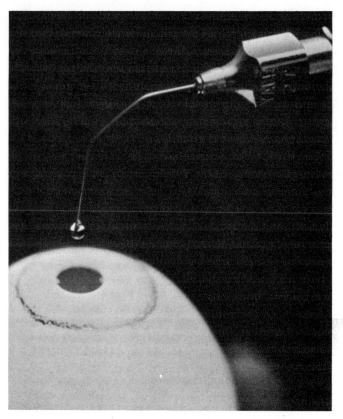

In chicken embryo toxicity test an aflatoxin preparation is injected into an egg to determine toxicity. The embryos and hatched chicks are examined for possible damage.

this screening method will offer a valuable tool for the Food and Drug Administration's District laboratories and research laboratories for expediting the collection of data on the mycotoxin problem.

A simple, rapid toxicity test using brine shrimp for the aflatoxins is nearing completion. Brine shrimp eggs are readily available in any pet shop. When these eggs are placed in sea water, they hatch in 24 hours to produce shrimp barely visible to the naked eye. These newly hatched shrimp are quickly killed when exposed to aflatoxin. Considerable interest has been shown in this test, because it can be completed in 2 days in most laboratories.

We now know that *A. flavus* produces several toxins, in addition to the four originally recognized aflatoxins. Analytical methodology is currently under development which, when completed, will provide a means for the detection of these other toxins so that surveillance can be carried out on agricultural commodities to establish whether or not they may present a health hazard.

Research programs are underway in the Food and Drug Administration's laboratories to seek out other mycotoxins which may be a health hazard to the consumer. Many toxic substances undoubtedly remain to be discovered in natural food products.

Much has been learned by the scientific community from the great amount of research which has gone on in many laboratories since the aflatoxins were discovered in 1961. This information has been quickly put to use to protect the health of the people throughout the world. These studies indicate that much is still to be learned about naturally occurring food poisons. Only through concerted research efforts of many laboratories will the basic scientific information be obtained for a sound evaluation of this newly recognized problem.

Juvenile Hormone Activity for the Bug Pyrrhocoris apterus

Karel Sláma
Carroll M. Williams

When transported from Prague to Boston and reared in the Biological Laboratories at Harvard University, the bug *Pyrrhocoris apterus* failed to undergo normal metamorphosis. Approximately 1500 individuals were reared from eggs. Instead of metamorphosing into normal adults, at the end of the 5th larval instar all molted into 6th instar larvae or into adultoid forms preserving many larval characters. Indeed, as illustrated in Figure 1, some continued to grow and molted into still-larger 7th instar larvae. Without exception, all individuals died without completing metamorphosis or attaining sexual maturity.

During 10 years of culturing *Pyrrhocoris* in Prague, not a single instance of this sort had been observed. Additional larval instars, in *Pyrrhocoris* as in other species, had been induced only by the implantation of active corpora allata (the endocrine source of juvenile hormone), or by the injection or topical application of substances showing juvenile hormone activity [1]. Evidently, when reared at Harvard University, the bugs had access to some unknown source of juvenile hormone.

An audit of the culture conditions at Harvard versus Prague suggested 15 differences. By systematic study, 14 were eliminated. The source of juvenile hormone activity was finally tracked down to exposure of the bugs to a certain paper towel ("Scott, brand 150") which had been placed in the rearing jars. When this toweling was replaced

Reprinted from the *Proceedings of the National Academy of Sciences, 54:* 411–14 (August 1965) with permission of the authors and the publisher. Investigation supported, in part, by Grant GB-3232 from the National Science Foundation.

Figure 1. The effects of contact with the active principle extracted from paper material is illustrated by these four specimens. On the left is a 5th instar *Pyrrhocoris* larva which normally transforms into the winged adult (*third from left*). When exposed to the paper extract, the larva continues to grow without metamorphosis to form a 6th instar larva (*second from left*) which, in turn, may form a still-larger 7th instar larva (*fourth from left*). (*This print was prepared by Frank White from a color transparency by Muriel V. Williams.*)

by Whatman's filter paper, the entire phenomenon disappeared and all individuals developed normally.

At first we thought that the effect of the toweling was due to some chemical added during its manufacture. However, of 20 other brands of American towels and tissues, 18 provoked the same extraordinary juvenile hormone effects when tested on *Pyrrhocoris*. Indeed, pieces of American newspapers and journals (*New York Times, Wall Street Journal, Boston Globe, Science,* and *Scientific American*) showed extremely high juvenile hormone activity when placed in contact with *Pyrrhocoris*. The *London Times* and *Nature* were inactive, and so were other paper materials of European or Japanese manufacture.

Extracts prepared from the Scott toweling were subjected to biological assay. The latter was accomplished merely by soaking a disk of filter paper in the extract, evaporating the solvent, and allowing young 5th instar *Pyrrhocoris* to walk upon it. After 5 days at 25°C, the presence of juvenile hormone activity was signaled by their molting to 6th instar larvae, or, in the case of weaker reactions, by molting to creatures which showed a mixture of larval and adult characters. The absence of activity was recognized by molting to normal adults after 7 days at 25°C.

Like all previous materials with juvenile hormone properties [2–5], the active principle in the toweling was found to be insoluble in water, but freely soluble in methanol, acetone, ether, and petroleum ether. The surprisingly large amount of material obtained by methanol extraction of toweling was purified by evaporation of solvent and extraction of the residue into petroleum ether. The active principle was found to be heat-stable (100°C) and destroyed by vigorous saponification. Further purification was achieved by chromatography on a column of silicic acid ("Unisil"). The active fraction was retained after perfusion with benzene but was eluted with an equal-part mixture of benzene and diethyl ether.

This partially purified extract showed extraordinary juvenile hormone activity when assayed on *Pyrrhocoris*. Contact with a 10-cm disk of filter paper impregnated with 100 μg of extract caused all of scores of larvae to transform into 6th instar larvae or adultoid forms. As little as 0.01 μg of extract provoked the formation of 6th instar larvae when topically applied to individual bugs. Even when the extract was placed on the tip of an antenna or leg, or at any other site, the full effect was realized. This demonstrated that the active principle readily penetrates the cuticle and is distributed throughout the insect. The extract was fully effective when tested on *Pyrrhocoris* larvae from which the corpora allata had been removed at the outset of the 5th instar—a finding which shows that the corpora allata are not involved in the reaction to the extract.

We would emphasize that the active material was without any detectable effects on the growth, molting, or viability of *Pyrrhocoris* larvae prior to the stage when metamorphosis ordinarily supervenes. This result is intelligible since larval growth normally proceeds in the presence of endogenous juvenile hormone secreted by the corpora allata [4]. Metamorphosis occurs only when the corpora allata stop secreting juvenile hormone; consequently, it is at this specific stage that the insect becomes sensitive to the materials possessing hormonal activity.

Through the kindness of Professor Irving W. Bailey, authentic samples of seven species of gymnosperms were obtained from the venerable wood collection of the Harvard Herbarium. Each specimen was first rinsed in acetone and then cut up on a drill press with an acetone-washed drill. The pulverata were shaken with acetone, filtered, and the solvent evaporated to obtain the acetone-soluble materials. The latter were dissolved in small volumes of methanol, impregnated onto filter paper, and assayed as described above.

Extracts of balsam fir (*Abies balsamea*), hemlock (*Tsuga canadensis*), and yew (*Taxus brevifolia*) showed high juvenile hormone activity. Extracts of American larch (*Larix laricina*) showed intermediate activity, while red spruce (*Picea rubra*), European larch (*Larix decidua*), and the southern pine (*Pinus echinata*) showed barely detectable activity. Evidently the substantial juvenile hormone activity in American paper products is mainly derived from the indigenous American pulp tree, the balsam fir.

We were astonished to find that our most active extracts were without any detectable effects when injected or topically applied to previously chilled pupae of the *cecropia* or *polyphemus* silkworms— even when they were tested in the ultra-sensitive wax-wound assay for juvenile hormone [3,5,6]. Equally surprising was the additional finding that purified extracts of *cecropia* oil, of extremely high juvenile hormone activity, when assayed on *cecropia* or *polyphemus* pupae, showed only a trace of activity when tested on *Pyrrhocoris apterus*.

What this implies is that molecules with juvenile hormone activity for one species of insect are not necessarily active on other species. Evidently during the millions of years of insect evolution, the detailed chemistry of the hormone has evolved and diversified. The scant sensitivity of *Pyrrhocoris* to *cecropia* hormone documents this fact and shows, moreover, that the evolution of the hormone has been accompanied by the biochemical "retuning" of the receptor mechanism at the cellular level.

At the present time additional studies are under way to clarify the chemistry of the active material and to define the types of insects sensitive to this particular variant of juvenile hormone. It is already clear that the towel extract is without any detectable effects on most laboratory insects, including two other species of heteroptera, *Oncopeltus fasciatus* and *Rhodnius prolixus*. In point of fact, the only sensitive species which we have thus far encountered is *Pyrrhocoris apterus* itself.

The family Pyrrhocoridae includes a substantial number of insect pests, such as the notorious "red cotton bug" (*Dysdercus cingulatus*) of eastern Asia, and various species of "cotton stainers" endemic to Australia, the West Indies, South America, and southern United States. It seems not unlikely that the hormonally active material may be effective in the selective destruction of at least certain of these pests, as well as any other insects which show the same hormonal sensitivities as *Pyrrhocoris apterus* [2]. This possibility is worthy of attention because the active material is available on an unlimited scale in American newspapers and journals.

Summary. Materials composed of American paper pulp contain an extractable, heat-stable lipid which exhibits extremely high juvenile hormone activity when injected or topically applied to the European bug *Pyrrhocoris apterus*. The active principle in the paper materials is derived from certain species of pulp trees, more particularly the balsam fir, *Abies balsamea*. Larvae exposed to the active material ultimately die without completing metamorphosis or attaining sexual maturity.

Despite its extremely high activity for *Pyrrhocoris apterus*, the extract is without any detectable effects on silkworm pupae; conversely, juvenile hormone extracts prepared from *cecropia* silkmoths show only a trace of activity when tested on *Pyrrhocoris*. These findings point to a diversification of the detailed chemistry of juvenile hormone during insect evolution.

The factor extracted from paper materials promises to be an effective agent for the selective control of insect pests which show the same endocrine sensitivities as *Pyrrhocoris apterus*.

references

1. K. Sláma, *Zool. Jb., Physiol., 70*, 427 (1964).
2. C. M. Williams, *Nature, 178*, 212 (1956).
3. H. A. Schneiderman and L. I. Gilbert, *Science, 143*, 325 (1964).
4. V. B. Wigglesworth, *Advan. Insect Physiol., 2*, 247 (1964).
5. C. M. Williams and J. H. Law, *J. Insect Physiol., 11*, 569 (1965).
6. H. A. Schneiderman and L. I. Gilbert, *Biol. Bull., 115*, 530 (1958).

Unidentified Substances

George M. Briggs

Some day—and the day may not be far off—a white-coated scientist is going to look up from his data books or his laboratory bench and tell himself, with no more excitement than his scientist's caution allows, "This is it!"

It will be a new vitamin or a new growth factor that he and perhaps many other laboratory workers have tried for a long time to find or identify exactly.

This new vitamin, or a food factor, will be a link between the first findings in nutrition years ago and today's research. It will push farther back the frontiers of man's knowledge. It will benefit people or animals or both. It will be as exciting as the solution of a mystery story and perhaps as outstanding as Dr. Jonas Salk's discovery of vaccine for poliomyelitis.

It may rank alongside the discovery of vitamins A, C, and D and the B-complex vitamins, which were complete mysteries before 1920 and minor mysteries between 1930 and 1955, when their chemical structures were discovered.

For there are still discoveries to be made of unidentified substances in foods.

Natural foods, such as milk, meat, eggs, vegetables, and cereals, contain at least several important nutrients and substances whose identity we still do not know. We call them unidentified factors. The list of them has been dwindling steadily as our knowledge has grown, but the ones remaining in 1959 seem to be important in nutrition.

How do we know that unidentified factors exist?

To find out, we start with a purified diet that contains all known

Reprinted from *The Yearbook of Agriculture, 1959*: 162–67 (1959), U.S. Department of Agriculture, with permission of the author and publisher.

nutrients in ample amounts in the form of a mixture of pure proteins, carbohydrates, vitamins, minerals, and fat. We feed it to an experimental animal and keep a record of the results. If we can get better results —such as improved growth or reproduction—by adding any natural food to this diet, we can be fairly certain that an unidentified factor is present in the natural food. White rats, mice, guinea pigs, chicks, and other small animals are the favorite "tool" for this work.

The next job is to identify the factor. That is not easy. We make concentrates—or extracts—of the factor from the natural food by chemical fractionation. We test the concentrates by adding them to the original purified diet and feeding the diet to the test animal. Thus we can follow the activity through repeated tests to the final isolation of the pure substance and to its identification. This is more difficult than it sounds and may take many months or years. There are many pitfalls and blind alleys, which can slow down the work considerably.

Often it is possible to find a 1- or 2-day test for the unknown factor if we use certain fast-growing microorganisms as the test "animals." That hastens the process. Most of the B vitamins were discovered in this way—by using bacteria.

The discovery of vitamin B_{12} in 1948 is an example of how unidentified factors become known and identified.

A number of supposedly different unidentified factors were being studied in different laboratories before 1948.

Many of these turned out to be vitamin B_{12}. As far back as 1926, Dr. George Richards Minot and Dr. William Parry Murphy, of Harvard and Boston, discovered that pernicious anemia, an incurable disease in man until then, could be treated by feeding large amounts of liver. Concentrates of the antipernicious anemia factor, as it was called, became available in the form of injectable liver extracts in a few years —but attempts to identify the active factor were unsuccessful.

Two groups of workers at the Agricultural Research Center at Beltsville, Md., had been working with unidentified factors for animals since the 1930's. Their investigations were along two different lines.

A number of investigators in the Poultry Division—Drs. Theodore C. Byerly, H. W. Titus, H. R. Bird, A. C. Groschke, N. R. Ellis, J. C. Hammond, M. Rubin, and others—studied an "animal protein factor." They learned that it occurred in protein concentrates from such sources as fishmeal and meat scraps and helped growth and reproduction of poultry. They discovered by a fortunate observation in 1946 that ordinary cow manure is an excellent source of a similar unidentified growth factor for chicks. It became known as the cow manure factor. Long and tedious attempts to purify and identify the substance were unsuccessful, but the scientists were able to prove that the factor is synthesized by microorganisms in the rumen.

C. A. Cary, A. M. Hartman, and their coworkers in the former Bureau of Dairy Industry of the Department of Agriculture were working at the same time on what was thought to be another unidentified factor in milk. It was necessary for the growth and reproduction of laboratory rats. This factor was different from all vitamins and minerals known at that time (1943 to 1947). They called it factor X. Many time-consuming studies were made to identify the factor, but it proved to be elusive and difficult to purify. These scientists found that antipernicious anemia factor concentrates were good sources of factor X, a finding that later proved to be useful to others (even though they believed at the time that the two factors were not identical).

In another laboratory, Lois M. Zucker and T. F. Zucker of Columbia University, a husband-and-wife team, were studying growth effects obtained by adding casein (the protein of milk), liver, or fish solubles to purified diets for rats. They obtained concentrates of an unidentified factor, which they named "zoopherin."

Other workers with rats and chicks in various laboratories, including the University of Wisconsin, Cornell University, and Lederle Laboratories, confirmed these findings and were actively attempting to identify the animal protein factor, as it was most commonly called in 1946 to 1948. All found the animal tests expensive and difficult.

Still another line of attack was being made to isolate this unidentified factor. Mary Shorb, a bacteriologist, working first at Beltsville in the former Bureau of Dairy Industry and later at the University of Maryland, discovered in 1947 that a certain bacterium, *Lactobacillus lactis* (Dorner), would not grow unless concentrates of the antipernicious anemia factor for humans were added to their food. She called this unknown substance the LLD factor, from the initials of the name of the bacterium.

Following this discovery, Dr. Shorb and I, at the University of Maryland Poultry Department, attempted to purify the LLD factor further. We had little success, but we were able to improve the assay enough so that it could be used by ourselves and others in short-time routine tests to identify the compound.

Using the Maryland test with bacteria, research workers in the Merck & Co. laboratories in Rahway, N.J., isolated a deep-red, crystalline compound from liver and other sources in 1948. Like others, the Merck laboratory had spent thousands of dollars and many years in attempts to find the antipernicious anemia factor. The goal was reached by the use of the 2-day bacterial test, which was better than testing each new batch on hospital patients suffering from pernicious anemia. The new compound was named vitamin B_{12}.

Thus a scientific mystery of long standing was solved in 1948, and many loose ends were brought together. After the discovery of vitamin B_{12}, scientists proved that it was not only the LLD factor but also the antipernicious anemia factor for humans, factor X, the animal protein factor, the cow manure factor, and zoopherin for chickens, pigs, and rats!

A discovery of this type leads to a large amount of experimental work and results in many benefits to mankind. It has had much practical use in animal feeding and in human nutrition and medicine. Workers in laboratories all over the world have written more than 1,500 scientific publications on vitamin B_{12} since 1948.

Another example of a recently discovered nutrient is selenium, a trace mineral. It was an unsuspected part of an unidentified factor until 1957, when scientists discovered that compounds containing selenium had important nutritional properties in feed given rats, pigs, chickens, turkeys, and mice.

The recognition of selenium as a trace element in nutrition goes back to 1951 to the work of K. Schwarz and his coworkers at the National Institutes of Health in Bethesda, Md. They discovered that some foods, such as milk, brewer's yeast, meat, and certain cereals (corn, soybeans, and wheat) contain an unidentified substance, which they called factor 3. It prevented liver damage and death in rats fed special diets low in vitamin E and low in cystine, an amino acid.

After 6 years of intensive study and purification, Dr. Schwarz and his group in 1957 discovered that highly purified concentrates of factor 3 contained selenium. Certain crystalline salts of selenium fed in small amounts (0.1 part per million or less) prevented liver damage in rats. This amount is far less than the amounts necessary to produce the well-known toxic effect of selenium in feeds.

Several groups of workers discovered soon thereafter that selenium-containing compounds are also exceedingly active in preventing exudative diathesis in chicks (a condition characterized by fluid under the skin), liver damage in pigs, and heart and kidney damage in mice.

Vitamin E had to be absent from the diet before the selenium compounds were effective in all animals. Vitamin E prevented the conditions, but it was only about one five-hundredth as active as the selenium compounds. Not all the functions of vitamin E could be replaced by the selenium compounds, however.

An active search began in 1957 to find the most active selenium-containing compounds in foods and to find out why selenium-containing compounds are necessary under these conditions. As is typical of such studies, complete answers will not be found until after years of devoted work on thousands of animals and much expense.

Nobody can say how many nutritional factors remain unknown or how soon they will be discovered.

I list some of the substances that seem to be necessary for animals and that were not identified in 1958. We have little information about their importance in human nutrition.

Strepogenin is the name given to a growth factor for certain bacteria by Dr. D. W. Wooley, of the Rockefeller Institute for Medical Research in New York, in the 1940's. It is present in many natural foods and is associated closely with proteins. Highly purified diets or synthetic media must be used in studies of it.

Certain peptides—compounds containing several amino acids—are known to have strepogenin activity in bacteria. Thousands of man-hours have been spent to identify the substance, but after 15 years of work the final answer has not been found. Its discovery must await the development of new techniques in protein and amino acid chemistry.

Studies with chicks in our laboratories at the National Institutes of Health and in other laboratories have indicated that this unidentified factor may be important for animal growth.

Protein sources, such as egg yolk, liver meal, dried whey, peanut meal, and fishmeal, have been reported to contain an unidentified vitamin (or possibly more than one) for the growth and reproduction of chickens and turkeys and for the growth of swine.

Drs. Henry Menge, Robert J. Lillie, and Charles A. Denton, of the Agricultural Research Service, have conducted extensive studies at Beltsville on this factor. Much work has been done at many State agricultural experiment stations and commercial laboratories.

In order to get growth responses with these materials, levels of as high as 5 to 12 percent of the material must be used in the diet. This would indicate that the protein portion of the crude materials might be responsible for the growth effect. The growth responses cannot be duplicated with pure proteins or with amino acids, however.

Little progress had been made up to 1959 in the identification of the factor (or factors), which at various times has been termed the egg yolk factor, liver factor, whey factor, and fish factor. Much has been written about it. It promises to be important in animal nutrition and possibly for people.

The grass juice factor, or the forage juice factor, was reported in 1938 to be necessary for guinea pigs. With the discovery of several other B vitamins in 1938 to 1948, the grass juice factor was almost forgotten. Now there is renewed interest in it. In studies in our laboratory and elsewhere, evidence has been found of this growth-promoting factor in grass, alfalfa, and possibly other green forage and pasture crops. It may also be present in plant seeds, such as corn, soybean meal, and wheat.

One might suspect that the factor would be important to grass-consuming animals, like sheep and cattle. It is not safe to make too many predictions about unidentified factors, however. The unexpected is more usual than the expected.

The grass juice factor is a good example of how long studies on unidentified factors often take. It takes particularly devoted scientists to stick to a problem, for example, that goes on for more than 20 years without a final answer.

Unidentified trace minerals, with nutritional activity for poultry, swine, and ruminants, exist, according to scientists' reports in 1957 and 1958.

A number of trace elements are known to have important functions in plants or in lower forms of life, but their importance to animal nutrition has never been proved. Among them are such minerals as nickel, aluminum, boron, silicon, and vanadium. These elements could not be considered as essential trace elements for animals in 1959, but no one can predict what will be found in future years.

Experiments with trace minerals are just as difficult to perform as studies with vitamins. It is extremely difficult to remove the very last amount of a mineral from purified diets so that their role in animal nutrition can be studied. Often a study becomes completely worthless if as little as one part in a million of a mineral remains in a test diet.

Promising new techniques are being developed, however, for studies on unidentified minerals. Scientists in some laboratories use animals that are the offspring of several generations of animals fed special diets. This is done in order to remove all traces of the mineral from the animal. In other laboratories, compounds are fed that are unique in being able to tie up the last remaining traces of an element within the animal.

In still other studies, animals are given special feeds produced on soils absolutely devoid of certain trace minerals. The curiosity of a nutritionist is unlimited, and he will go to any extremes possible to discover new facts.

The unidentified antitoxic factors found in natural foods counteract the effects of toxic agents in animal nutrition.

Factors in meat and liver, for example, are known to prevent the toxic effect of large doses of the thyroid hormone and cortisone. Unidentified factors in meat overcome the toxicity of the drug thiouracil.

The study of antitoxic factors is but one pathway that may lead to the discovery of a new vitamin or growth factor. It is possible that a small amount of an antitoxic factor may be necessary for animals even in the absence of the toxic factor. The importance of these factors in animal or human nutrition was not known in 1959.

Growth factors in microbial products (such as brewer's yeast, distiller's solubles, bacterial and mold cultures, and fermentation residues) continue to receive attention by men who study nutrition of animals. Such products appear to contain unidentified factors for bacteria as well as for animals. It is possible that short-time tests for these factors can be developed with bacteria to replace the much longer animal tests.

No predictions can be made at this stage of research as to the actual importance of the factors in animal and human nutrition. However, even now crude sources of these factors are being used with apparent benefit in commercial poultry and swine rations: It is possible to make good use of unidentified factors in nutrition even before they are identified.

Bacteria, protozoa, insects, and other lower forms of life are known to require unidentified factors besides those I mentioned previously.

Such compounds, when they are identified, are known as growth factors, rather than vitamins, because, by definition, a compound must be shown to have a beneficial physiological function by one or more of the higher animals—vertebrates—before it can be called a vitamin. Furthermore, by definition, the compound must be an organic substance in natural foods but not a fat, carbohydrate, or amino acid.

Unidentified growth factors for lower forms of life include one or more substances in bacterial cultures for *Lactobacillus casei;* a growth factor in liver for *Lactobacillus leichmannii;* a corn-leaf factor for the European corn borer larva; and an unknown substance in spleen for *Escherichia coli.*

Many others have been reported. We do not yet know the importance of these growth factors in the nutrition of higher animals, including people. The answer can only be obtained by further study.

On the one hand, many of our present B vitamins were discovered to be needed by bacteria (folic acid, vitamin B_{12}, and biotin, for example) before we knew they were needed by animals.

On the other hand, many important growth factors for lower forms of life have no known role in vertebrate nutrition. These should not be considered as vitamins. Among them are the purines and pyrimidines, the bifidus factor, para-aminobenzoic acid, melvalonic acid, inositol, lipoic acid (thioctic acid), various sterols (including cholesterol), nucleosides, orotic acid, asparagine, carnitine, shikimic acid, and others.

Growth promotants are compounds that stimulate the growth of animals by indirect ways, usually by some type of action in the intestinal tract. Some may improve absorption or stimulate the synthesis of nutrients in the intestine. Some may prevent subclinical diseases—diseases that are present but do not severely affect an animal.

Such growth-promoting compounds as the antibiotics, surface-acting agents (such as ordinary detergents), organic arsenicals, several sulfa drugs, various drugs used for the prevention of coccidiosis, and other drugs act in this manner. These substances, not present in most natural foods, should not be confused with vitamins, which the body cells need for normal metabolism.

Some of the unidentified factors reported to be necessary for animals undoubtedly will fall into the class of growth promotants rather than vitamins when they eventually are isolated.

It is highly possible, for instance, that the so-called vitamin B_{13}, found in fermentation products and distiller's solubles, is really a growth promotant. The only way one can be sure is to characterize chemically the growth-stimulating compound and study it in animals in the laboratory.

A vitamin B_{14} and vitamin B_{15} have been mentioned since 1948, but their real importance to animal or human nutrition is not known, and the terms should be dropped until such information is available.

Known nutrients have been inadvertently rediscovered many times, because of inadequate levels of minerals or vitamins in experimental diets or because of nutritional imbalances. Because of the complexities of experimental work in this field, one should regard unconfirmed announcements of new unidentified factors with caution.

Nutritional knowledge has improved so much since 1930 that today animals are being reared on synthetic diets of known composition composed of highly purified ingredients—sugar, fat, proteins, vitamins, and minerals—with no natural foods at all. In fact, white rats and chickens have been carried through several generations on such diets.

These are convincing demonstrations that the most essential vitamins for these animals have been discovered, except perhaps the substances present in protein. Similar statements cannot be made for the guinea pig, the turkey, or the pig.

Studies with synthetic diets in human nutrition over long periods are especially incomplete.

Because we know that unidentified factors do exist in foods of plant and animal origin, it obviously is wisest to eat a wide variety of foods from the many excellent food groups—milk and milk products, meats, eggs and poultry, fish, cereals and grain products, vegetables, and citrus and other fruits. One who does this routinely does not need to eat vitamin pills or the so-called health foods (like wheat germ, molasses, yoghurt) to supply known nutrients and the unidentified factors that may be necessary for optimal health except on the advice of a physician or except by personal preference.

When scientists develop further information on the present unidentified factors in food, people will benefit.

Mutagenicity of Cycasin Aglycone (Methylazoxymethanol), a Naturally Occurring Carcinogen

David W.E. Smith

Cycasin (methylazoxymethanol-β-D-glucoside) is a carcinogenic and hepatotoxic compound occurring in plants of the family Cycadaceae. The frequent ingestion of various parts of these plants by people and domesticated animals in tropical parts of the world makes the compound of special interest [1]. In its naturally occurring form cycasin is a β-glucoside, but there is mounting evidence that it is the aglycone methylazoxymethanol that is actually toxic and carcinogenic, and that deglucosylation must be performed by intestinal microorganisms before the toxicity can be manifested [2]. Matsumoto and Higa [3] have demonstrated that methylazoxymethanol is a methylating agent, with 7-methylguanine being formed by its reaction with DNA or RNA. The genetic damage resulting from such methylation should be reflected in an increased mutation rate in the presence of this aglycone. The following results will show that methylazoxymethanol is a good mutagen in the bacterium *Salmonella typhimurium*.

Methylazoxymethanol was prepared from crystalline cycasin which had been purified from the seeds of *Cycas circinalis*. Enzymatic deglucosylation (almond emulsin, Sigma Chemical Co.) and purification were carried out according to the method of Kobayashi and Matsumoto [4]. The mutagenic activity of both cycasin and the aglycone was tested by measuring the frequency of reversion to histidine independence of several histidine-requiring mutants of *Salmonella* [5]. The bacteria were exposed to these compounds on petri plates which were prepared by mixing 0.2 ml of freshly grown cultures (2×10^9 bacteria per milliliter) of the mutants with 2 ml of 0.6-percent agar at 45°C. The soft agar, which contained a trace (0.20 μmole) of histidine as well as the bacterial inoculum, was then poured onto plates of a histidine-free minimal agar medium. The aglycone (1.5 mg), on a disc of absorbent filter paper, was introduced onto the surface of each plate after the agar had hardened.

In experiments with cycasin, 9 mg was applied to each disc, this amount being sufficient to release 3 mg of aglycone after deglucosylation. The trace of histidine present permits a small amount of growth so that zones of inhibition caused by some mutagens are visible around the discs. Revertant colonies usually could be seen clearly after 40 hours of incubation at 37°C, but on some plates the number of revertants increased between 40 and 70 hours, and revertants of one of. the mutants used, C 151, did not appear until 70 hours. A control plate containing no cycasin or its aglycone was prepared for each of the mutants tested. The spontaneous reversion rate of the mutants was low (0 to 15 colonies per plate).

Cycasin neither inhibited nor caused reversion in any of the mutants. This suggests that the *Salmonella* lack the necessary deglucosylating enzyme. In contrast, methylazoxymethanol caused all but two (C 120 and C 207) of the ten different mutants tested to revert. Most sensitive was G 46 (Figure 1), with hundreds of revertant colonies appearing; C 50 and D 130 were also quite sensitive, with about 100 colonies appearing on each plate. Only 20 to 40 colonies (3 to 5 times the number seen on control plates) appeared in tests with the other mutants (for example, C 496, C 527, and C 151). Zones of inhibition, 3 cm in diameter, surrounded the discs of the methylazoxymethanol. A mutagenic effect resulted in the obvious localization of the revertants just outside the zone of inhibition (Figure 1). These results were reproduced two to four times with each of the mutants.

Most of the mutants tested are known to have a histidine requirement because of the substitution of a single base in one of the genes coding for the enzymes of histidine biosynthesis [6]. These mutants are revertible with a variety of alkylating agents, and many are suppressible if amber and ochre suppressors are introduced. The mutant C 207, however, appears to be a reading-frame error [6], and alkylating agents including methylazoxymethanol do not cause it to revert.

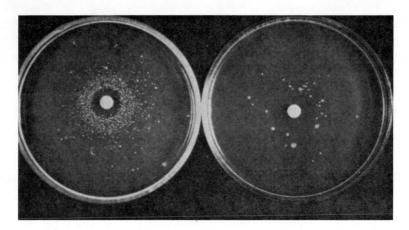

Figure 1. (Left) The numerous revertants of the mutant G 46 histidine independence as a result of exposure to methylazoxymethanol. (Right) The smaller number of revertants seen when less sensitive histidine-requiring mutants (C 496 in example shown) are placed under the same condition. The localization of mutants around the disc containing methylazoxymethanol is typical.

It is likely that in aqueous solution methylazoxymethanol breaks down, forming diazomethane, which is a well-known methylating agent [7], mutagen [8], and carcinogen [9]. Structurally related nitrosamides and nitrosamines, many of which are mutagenic, hepatotoxic, and carcinogenic, are also thought to be converted enzymatically and spontaneously to diazomethane [10].

Genetic damage, presumably by methylazoxymethanol, has also been described by Teas *et al.* [11] who showed that chromosome breakage occurred in onion-root tips treated with cycasin. Although it has not been demonstrated, mutation may occur in animals and humans ingesting cycasin, and mechanisms can be imagined by which both the carcinogenicity and hepatotoxicity of methylazoxymethanol could be consequences of the alkylation of DNA and RNA.

references

1. The toxicity of cycads was the subject of a conference reported in *Fed. Proc. 23,* 1337 (1964).

2. G. L. Laqueur, *ibid.,* p. 1386.

3. H. Matsumoto and H. H. Higa, *Biochem. J. 98,* 20c (1966).

4. A. Kobayashi and H. Matsumoto, *Arch. Biochem. Biophys. 110,* 373 (1965).

5. P. E. Hartman, J. C. Loper, D. Serman, *J. Gen. Microbiol. 22,* 323 (1960); P. E. Hartman, Z. Hartman, D. Serman, *ibid.,* p. 354; C. E. Kirchner, *J. Mol. Biol. 2,* 331 (1960).

6. H. Whitfield, R. G. Martin, B. N. Ames, *Fed. Proc. 25*, Part 1, 337 (1966).

7. O. M. Friedman, G. N. Mahapatra, B. Dash, R. Stevenson, *Biochem. Biophys. Acta 103*, 286 (1965).

8. K. A. Jensen, I. Kirk, G. Kølmark, M. Westergaard, *Cod Spring Harbor Symp. Quant. Biol. 16*, 245 (1951).

9. R. Scohental, *Nature 188*, 420 (1960).

10. H. Marquardt, F. K. Zimmerman, R. Schwaier, *Z. Vererbungslehre 95*, 82 (1964); H. Marquardt, *German Med. Monthly* (Engl. ed.) *10*, 107 (1965); P. N. Magee and R. Schoental, *Brit. Med. Bull. 20*, 102 (1964).

11. H. J. Teas, H. Sax, K. Sax, *Science 149*, 541 (1965).

8

Life Savers

As he brews, so shall he drink.

—BEN JONSON

In prehistoric times life expectancy at birth is thought to have been about 18 years. At the time of the Roman Empire the odds were that a person would live 25 to 30 years and, as late as 1900 in the United States, life expectancy was still less than 50 years. Today the life span of North Americans and Europeans is 70 to 72 years in terms of life expectancy at birth. Life is far shorter in many parts of the world. For example, a person born in southeast Asia can expect to live only 45 to 50 years and in western Africa the expectancy of life is merely 30 to 35 years.

The prospect of a long and healthy life in the more advanced parts of the world has many causes. Agricultural mechanization and the use of fertilizers control famine and greatly improve diet; prosperity is accompanied by better working conditions and protection from the elements; pesticides subdue the arthropod carriers of disease; and modern sanitation practices remove the sources of many of the most deadly microorganisms. Most spectacular of all the developments that prolong life and alleviate human suffering is the modern discovery and use of medicines.

Little more than a hundred years ago Pasteur, the French chemist-microbiologist, not only demolished the concept of spontaneous generation of life but, more importantly, derived the germ theory of disease. Great discoveries in medicine followed the initial scientific breakthrough from his studies in fermentation beginning in 1857 and from his work on the diseases of silkworms from 1865 to 1870. The basic techniques of asepsis and sterilization were worked out between 1860 and 1880 largely on the basis of Pasteur's work.

Vaccination had already been discovered before Pasteur was born but there was little knowledge of why it worked. The British physician Edward Jenner (1749–1823) was said to have diagnosed the ailment of a Gloucestershire dairymaid as smallpox whereupon she replied, "I cannot get smallpox because I have had cowpox." Many people in eighteenth-century England believed that if a person had cowpox, a skin disease contracted by contact with an infected cow, he or she could not thereafter contract smallpox. The incident set Jenner off on a systematic study of the protective effect of cowpox. He conducted experiments on human subjects and introduced the practice of immunization against smallpox by injecting material from the pustules of the cow. The word "vaccination" is derived from the latin *vacca* for cow.

Later, Pasteur found that old cultures of chicken cholera, which an unexpected interruption forced him to set aside during the summer of 1879, would no longer produce the disease when injected into chickens. He again injected the chickens with a culture of the cholera bacteria obtained from a natural outbreak of the disease. At the same time he injected the virulent culture into new chickens recently from the market. To Pasteur's astonishment only the new chickens succumbed to the disease. Pasteur was hot on the trail of the science of immunology. He devised a method of vaccinating for anthrax, a dreadful disease of livestock, developed a dramatic prophylaxis for rabies, and set the stage for the widespread prevention of disease by immunization as practiced in modern medicine.

Since the beginning of recorded history malaria has been man's worst enemy. Swamps and dank air were believed to have something to do with causing the disease. It was not until the early 1880's that Patrick Manson, a British physician in Hong Kong, made the observation that swamps were breeding places for mosquitos and suggested that there might be a connection between mosquitos and malaria. Ronald Ross, another British doctor in India, was intrigued by the idea and proceeded to prove that the *Plasmodium* of malaria passed part of its life cycle in the *Anopheles* mosquito. Ross was awarded the Nobel prize in 1902. Ross's discovery was one of the most revolutionary developments of modern medicine. For the first time, an arthropod was demonstrated to be the carrier of disease, and the knowledge made it possible to stop the disease by destroying the insect vector.

When in 1880 Charles Laveran, a French microbiologist, discovered
the protozoan parasite in the red blood cells of people who were
stricken with malaria, quinine from the bark of the cinchona tree was
already widely used as a remedy. The bark had been chewed by the
Indians of Peru to cure the disease. Quinine still is the most effective
treatment for some forms of malaria but chemists and biologists have
developed other potent medicines for the disease. Some of the drugs—
proquanil and pyrimethamine—prevent the parasite from becoming
established in the liver and, hence, are prophylactics. Others—mepa-
crine (atebrin), amodiaquin, and chloroquine[1]—act like quinine by
attacking the parasites in the red blood cells. Pamaquine and prima-
quine, in addition to having therapeutic value, kill the gametocytes, the
stage in the life cycle taken up with human blood by the mosquito. Mass
chemotherapy was tried in Brazil by adding chloroquine to salt similar
to the way iodine is used to prevent endemic goiter.

The protozoan parasite shows an amazing ability to develop resistance to drugs. Meanwhile, insecticides gradually lose their effectiveness
because of mounting resistance on the part of the mosquitos. The battle
against the parasitic *Plasmodium* and its partner and carrier, the
Anopheles mosquito, continues.

Few, if any, of the discoveries of medicine outrank the miracle of
antibiotics. Their development demonstrates the indirect way in which
science often reaches a useful objective. Alexander Fleming, a British
microbiologist, noticed one day that some of his cultures of the pus-
forming staphylococcus bacteria had formed spots in the agar nutrient
that were clear and free of any growth. Fleming may have been especially alert for he had already discovered the bactericidal properties of
an enzyme, lysozome, in teardrops. In the middle of the areas of no
bacterial growth, Fleming noticed there was a spot of fungus which
turned out to be the common bread mold, *Penicillium notatum*. Fleming's results were printed in 1929 but nobody at that time got very
excited over the aggressive nature of bread mold. Perhaps others had
absent mindedly observed the same thing many times. In fact, the
not-so-absent minded Pasteur long before noted the antibiotic properties of onion juice and wrote in his first paper published in 1857,
about how onion extract added to a sugar solution prevented the
growth of yeast. No one followed up the lead. It was not until 10 years
after Fleming's report that the British biochemist, Howard Florey, and

---

[1] See paper by Jennie Ciak and Fred E. Hahn.

his colleague, Ernst Chain, decided to embark on a serious investigation of the bread-mold mystery and isolated an extract that led to the development of what may have been the greatest of all medical contributions, penicillin. Fleming, Florey, and Chain were awarded the Nobel prize in 1945 for their contribution to medicine and physiology.

Medicines have been devised to treat nearly every affliction of man. *The Physician's Desk Reference*[2] lists over 2,600 pharmaceutical specialties, biologicals, and antibiotics. Mankind owes a debt of gratitude to the men and women who have made contributions to the discovery and development of health-giving medicines. That there are great risks in using such powerful and biologically effective substances is self-evident.

Medicines have become a way of life for millions of civilized men, women, and children. In America alone, drug industry sales reached nearly $10 billion in 1968 and computer calculations show that the volume is increasing at the rate of a billion dollars a year,[3] five times the population growth.

Most people are, or should be, grateful for the magic gift of health and life provided by the medicinal products of chemical and biological laboratories. Yet the shelves of the apothecaries have become filled with so bewildering an array of potent drugs intended for nearly every conceivable malfunction that even the experts have become alarmed at their potential for misuse. Any substance found to drastically modify cellular or physiological functions may have profoundly injurious effects as well. Such toxic or otherwise unwanted results are referred to in the medical trade as "side effects." Not infrequently, a second medicine is needed to counteract the side effects of the first, and a chain of undesirable events may take place that calls for a half dozen or more drugs to be administered simultaneously—by no means an unusual occurrence.

Aspirin (acetylsalicylic acid) is the most widely used drug in the world. At about a cent a tablet, it is also the cheapest. Americans consume an estimated 20 million pounds a year. Aspirin, alone and in combination with other tension-reducing drugs, helps to make life livable in what we call the modern civilized world. Moreover, it is one of the safest of medicines, having few side effects and being beneficial to adults

---

[2] *Published by Medical Economics, Inc.*

[3] *Arthur Poulos, "Booming Demand Adds Billions to Sales,"* Chemical & Engineering News: *93A–97A (September 4, 1967).*

and children alike. Of more concern are dozens of more potent chemical substances in medicinal use, some of which have profound physiological action. The margin of safety between therapeutic dose and serious damage is often alarmingly narrow and not always possible to estimate accurately.

The thalidomide episode (see Chapter 5) made the public sharply aware of the frightening possibilities of inadequate biological evaluations of medicines. Yet other drugs, less publicized, may be equally dangerous and may have caused as much suffering. An estimated billion dollars a year are spent on antibiotics alone. It is widely recognized that these potent products are often used for infections against which antibiotics are known to be ineffective, yet it is also well known that indiscriminate use of antibiotics is dangerous, not only by reason of the common occurrence of the development of allergic conditions but also because of the possibility of development of strains of pathogenic organisms that are resistant to the antibiotic. The practice of using antibiotics in agriculture and animal husbandry presents an additional and largely unknown hazard. Estrogenic materials used to promote weight gain in beef cattle are found in human fat.

Chloramphenicol is an antibiotic obtained from a species of the fungus *Streptomyces*, but it can also be synthesized. The drug has a broad spectrum of biological activity. Its sales reportedly achieved a volume of $86 million in one year. Before its use was restricted to treatment of typhoid fever—a disease for which no safe medicine exists —and as an alternate drug for treatment of certain other diseases, the antibiotic was found to be the cause of a form of aplastic anemia, often fatal, especially in children.

The effects of thalidomide and chloramphenicol are dramatic and well documented. Other examples are less spectacular and their effects may be more obscure. Tens of millions of men, women, and children have used and are using tranquilizers. Some of the most commonly used sedatives and tranquilizers can cause serious side effects, including coma, stupor, apathy, mood depression, toxicity, and changes in personality. Oral contraceptives are used by at least ten million women. Thrombophlebitis, a painful inflammation from a clot in a vein, has been linked in some cases to the use of oral contraceptives and the possibility of its occurrence has been highly publicized. Other side effects less widely reported are also matters of concern. All manufacturers warn physicians—not necessarily patients—against the use of oral contraceptives by breast-feeding mothers because detectable amounts have been found in the milk. Oral contraceptives contain steroids that affect the endocrine system and its many profound ramifications. Masculinization of the female fetus (or feminization of the male fetus) is a possibility that remains to be completely resolved.

The National Academy of Sciences–National Research Council announced in 1966 that at the request of the Food and Drug Administration it would undertake the evaluation of the effectiveness of 3000 to 4000 drugs introduced during the period from 1938 to 1962.[4] Beginning in 1962, amendments to the Food, Drug and Cosmetics Act required that manufacturers provide evidence supporting therapeutic claims. Similar evidence for drugs introduced between 1938 and 1962 was required by the amendments only when proof of safety was called for. Despite the tightened legal restrictions, an avalanche of new drugs descends on the public. In the meantime, the FDA struggles on the one hand with the demand for health potions and life savers and, on the other, with the injurious potential inherent in any biologically active chemical.

---

[4] Scientific American, *p. 42* (*August 1966*).

Establishing and Monitoring Drug Residue Levels

Fred J. Kingma

When a New Drug Application involving a drug intended for use in a food-producing animal is submitted to the Food and Drug Administration, personnel responsible for review are confronted with two basic problems: (1) Is the drug safe and effective for the animal when used as recommended? (2) Are edible products from the treated animal safe for human food?

Examination of Subpart D of the Food Additive Regulations will make it clear that practically all NDA's and food additive petitions for drugs intended for use in food-producing animals have been approved by the FDA because it was established that none of the drugs or their metabolites remained in the edible products from treated animals when the drugs were used as recommended. Almost invariably the elimination of the drug substance is accomplished after a certain number of hours or days following the last exposure to the material. In a few instances a safe tolerance, or permitted level, is established for the drug in edible products from the animal receiving the drug, thus shortening the withdrawal time.

Until proved otherwise, the addition of a new chemical entity to the diet of man—even· in apparently infinitesimal amounts—presents a potential hazard to health. Before the FDA permits the inclusion of such substances in the diet, convincing evidence of their safety must be submitted. Although certain routine or standard tests have to be included in a request for a tolerance in foods, it should be understood that each drug substance must be regarded individually. The individual

Reprinted from *FDA Papers*: July–August 1967 with permission of the author and publisher.

characteristics of each substance may dictate additional tests totally unforeseen when the safety testing program is originally planned and organized. FDA demands the submission of all data deemed necessary to demonstrate the absence of any human health hazard before establishing a permitted level of a drug in the diet of man.

The present minimum requirements for establishing a tolerance demand the demonstration of an adequate margin of safety in studies with two species of laboratory animals—one a nonrodent. The studies involve acute toxicity, subacute toxicity and chronic toxicity experiments—the latter of two years' duration. In most instances, a three-generation reproduction study is also required. Some drugs may require additional studies depending on their specific activity. This is especially true if the studies indicate a species variation.

acute toxicity studies

Acute toxicity is the effect which a drug or a compound produces when given to a test animal in single or multiple doses over periods of 24 hours or less. Multiple doses are required when the volume of the chemical or its solvent is too high for single administration. The most convenient expression of the acute toxicity of a substance is the ED50. This is the amount of the substance (usually expressed in milligrams, grams, or milliliters per kilogram of body weight) which, on the average, will affect one-half of a group of animals of a certain species under specified conditions. This standard of comparison was selected because the dosage required to effect a response in 50 percent of the animals is more reproducible than any other dosage.

Experience has shown that the ED50 will vary from species to species and with environmental conditions so that it is necessary to specify the conditions of the experiment. Species, habitat, route of administration, sex, age, weight range, and state of nutrition of the test animals, as well as the physical state of the chemical, solvent, and its concentration, are the conditions usually specified.

Although the effect most frequently reported is mortality (LD50), an acute toxicity determination is not necessarily limited to the estimation of the lethal dose. Any toxic manifestation, such as emesis, convulsions, hypnosis, etc., may be reported in terms of the ED50.

Because different species of animals and even various strains of the same species may differ widely in sensitivity to drugs, the LD50 should be determined on at least three species of animals, one of which should be nonrodent. An evaluation of these results will give a measure of the species variability, and thus permit the pharmacologist to estimate the toxicity of the test substance for man.

If all of the LD50's are of the same order of magnitude, it is usually safe to assume a similar LD50 for man. If, however, there is a wide variation of LD50's among species of test animals, the estimation of the probable LD50 for man is much more difficult.

In some cases the estimate can be based upon man's position in the phylogenetic scale in relation to the test animals. In other cases the estimate must be based upon biochemical and metabolic similarities of man with the test animals. For example, a chemical that may produce methemoglobinemia as its characteristic effect can be tested in the cat or dog, known to yield this response similarly to man. Tests in monkeys, rats, and rabbits, which are known to produce practically no methemoglobinemia in response to such chemicals as acetanilide and nitrobenzene, would obviously be of little value in estimating this particular hazard for man. Where adequate knowledge of similarities between man and the test animal is not available, it is safest to assume that man is at least as sensitive as the most sensitive species of animal tested.

Of all the factors which influence the LD50 of a drug, the route of administration is the one most apt to modify the toxic effects. For most chemicals the oral and intravenous LD50's are sufficient. However, for drugs which may enter the body by some other route, such as inhalation, the acute toxicity determination must be designed so that the results are applicable to actual use conditions. Other factors which influence absorption and, thus, indirectly the toxicity are: (1) the physical state of the drug—dry chemicals are more slowly absorbed than those administered in solution; (2) solvents—substances dissolved in oil are absorbed more slowly than those in water; (3) concentration of the drug—concentrated solutions are usually more rapidly absorbed than the administration of the same amount in a more dilute form; and (4) presence of other substances—suspending agents may hinder absorption partly by absorption of the drug, partly by blocking its access to the absorbing surface. Food in the alimentary tract has this action. On the other hand, the presence of surface active agents may hasten absorption.

In practice the chemical or drug is usually given orally to animals which have been fasted overnight. The substance may be administered by stomach tube, capsules, or by mixing with the animal's food. Where the recommended administration of the drug is by the parenteral route, the experimental administration of the drug (subcutaneous, intraperitoneal, intramuscular, or intravenous injections) must be related to the recommended usage. In no case is it necessary or advisable to anesthetize the animals in order to administer the test dose. The relationship between the intravenous and oral LD50 usually indicates the extent and rate of intestinal absorption.

The interpretation of the acute toxicity data for the purpose of estimating a safe or therapeutic dose is not based upon a simple mathematical formula. Among the factors which are weighed in evaluating the data are:

1. Adequacy of the data from a statistical viewpoint—a sufficient number of animals is employed so that the chemical can be characterized with respect to its LD50 and slope of the dosage-response curve and the errors of these estimates;

2. Interspecies variation—susceptibility of man as compared to the experimental animals; generally, man is six times as sensitive as the dog and 10 times as sensitive as the rat to the toxic effects of drugs;

3. Intraspecies variation—differences in susceptibility which normally occur in a general population (age, sex, state of health and nutrition, stress, etc.);

4. Usefulness of chemical or drug—whether the benefits derived warrant the risks.

subacute toxicity studies

Fitzhugh and Schouboe define subacute toxicity as the type of toxicity that produces functional and/or anatomical changes in animals when repeated exposure to a compound is experienced for periods ranging from a few days to a year. Subacute toxicity studies should be conducted after the acute and before the chronic toxicity studies are done. These experiments are designed to pinpoint the maximum tolerated and the minimum grossly toxic doses; establish the biological nature of the toxic effects; determine variations in species sensitivity; and permit decisions as to the desirability and exact design of chronic studies. Subacute experiments are designed to cover a 3-month period. In some special cases they are extended to 4 or 6 months or even to a year.

Properly designed and conducted, the subacute experiment will provide many of the basic observations for screening purposes, for an understanding of the pharmacology of the chemical, and for a guide for additional toxicity study. Even when chronic experiments are to be conducted later, the observations made here will help to evaluate the safety or the potential hazard of the substance. Therefore, a concentration of effort should be made in performing the subacute experiment to provide the best available information on the possible deleterious changes.

The first step in this procedure should be the literature search. A thorough understanding of the chemical nature, purity, and stability of the compound, the physiological activity of similar compounds, and a knowledge of techniques for measuring suspected chemical and biological changes is essential to the proper design of the experiment.

Another necessary step preliminary to the initiation of the subacute study is the range-finding experiment. Results of the range-finding experiment provide essential information on the order of magnitude of dosages to be selected. At this time two important decisions must be made: namely, selection of the experimental species, and route of administration.

The techniques employed should determine the effects of the compound, both anatomical and functional, if any. The lowest dosage level at which these effects occur should be determined. The evaluation of all effects in relation to dosage and use will indicate the desirability and the exact design of any proposed chronic toxicity experiments.

The following points should be observed when conducting subacute toxicity studies:

1. At least two species should be employed, one of which is a nonrodent.

2. Studies should be designed for at least 90 days.

3. At least three dosage levels should be used—plus a control group. One dosage level should be toxic.

4. If rats are employed, use at least 20 animals per group with the sexes equally divided. When dogs are employed, there should be at least two males and two females in each group when testing with drugs. This number must be doubled if a pesticide is being tested.

5. The following minimum observations should be made: growth, food consumption, general appearance and behavior, mortality, organ weights, clinical laboratory tests (blood, urine, organ function, enzymatic, and metabolic), and gross and microscopic tissue examinations.

All animals which die before the termination of the study should be subjected to careful and detailed gross and microscopic examination.

A successful study should establish the maximum tolerated dosage, the biological activity of the drug, and an estimate of the "no-effect" dosage.

chronic toxicity studies

The third of the basic or minimum studies essential when requesting the establishment of a tolerance for drug residues in edible products from treated animals is described by Fitzhugh. The purpose of such basic studies is to provide data adequate to evaluate the safety of drug residues when ingested by man. In this respect toxicity should be interpreted broadly to include *any* change from the normal. It may be a result of changes in nutritional values of the food as well as direct effects of the chemical on any of the physiological systems of the experimental animals. When a drug is to be used in conjunction with the intake of food, or in certain cases of repetitive usage, evidence must be obtained to indicate the absence of any chronic toxicity. When metabolic pathways are not known or cannot be explained, and where subacute toxicity tests have produced only minor effects, chronic toxicity tests should be carried out on the proposed drugs. Chronic tests, in contrast to subacute studies, will determine with certainty that we are not encountering a case where the effect of exposure to a *small amount* of a compound for a *long time* differs markedly from an exposure to a *large amount* of the drug for a *short time*.

If a drug appears in animal feeds, the following factors must be considered: the form in which the drug will be found in the animal; the concentration of the drug or harmful metabolite in edible parts of the animal; the form and concentration level at which the drug can be tolerated without adverse effect when ingested by humans for prolonged periods; the pharmacodynamics of the drug in the form in which it is encountered and how the drug is metabolized; any harmful metabolites that might be produced during the breakdown of the drug in the body; and the ultimate pathological manifestations, functional or organic, which might be expected from exposure to excessive quantities of the drug. In other words, the drug must *not only be safe for the animal, but also any drug residue, including metabolites, in the food must be demonstrated to be safe for man.*

The lowest dosage level is adjusted so that no damage can be expected to occur within the experimental period, and the highest dosage *should* cause some deaths. No general statement is adequate to define feeding levels for food additives, including pesticides. In most instances a drug must show "no effect" when fed for 2 years to the most sensitive laboratory species at a minimum of 100 times the requested tolerance before it can be permitted in the total human diet.

Although data from all dosages bear on the evaluation of safety, *only* the "no-effect" level in the most sensitive species can be used to establish the definite margin of safety. Where there is a broad interval between the "no-effect" dosage and the next one with a slight effect, this factor may cause an interpretation of toxicity greater than the actual.

In some studies it is desirable to sacrifice one or two rats of each sex at various intervals, such as 6, 12, and 18 months. If this is done, the total number in each group should not be reduced below 40 rats. Since the usual strain of albino rats is not inbred, weanling animals are assigned to the various groups according to litter mates. A litter of four males and four females, with a variation of no more than five grams within the litter, is distributed with one male and one female in each of the four groups as follows: (1) a control group; (2) a group on a low level which is expected to produce no damage; (3) a group in a middle level which may or may not produce damage; (4) a group on a high level which approaches the tolerated amount.

In a similar experiment, dogs are used in groups of eight each on the four dosage levels. Since there should be a minimum of four dogs remaining in each group at the termination of the experiment, the exact number used at the beginning depends upon the desirability of sacrificing animals during the experimental period and the accepted risk of losing animals from natural causes. Animals are selected from litters of young from a known breed, and are assigned in groups of four males and four females to each dosage in a manner which will give an even distribution according to age and weight.

A critical evaluation of all data on the effects of a compound, whether biochemical, pharmacological, or morphological, will permit a logical decision to be reached regarding any possible hazard resulting from the use of the proposed substance. Usually, for a substance proposed for use in food, the chronic experiments in *two* species of animals will be adequate for this evaluation. However, for certain types of additives, such as a drug residue in milk, a dietary constituent necessary for the very life of the young, the invalid, and the old, more extensive investigations are necessary. To assure an added margin of safety in this instance, supplemental studies are recommended as follows:

1. The regular reproduction studies which are described below for rats;

2. A breeding study in another mammal (dogs may be used in groups of two females each, with establishment of a "no effect" and a toxic dosage to the newborn and to the young up to 4 months of age);

3. A 90-day study in rats and dogs in which milk is a major component of the diet; and

4. Groups of animals with injured livers are given different test dosages of the drug to simulate conditions found when milk diets containing the drug are given to persons with liver ailments.

It must be remembered that chronic toxicity studies do not stand alone but are part of the overall picture, following and adding to information gained in acute, subacute, and biochemical tests, and possibly indicating the necessity of further work. Each drug tested presents different problems and must be approached in a sound and practical manner. Since the effect of a drug in man can never be predicted with certainty from other species, the effects on the most susceptible species will be adopted in making extrapolations. In the absence of reasonable certainty concerning a "no-effect" level for food additives, *no risk will be taken.*

The following points should be observed when conducting chronic toxicity studies:

1. At least two species should be employed, one of which is a nonrodent.

2. The studies should be designed to cover a 2-year period.

3. At least three dosage levels should be used—plus a control group. One dosage level should be toxic.

4. If rats are used, each group should consist of 50 animals with the sexes equally divided. When dogs are used, there should be at least four males and four females in each group.

5. The following minimum observations should be made: growth, food consumption, general appearance and behavior, mortality, organ weights, clinical laboratory tests (blood, urine, enzymatic, metabolic, and organ function, especially as related to the expected type of response demonstrated in short term tests), gross examination of ani-

mals throughout the experimental period, and gross and microscopic examination of tissues and organs at autopsy. Animals which die before the termination of the study should be similarly examined.

reproduction studies

Reproduction studies must be performed when requesting a tolerance for drug residues in edible products. These studies should be designed as follows:

1. A minimum of one species shall be used—two species are preferable.

2. There should be at least two dosage levels, plus a control group.

3. One of the dosage levels should be toxic, another should have no effect.

4. The group should consist of at least 20 females and 10–20 males.

5. The study should extend over three successive generations in the rat.

6. It is desirable to have two litters per generation.

7. Both the males and females should be treated for 60 days prior to breeding. The second and third generations are treated from weaning throughout the breeding period.

8. The following minimum observations must be made: fertility, length of gestation, number of live births, stillbirths, survival at 4 days and at weaning, sex of newborn and of weanlings, body weight, gross abnormalities, and microscopic examination of tissues of young in last generation (10 animals per group).

monitoring permissible drug
residue levels

Since the enactment into law of the Food Additives Amendment of 1958, tolerances for drug residues in edible products derived from treated animals have been established for about 50 drugs. Zero tolerances have been established for 45 of these drugs, and finite tolerances for five drugs: zoalene, amprolium, arsenic, chlortetracycline, and oxytetracycline.

Various meat and poultry products may be sampled and tested by the Government for any of these drugs at any time.

Recently, the FDA has requested and obtained considerable data regarding the duration of antibiotic residues in edible tissues of treated animals. The long withdrawal times needed for animals and poultry to excrete all traces of some of the antibiotics have convinced FDA that a large-scale residue surveillance program for antibiotic residues should be instigated.

This anticipated program will be a cooperative venture with the Consumer and Marketing Service, USDA. C & MS will do their sampling at the packing plants. A total of 5,200 samples per year, with approximately 3,900 red meat and 1,300 poultry samples, are to be analyzed for the presence or absence of antibiotic residues. The tissues will be tested for as many antibiotics as possible, including penicillin, streptomycin, chlortetracycline, and tylosin. The current procedure of sampling all carcasses which show possible injection lesions will continue. Carcasses and edible organs found to contain antibiotic residues will be condemned for food.

The FDA plans call for a random sampling of meat and poultry products at the retail level. This will include processed foods. When the results of this survey are compiled, we will then know if a hazard to human health actually exists.

Detoxication—Nature's Margin of Safety

L. C. Terriere

When one considers the vast array of drugs, cosmetics, preservatives, flavoring agents, dyes, surfactants, highway gases, pesticides, and nature's own complex materials to which man and the other animals are exposed, he could well become fearful that the chemicals in our environment are doing us harm. We indeed live in a chemical age and it is no wonder that the several crescendos of worry have occurred during the last 15 years. What we have forgotten in our concentration on this worry is that animal life has always encountered chemicals in its environment and that nature has evolved a defense against them.

When a foreign organic compound enters the animal body, it immediately becomes involved in a series of biochemical reactions designed to assist in its speedy removal from the tissues and cells. These reactions, often referred to as detoxication processes, are efficient, versatile, and ubiquitous. They are as much a natural defense against environmental dangers as the sensory and morphological defenses.

The modern entomologist encounters the processes of detoxication in several aspects of his professional and personal life. The specificity or selective toxicity of a toxicant; the resistance or tolerance of an insect to a toxicant; synergism, antagonism, and potentiation; and even the survival of higher animals ingesting poisonous substances all depend in part on the organism's complement of detoxication systems. Let us summarize our knowledge of these processes and then see how it applies to some of these phenomena.

As mentioned earlier, the animal organism is exposed to a wide variety of natural and synthetic chemicals not required in the life processes. Obviously these things must be eliminated from the organism

From a Paper before the Pacific Branch of the Entomological Society of America, Gearhart, Oregon, June 1963, with permission of the copyright owner and the author.

whether they are toxic or not. A variety of biochemical reactions are available to do this. In the process a foreign compound may be detoxified, a fortunate circumstance arising from the peculiar specificity of structure required of a toxicant. Thus the mere modification of a foreign compound in preparation for its transport and disposal from the cell or organ, at the same time will usually "disarm" or detoxify it. This is not always the case, especially as we view the individual steps in the detoxication reaction. What is important to remember at this point is that the specificity of structure of toxic compounds and the tendency of detoxication to modify structures go hand in hand in protecting an organism. Thus p,p **DDT** is toxic, p,p **DDE** is not—a slight change in the molecule neutralizes it.

detoxication reactions

Biochemically the detoxication process is one of transforming chemically inert, water insoluble compounds into water soluble compounds. In this state they can be transported to the excretory organs, pass through the necessary membranes, and out of the animal body. Normally such foreign compounds go through two stages of biochemical reactions as excretion is achieved. During the first stage the unreactive insoluble compound (toxicant) is modified by oxidation, reduction, or hydrolysis to become chemically reactive at one or more points. It's something like drilling the finger holes in a bowling ball, or attaching a handle to a briefcase or cooking utensil. Examples of these modifications are shown in the first figure.

First Stage Detoxication Reactions

Here we see three of the half dozen or so reactions by which hundreds of kinds of foreign molecules can be modified. In the first case a hydrocarbon is converted to a phenol. In the second case a phenol group is uncovered by the removal of a methyl radical and in the third case a nitro group is reduced to an amine. Thus the products of these three reactions are reactive molecules in contrast to their precursors which were comparatively inert.

At completion of the first stage of detoxication the compound may be more toxic but it will be in condition to enter the second stage, if necessary to further increase its water solubility or transportability. Some compounds may not require further modifications, for example, organic phosphate insecticides may be both detoxified and solubilized by hydrolysis reactions and are excreted without further change. If a further reaction is necessary it is one of synthesis. That is, the product of oxidation, reduction, or hydrolysis is connected to another compound to form an ester, amide, ether and so on. This new product will almost certainly be more water soluble and much less toxic than the original compound. Some examples of this stage are shown in the second

Second Stage Detoxication Reactions

$$R \langle \rangle OH + H_2SO_4 \longrightarrow R \langle \rangle OSO_3H$$

$$R \langle \rangle OH + gluc \longrightarrow R \langle \rangle O-gluc$$

$$R \langle \rangle NH_2 + HAc \longrightarrow R \langle \rangle \overset{H}{N}-Ac$$

figure. You will note that the second molecule involved in each of these reactions is of "natural" origin, i.e., it is a common amino acid, sugar, or salt, already present in the animal body. The handle or finger hole put in the toxicant molecule during stage one provides a connecting link with the natural amino acid, sugar or salt. Together the two make a new compound easily diffusable across membranes and sufficiently soluble in blood or other liquids to allow excretion without problems.

The various oxidative, reductive, hydrolytic, and synthetic reactions involved in detoxication are chemically simple. They are rather general reactions, too, the kind that nature uses in transforming one nutrient into another, in activating hormones, in building tissue. A perplexing question then is, what prevents the detoxifying reactions from going too far, running amok, modifying the natural and essential constituents of the cell? The most logical explanation so far advanced is that the detoxication processes are localized in non-aqueous tissues or behind lipoidal membranes. Thus only the fat soluble molecule gets into the detoxifying factory. Since nature's essential molecules are usually water soluble while the toxic or non-essential compounds are usually fat soluble, this unique arrangement provides a means of selecting the foreign compound for modification without at the same time destroying the desirable constituents.

Recent research, conducted since 1956, has lead us to the cell where important steps in detoxication occur. These are the microsomes, a sub-cell material much smaller than the nuclei or the mitochondria. I believe it is still safe to say that they are the smallest particles yet discovered in the cell. The microsomes are thought to be part of a membranous network in the cytoplasm. What we call the microsome is really a fragment of this membrane, created when we macerate and fracture the cell. Associated with the microsome as an organized particle is the ribosome where protein is synthesized. The microsome might be considered a piece of lipoidal membrane in which is enmeshed ribosome particles. The detoxifying enzymes are probably located in the lipoidal membrane. Microsomes are prepared for study by first thoroughly macerating the tissue. Liver is a rich source in higher animals —although in studying insects we of course must use the entire animal. After the homogenization, which liberates or creates the microsomes, they are separated from the other tissues and cell particles by high speed centrifugation in the cold. Centrifugal forces of 90 to 100 thousand times gravity are required.

detoxication by microsomes

Detoxication has been studied for over 100 years and until recently the method has been to feed the drug or toxicant in question, collect excretory products, and examine them for fragments or products of the original compound. In this way, the various transforming reactions available to animals have been pieced together. This approach is still popular and productive, especially with the use of radioactive test compounds. The discovery of the microsome as a site of detoxication has opened a new avenue of study. It is now possible to get at the enzymes themselves under controlled conditions and in a quantitative manner never before realized.

The method is very simple, once the microsomes are isolated. This done, one mixes the compound he is studying with some microsomes, a few essential chemicals and in a few minutes returns to examine the results. Tracer methods, gas chromatography, and spectrophotometry are put to work to identify the products.

The point of all this is that when an animal ingests a foreign organic molecule, a variety of biochemical processes go into action so as to relieve the animal of this unwanted molecule. It is a rare compound, indeed, which cannot be so modified. The extent of and speed of these various reactions determines how long the foreigner remains in the tissues and how extensive its deleterious effect shall be.

detoxication mechanisms of insects

With this background and review of the biochemistry of detoxication, let us now turn to the insect and see what this animal can do in protecting itself against the chemicals of its environment. Our own laboratory has been quite active in this field but we were preceded by some ten years by others, especially a group in England, that of J. N. Smith [1]. As a result of their investigations of some fifteen species, mainly Orthoptera, Coleoptera, Lepidoptera and Hemiptera, these workers have found that insects oxidize, reduce, hydrolyze, and conjugate non-essential materials very much according to previously known pathways. One exception, which has been labeled a biochemical peculiarity of insects, is the formation of glucosides (using glucose) instead of glucuronides (using glucuronic acid).

Our own interest in the detoxication mechanisms of insects began when we attempted to follow the metabolism of DDT by resistant and susceptible houseflies. We found that DDT was detoxified and excreted as a water soluble and hydrolyzable metabolite, indicating that conjugation has occurred. We made little progress beyond this point, however, because the chemistry of this compound was so complex and the biochemical defenses of the insect so mysterious. We decided we should go back to the beginning and learn more about the basic biochemical reactions utilized by insects. We were interested in the hydroxylation of aromatic compounds because it would provide in one simple reaction a means of detoxifying a variety of insecticides and thus might explain resistance and cross tolerance.

The next experiments were therefore made with a simple compound, naphthalene. To be metabolized and excreted, this compound almost had to be hydroxylated because it had no handles at all. The results of our studies with naphthalene are summarized in the following figures and tables.

Detoxication of Naphthalene—First Stage

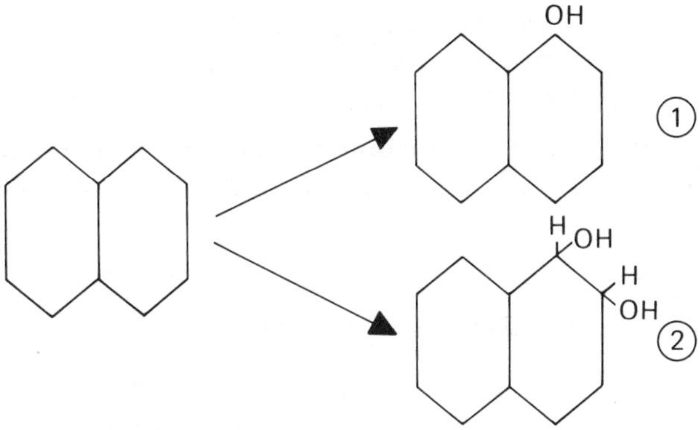

Detoxication of Naphthalene—Second Stage

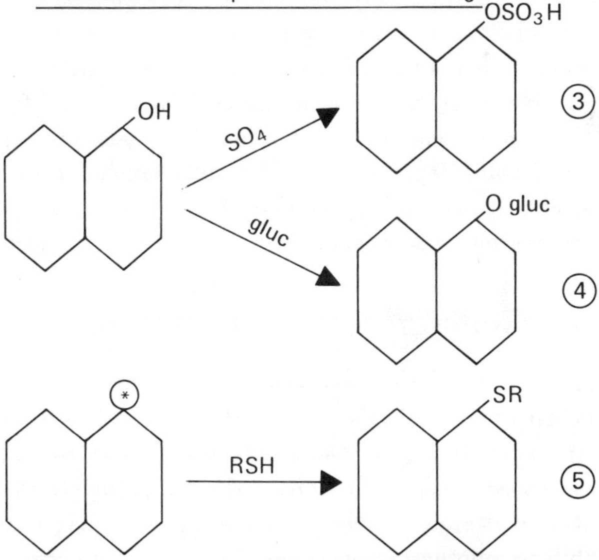

We were pleased to find that houseflies metabolize naphthalene in much the same way, qualitatively, as the higher animals in which this compound has been extensively studied. Several of the classical second-ary synthetic steps are used as well as the important primary step, hydroxylation. There is good evidence that flies convert naphthalene into glucuronides, thus contradicting the theory that insects are abnormal in this respect. We are still working on this to gain confirmation of it and we are still trying to clinch other aspects of the picture.

Having learned that flies do hydroxylate the aromatic ring, we began a study of this primary process using microsomes. We have performed many experiments with this tiny fragment of the insect cell.

Our original hypothesis that hydroxylation might be a key to the resistant insect's ability to defy groups of insecticides seems to be holding up. Microsomes of DDT resistant flies hydroxylate naphthalene three or four times more rapidly than S flies. Blowflies, which apparently do not become resistant to chlorinated hydrocarbons, contain microsomes which are only one tenth as active as those of houseflies.

detoxication and resistance

From what has already been said, we need only to tie up some loose ends to see how detoxication fits into the picture of an insect's resistance to an insecticide. Detoxication is done by enzymes and the production of enzymes is controlled by genes. In an environment contaminated with insecticides the insect with the best complement of detoxication processes will survive, pass this inheritable trait on to his offspring, and thus start a process wherein detoxication methods are concentrated. The resulting populations are thus able to detoxify lethal amounts of insecticides. There are other avenues by which resistance may be gained, of course, but this is certainly one of the most important.

synergism and detoxication

Early theories of synergism were several in number. One held that the synergist sensitized the tissue at the site of action of the toxicant, increasing its susceptibility to the poison. Another theory was that the synergist improved the penetration of the cuticle by the toxicant. In more recent years several authors have suggested that the synergists acted by inhibiting detoxication of the pesticide. If we keep in mind the biochemical activities of a cell exposed to a toxicant, we can see how this latter theory operates. A toxicant immediately undergoes two general types of activities once it enters the insect body; a toxication and a detoxifying action. The latter process "wastes" some of the toxicant molecules preventing their deleterious effect. Thus if the detoxifying action is stopped by a synergist, more molecules are available for the lethal action. This would explain the principal characteristic of synergistic mixtures—greater activity by the mixture than by either component alone.

Proof of the anti-detoxifying theory is now coming in. Dr. Sun [2], of Shell Chemical Corp., has advanced evidence of this using the pyrethrin synergists and a wide variety of organic phosphate and chlorinated hydrocarbon insecticides. He has found that compounds which need activation for maximum effectiveness, such as the conversion of parathion to paraoxon, are antagonized, that is, made less toxic, by the pyrethrin synergists. On the other hand, compounds which are active per se are frequently greatly synergized, up to 15 or more times. In either case the synergist is thought to be interfering with a biochemical reaction, activating the toxicant on the one hand and inactivating, or detoxifying it on the other. Some data from Dr. Sun's paper is shown in the following table.

Synergism and Antagonism By Sesamex

Insecticide	Co-Tox Coef [a]
Phosphamidon	14.6
Me-Parathion	0.41
Me-Poraoxon	1.8
Aldrin	0.60
Dieldrin	1.6
Heptachlor	0.57
Hep-Epoxide	1.3

[a] Toxicity with synergist divided by toxicity without synergist.

We should be able to show support for the anti-detoxication theory of synergism in our experiments with microsomes. If hydroxylation is an important reaction in the detoxication of insecticides, a synergistic compound might be a strong inhibitor of it. This has proven to be the case. The same four pyrethrin synergists tested by Dr. Sun have been used at very small concentrations in our test tube experiments with housefly microsomes and have been found to prevent the hydroxylation of naphthalene.

Taking this hypothesis a step further, one would conclude that if hydroxylation is an important detoxifying step in the fly's metabolism of naphthalene and the pyrethrin synergists prevent this process, then it should be possible to make naphthalene more toxic to houseflies by using it with such synergists. The next table shows typical results when such experiments were performed. It can be seen that the four synergists did increase the toxicity of naphthalene, although they varied considerably in this respect.

Housefly Toxicity of Naph + Synergist

Synergist Pre. Treat	Mort, % ⟶	
	without Naph (no naphthalene)	*+2 Hrs. Exp. Naph*
None	0	0
Sesoxane, 1 m %	7	46
Pip-Butoxide, 1 ml %	9	50
Sulfoxide, 2 ml %	7	28
N-Propyl Isome 5 ml %	3	23

Dr. Hoskins [3] and co-workers have observed that the insecticide, Sevin, is synergized by the pyrethrin synergists. This may be due to inhibitory reactions such as those described here since hydroxylation has been shown to be an important step in the metabolism of this insecticide.

I believe it will be clear now how the biochemical reactions occurring in the cell—the ones we call detoxication processes—protect the insect. A little reflection will show how these processes help explain selective toxicity or the specificity of action of toxicants. Some workers are now beginning to use their knowledge of detoxication differences between species to develop toxicants with wider margins of safety between the higher animals and our insect pests. Malathion has provided a clue to how this is to be done. I am quite confident that progress towards the selective pesticide, safe to man and wild life, livestock, and beneficial insects, but effective against insect pests, will come as a result of further comparisons of detoxication mechanisms.

detoxication in higher animals

Now that we have seen how detoxication works biochemically and how it fits into some of the biological phenomena, let's turn to the higher animals for evidence of its operation. There is plenty of evidence that the detoxication processes protect the higher animals. When you take an aspirin tablet, does it protect you against headaches from that point on? Or when your doctor gives you a narcotic as an anesthetic do you remain asleep indefinitely? Of course the answer to these questions is no. It is true, in fact, that your doctor depends upon these biochemical defenses to neutralize and eliminate such drugs soon after they are taken so that side effects will be minimal. Drugs are actually designed with these detoxication processes in mind in order to take full advantage of their protective action. Many well-informed people know very well that pesticides are detoxified by the human body just as are the cosmetics, drugs, pigments, dyes, surfactants, preservatives, flavoring agents and so on. Pesticide residues do not remain in the body like so many chunks of slag. They are metabolized, detoxified, and excreted.

It has been known for years that DDT is metabolized to DDA in the vertebrate animal. While this route of detoxication might not have been predicted by biochemists they should now take some comfort in its discovery because it illustrates once again that our detoxicative defenses are indeed versatile. This relatively inert, insoluble toxicant is made into a polar compound of considerably greater water solubility. Details of its excretory state, that is, whether it is a conjugate, may still be vague, but excreted it is, that is certain. There is evidence that other things also happen in the way of detoxication of DDT for men given DDT regularly for several months dispose of 75 percent of it in some manner, only one-fifth to one-seventh by way of DDA.

Over 100 humans have been used in studying the intake and excretion of DDT. Intake levels ranged from the normal dietary level of DDT, about 0.2 mgs per day, to 200 times that amount, 35 mgs per day. Other subjects encountered DDT in their work—in manufacturing or applying it. The data from these tests show that as the DDT intake increases, its detoxication to DDA also increases. This is shown in data from a recent paper by Ortelee [4]. The conversion of DDT to DDA is so dependable, according to these scientists that the urinary excretion of DDA can be used as a measure of exposure to DDT. The men studied in these tests had DDT exposure histories up to 8 years in length yet showed no measurable ill effects or symptoms.

Fate of DDT in Humans

Treatment, Mgs/Day	Total Intake, 1 Year	Total Stored, 1 Year	Intake Retained	Excreted as DDA
	gms	gms	%	%
0 (.18)	0.06	0.15	—	—
3.5	1.28	0.61	47	10
35.0	12.8	3.28	26	19

The next table has been prepared from data found in Hayes [5] and Durham's paper describing their experiments with human volunteers fed DDT. We can see here that about 75 percent of a 35 mg per day dose will have been eliminated in some form by the end of the first year. This kind of data, like that shown by Ortelee correlating DDT intake with DDA output, supports the idea that detoxication mechanisms are self-adjusting, picking up larger proportions of toxicants as the intake increases.

The metabolism of dieldrin has been difficult to trace until just recently, leading to the impression that this compound is biochemically inert. Recent experiments [6], however, show that this is not the case. Humans exposed to dieldrin excrete at least two metabolites in the urine, metabolites more polar than their precursor, just as the student of detoxication would have predicted.

In the case of parathion, PHS workers [7] have found that its conversion to and excretion as p-nitro phenol is so reliable and efficient that urine tests for this metabolite are more accurate indicators of exposure than cholinesterase measurements. Subjects tested were excreting PNP long before cholinesterase levels were affected. Here is another good example of the body's detoxication at work. In this case it is the hydrolysis function that we mentioned as one of the primary reactions. The detoxifying capacity by this route is at least 10 mgs of parathion per day. This would be the equivalent of the parathion ingested in eating 20 pounds of food containing 1 ppm.

Still another example of insecticide detoxication by humans [8] is that of malathion. Like parathion this organic phosphate is transformed into fragments by hydrolyzing enzymes. About one-fourth of a heavy dose of malathion is excreted in 8 hours.

There are not many instances where tests with humans have been used to study detoxication of pesticides. There are, of course, numerous examples with experimental animals, nearly always providing evidence that such processes do occur. These tests do bring out one fact of life that sobers any optimistic feeling that detoxication is a guarantee in all cases. It has been found that detoxication capacities and routes vary, from species to species, individual to individual, and even with respect to sex and age. We find, for example, that aged flies (microsomes) can hydroxylate naphthalene 5 times faster than one day old insects. In work with the microsomes of male and female rats, we find that males epoxidate aldrin four times more rapidly. Pharmacologists have seen these aberrations between species and sexes in studies with narcotic drugs. Such differences are, in fact, one of the main sources of drug and pesticide specificity. We must recognize, therefore, that the sword cuts two ways and not proceed on the blithe assumption that nature's detoxication mechanisms will protect all animals equally well. This is certainly one of the reasons for conservatism in the establishment of tolerances.

When one pulls all considerations together, he finds himself with these facts and concepts: foreign organic molecules are actively modified and excreted by the animal ingesting them; no compound with any toxic or biochemical value is completely inert to degradative reactions; animals survive or succumb depending in part, at least, on the versatility and efficiency of their detoxication processes; and, animals differ in their detoxication powers. Summing this up, it seems to me that detoxication is a definite and reliable defense mechanism and that used with reason by man, can provide him with a real margin of safety in an environment contaminated with chemicals.

references

1. J. N. Smith, *Annual Review of Entomology, 7:* 465 (1962).
2. Yum-Pei Sun and E. R. Johnson, *Agricultural and Food Chemistry, 8(43):* 261 (1960).
3. W. M. Hoskins, R. Miskus, and M. E. Eldefrawi, *Science, 129:* 898 (1959).
4. M. F. Ortelee, *A.M.A. Archives of Industrial Health, 18:* 433 (1958).
5. W. J. Hayes, Jr., W. F. Durham, and C. Cueto, Jr., *J. of the American Medical Association, 162:* 890 (1956).
6. C. Cueto, Jr. and W. J. Hayes, Jr., *Agricultural Food Chemistry, 10:* 366 (1962).
7. J. D. Arterberry, W. F. Durham, J. W. Elliott, and H. R. Wolfe, *Archives of Environmental Health, 3:* 476 (1961).
8. A. M Mattson and V. A. Sedlak, *Agricultural and Food Chemistry, 8(2):* 107 (1960).

Chloroquine: Mode of Action

Jennie Ciak
Fred E. Hahn

The antimalarial drug, chloroquine [Resochin, 1], forms a complex with DNA [2, 3] and inhibits in vitro reactions catalyzed by DNA polymerase [4], RNA polymerase [4], and deoxyribonuclease [3]. It also inhibits incorporation of P^{32}-orthophosphate into the nucleic acids of two plasmodia [5]. Although bacteria are relatively insensitive to the drug [6] we have found a strain of *Bacillus megaterium* to be susceptible to chloroquine [7] and have studied the mode of action of the drug with this organism; these studies are the subject of this report.

Addition of chloroquine to cultures of *B. megaterium* in exponential growth resulted in rapid decline in bacterial viability (Figure 1). During the first 20 minutes after addition of the drug, bacterial density, measured turbidimetrically, increased approximately 10 percent and then remained constant. Chemical analyses for DNA [8] and RNA [9] of bacteria in samples of culture taken at intervals showed not only that nucleic acid biosynthesis was blocked by chloroquine but also that the bacteria lost approximately 10 percent of their total RNA during 1 hour of exposure. When global RNA was labeled with uracil-C^{14}, radioactive label was lost progressively from chloroquine-exposed organisms but not from drug-free control bacteria (Figure 2). During 1 hour of incubation, this loss amounted to 10 percent of the total radioactivity present; the result is in agreement with the results of chemical analyses for RNA.

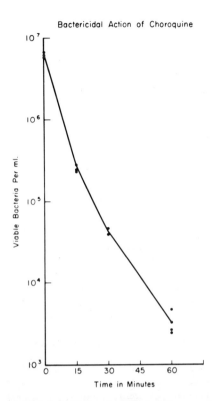

Figure 1. Decrease in viability of chloroquine-treated *B. megaterium*. The test strain 46-U-1 (furnished by the Department of Bacteriology of Walter Reed Army Institute of Research) was grown in Sauton's medium [16] in which DL-glutamic acid was replaced by the L-isomer, and 0.2 percent glucose was substituted for glycerol. Chloroquine was added as the hydrochloride (a commercial product) to exponentially growing cultures to a concentration of $10^{-3}M$; samples were removed at intervals for serial dilution plate counting.

Chromatographic analysis of the phenol-extracted global nucleic acids revealed that *B. megaterium*, upon exposure to chloroquine for 1 hour, dissimilated all 16S and most of the 23S ribosomal RNA's; transfer-RNA and DNA were not degraded (Figure 3). Evidently only a small fraction of the ribosomal RNA was degraded to products sufficiently small to be excreted by the test bacteria; most of the ribosomal RNA remained inside the bacterial cells in the form of products of no preferred molecular size. This dissimilation of ribosomal RNA suggested that the ribosome particles themselves were breaking up. Figure 4 depicts the time course of ribosome degradation in chloroquine-exposed *B. megaterium* and indicates that the organisms de-

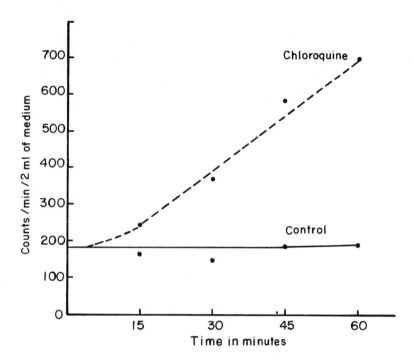

Figure 2. Release of radioactivity from *B. megaterium* labeled with uracil-C[14] upon incubation with chloroquine ($1.6 \times 10^{-3}M$). The bacteria were grown for 2 hours in modified Sauton's medium (Figure 1) containing 332 μg/liter of uracil-C[14] of specific activity 0.7 μc/μmole; they were then collected and resuspended in fresh uracil-free medium with (top line) or without (bottom line) added chloroquine. Radioactivities were measured in membrane filtrates of samples taken at intervals; a Nuclear-Chicago liquid scintillation counter and a dioxane-based scintillation fluid were used.

graded 70 percent of their ribosomes during the first 10 minutes of drug action.

When phenylalanine-C[14] was supplied to test cultures immediately before addition of chloroquine and the radioactivities of the bacterial proteins were determined at intervals by a membrane filter technique [10], no significant quantities of the amino acid were incorporated. The conclusion that protein synthesis was inhibited is in accord with the observation that bacterial density failed to increase significantly after addition of chloroquine.

Oxidation of glucose by washed suspensions of *B. megaterium* as measured manometrically [11] was inhibited by only 10 percent at a bactericidal concentration of chloroquine of 7.8×10^{-4} mole/liter. A graphic probit transformation [12] of inhibition of oxygen consump-

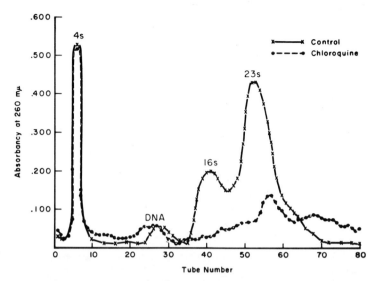

Figure 3. Chromatographic analysis of nucleic acids of *B. megaterium* incubated for 1 hour with $1.6 \times 10^{-3}M$ chloroquine (solid circles) or without the drug (crosses). Bacteria were collected and disrupted by sudden release from hydrostatic pressure in a French pressure cell (Aminco). Nucleic acids were obtained by phenol extraction [17] and chromatographed on a methylated albumin-kieselguhr column [18] by elution with a linear gradient of NaCl from 0.5 to 1.0*M*, buffered with phosphate at *p*H 6.7.

tion as a function of chloroquine concentration yielded a straight line with a value of ED_{50} (the 50-percent effective dose) of 760 μg/ml, that is, 2.4×10^{-3} mole/liter. Evidently the inhibitions of macromolecular biosyntheses we report are not results of a general anabolic failure owing to blocking of electron-transfer reactions; oxidative phosphorylation is insensitive to chloroquine in cells whose growth is inhibited by the drug [13].

Our finding that DNA synthesis in bacteria is inhibited in vivo by chloroquine is in essential agreement with observations that incorporation of radiophosphate into nucleic acids of plasmodia is inhibited by this drug [5]; blockage of DNA replication per se explains, in our opinion, the bactericidal effect of chloroquine.

The breakup of ribosomes and the dissimilation of ribosomal RNA were unexpected findings, although another instance is known [14] in which blocking of DNA replication was accompanied by similar phenomena. Degradation of ribosomes and their RNA in our experiments with chloroquine explains the observed net loss of RNA from *B. mega-*

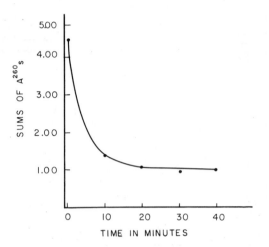

Figure 4. Decrease in ribosome content of *B. megaterium* during exposure to chloroquine ($1.6 \times 10^{-3}M$). Samples (1000 ml) of experimental mass cultures were taken at intervals, the bacteria were collected and disrupted as described in the legend to Figure 3, and the samples were clarified by low-speed centrifugation and dialyzed for 24 hours at 4° C against a buffer mixture introduced by Nirenberg and Matthaei into experimentation with ribosomes [19]. The samples were then subjected to molecular sieve analysis [20] by being placed on columns of Sephadex G-100 and eluted with fresh buffer. Relative quantities of ribosomes in eluted fractions were estimated spectrophotometrically (wavelength 260 mμ), and the sums of the absorbancies (A^{260}s) in fractions comprising entire ribosomal peaks were plotted as a function of the time of bacterial exposure to chloroquine.

terium as well as the failure of protein synthesis and may have contributed to the bactericidal effect of the drug upon this organism.

We propose that inhibition of DNA replication, based upon a direct action of the drug on DNA, is the general mode of antimicrobial action of chloroquine. This idea has certain implications for observations of natural or acquired resistance to the drug. The molecular architecture of double-stranded DNA is evidently universal, and susceptibility or resistance to chloroquine cannot be explained on the basis of structural or compositional differences between the DNA's of susceptible or resistant cells. It is more likely that susceptibility to chloroquine, like that to actinomycin D [15], is based upon the capacity of susceptible cells to permit passage and accumulation of critical concentrations of the drug while natural or acquired resistance may be results of impermeability or of an impaired concentration mechanism. This is borne out by two observations. (i) Chloroquine-exposed and packed cells of susceptible *B. megaterium* contained ten times as much of the drug as did identical volumes of packed, chloroquine-resistant *B. cereus* [11]. (ii) The

DNA-polymerase reaction in cell-free experiments in vitro is highly susceptible to chloroquine [4] in spite of the fact that the priming DNA as well as the enzyme has been prepared from *Escherichia coli* which is resistant to chloroquine [6].

references and notes

1. H. Andersag, S. Breitner, H. Jung, German patent 683, 692 (1939).

2. F. S. Parker and J. L. Irvin, *J. Biol. Chem. 199*, 897 (1952); D. Stollar and L. Levine, *Arch. Biochem. Biophys. 101*, 335 (1963); S. N. Cohen and K. L. Yielding, *J. Biol. Chem. 240*, 3123 (1965); J. L. Allison, R. L. O'Brien, F. E. Hahn, *Science 149*, 1111 (1965).

3. N. B. Kurnick and I. E. Radcliffe, *J. Lab. Clin. Med. 60*, 669 (1962).

4. S. N. Cohen and K. L. Yielding, *Proc. Nat. Acad. Sci. U.S. 54*, 521 (1965).

5. K A. Schellenberg and G. R. Coatney, *Biochem. Pharmacol. 6*, 143 (1961).

6. F. Kradolfer and L. Neipp, *Antibiot. Chemothap. 8*, 297 (1958); L. B. Robinson, T. M. Brown, R. H. Wichelhausen, *ibid. 9*, 111 (1959); V. Houba and M. Adam, *Cas. Lek. Ceskych 103*, 540 (1965).

7. J. Ciak and F. E. Hahn, *Fed. Proc. 24*, 454 (1965).

8. Z. Dische, "Color reactions of nucleic acid components," in *The Nucleic Acids*, E. Chargaff and J. N. Davidson, Eds. (Academic Press, New York, 1955), vol. 1, p. 285.

9. W. Mejbaum, *Z. Physiol. Chem. 258*, 117 (1939).

10. C. Levinthal, A. Keynan, A. Higa, *Proc. Nat. Acad. Sci. U.S. 48*, 1631 (1962).

11. These experiments were carried out by Dr. R. L. O'Brien of [the Department of Molecular Biology, Walter Reed Army Institute of Research].

12. H. P. Treffers, *J. Bacteriol. 72*, 108 (1956).

13. H. Greiling and G. Doerner, *Z. Rheumaforsch. 21*, 316 (1962); M. W. Whitehouse, *J. Pharm. Pharmacol. 15*, 556 (1963); M. W. Whitehouse and H. Boström, *Biochem. Pharmacol. 14*, 1173 (1965).

14. H. H. Kersten and W. Kersten, *Z. Physiol. Chem. 334*, 141 (1963); H. Suzuki and W. W. Kilgore, *Science 146*, 1585 (1964).

15. B. Mach and E. L. Tatum, *Science 139*, 1051 (1963).

16. F. E. Hahn, C. L. Wissman, Jr., H. E. Hopps, *J. Bacteriol. 67*, 674 (1954).

17. A. Gierer and G. Schramm, *Nature 177*, 702 (1956).

18. J. D. Mandell and A. D. Hershey, *Anal. Biochem. 1*, 66 (1960).

19. M. W. Nirenberg and J. H. Matthaei, *Proc. Nat. Acad. Sci. U.S. 47*, 1588 (1961).

20. M. Takanami and G. Zubay, *ibid. 51*, 834 (1964).

21. We gratefully acknowledge the technical assistance of H. L. Whitfield and Angelo Zegna and the efforts of the Medical Audio-Visual Department of [the Walter Reed Army Institute of Research] in producing the figures.

9

Pests or People

You might as well say that's a valiant flea that
dare take his breakfast on the lip of the lion.
—ORLEANS, IN *Henry the Fifth*

Insects, rats, worms, snails, and similar vermin are the most prolific
and competitive creatures on the face of the earth. Those that plague
man and domestic animals and plants belong to a broad spectrum of
animal life from the simplest protoplasmic cells to successively more
complex forms, including people. Fungi and many higher plants are
also "pests" depending on which viewpoint is taken, that of the aggres-
sor or that of the victim.

There are two widely held misconceptions concerning living things
that, together, might be said to constitute the pseudoscience of biomythology. The first myth is that parasitism is an unnatural condition of
animals and plants. The exact opposite is true, for competitiveness is
one of the most characteristic features of living things. Some have
learned to live off the labors of others. Animal life depends on chlorophyll produced by higher plants; however, some plants cannot produce
chlorophyll and must live off those that can; some animals cannot
survive except at the expense of the flesh and blood of others that have
derived their sustenance from plants. Parasites, predators, and pathogens are ever present and are a normal part of the biosphere including
the microsphere of man.

The other great misconception of biomythology is the idea of the
"balance of nature." Nature, especially with respect to animals and
plants, is molded by incredibly powerful forces. Dynamic change is the
second, or perhaps the foremost, characteristic feature of living things.

Climates change; habitats change; genes change; chromosomes change; new species appear and thrive, then perish from the earth. There is no "balance"—only the brutal impact of the carnival of forces that create, modify, and destroy not only individuals, but entire populations of animals and plants.

Man has always sought advantageous ways to upset the forces of nature: selection and cultivation of plants, drainage of swamps, diversion of rivers, and irrigation of crops. Sometimes, however, he displays poor judgment, as when he chops down a forest and lets the soil erode and go to weeds, or when he builds a city and neglects to leave enough open spaces or to provide for prevention and disposal of pollutants. But man has exhibited perhaps his most diligent ingenuity in trying to thwart the multitude of pests that strive to deprive him of food, fiber, shelter, and health.

"Over one-thousand million human beings live and die without ever having a really adequate amount of the right kind of food."[1] Moreover, it is estimated that 10,000 people, including children, starve to death every day. Yet with mankind increasing at the rate of 7,000 babies an hour, or at about 100 per minute, most of the food grown would be harvested by pests if the war against them were not diligently pursued.

The most abundant of all the pests are the arthropods (jointed-leg invertebrates), which alone comprise 700,000 known species, three times the number of all other animals combined. Spiders, centipedes, scorpions, mites, ticks, and insects are arthropods. It is not surprising that so numerous an aggregation of crawling creatures include many that test the ingenuity of man, for survival depends on adequate protection against their depredations.

Many of the crawling and other lowly organisms are beneficial to man. For example, clams, lobsters, and crabs are edible, earthworms and other primitive earth dwellers help fertilize the soil, insects pollinate food crops, and, of great economic importance, the shells of small marine organisms that lived in abundance when deep seas covered the continents built vast deposits of limestone and chalk.

In contrast, other creatures of their kind are some of the most malevolent enemies of man. Their depredations on agricultural crops have always demanded ceaseless battle. Malaria organisms, blood flukes, and intestinal parasites of various kinds, as well as insects and

---

[1] The World Must Eat, *United Nations' Study Guide* (1962).

related species that transmit diseases, have caused pestilence and death throughout the history of mankind.

Of the ten biblical plagues of Egypt, three were insect pests. As related in the Book of Exodus, ". . . the dust became lice in man and in beast throughout all of the land," ". . . there came a grievous swarm of flies [mosquitos?] into the house of Pharaoh and the land was corrupted," ". . . The east wind blew and when it was morning the locusts went up over all the land."

The decline of civilization in ancient Rome is attributed partly to decimation and loss of vigor and vitality from malaria. There and elsewhere through the centuries the anopheline mosquito disease has been and is one of the most prevalent diseases and worst killers known to man. Bubonic plague, carried by diseased rats and from rats to man by fleas, lashed across Asia and Europe in a series of epidemics during the Middle Ages. During one epidemic in the fourteenth century, the Black Plague wiped out what was estimated to have been 25 million people or nearly a fourth of the population of western Europe. Since ancient times in the Nile Valley of Egypt, the blood fluke disease called *bilharzia* has subjugated the *felahin* in farming areas to the dreaded snail-borne disease.

Diligent use of modern pesticides is the only real remedy. For generations on end, malaria, yellow fever, typhus, black plague, sleeping sickness, and other pest-borne diseases have held men's progress in check when and where people have been unable to cope with the arthropod carriers.

Today, partly from the discovery of effective pesticides, millions of people enjoy health and productivity in densely populated areas of the earth, formerly sickness-ridden with insect-carried diseases. Moreover, effective pesticides have helped raise the standard of living by improving agricultural efficiency, yield, and quality, while lowering the cost of products from the soil.

The insecticidal properties of the most dramatic insecticide, DDT, were discovered in Switzerland in 1942 by Paul Müller. For this he was awarded, in 1948, the Nobel prize for physiology and medicine. DDT, relatively safe to humans yet deadly to a wide variety of insects, was used during the closing days of World War II in eastern Europe where it kept tick-borne typhus fever under control. DDT quickly demonstrated its effectiveness as a crop protectant and a spectacular fly and mosquito killer. Large populations in malaria-riddled parts of the world were suddenly given health and hope. Ireland's potato blight, which left famine and destitution in its wake and caused one of the greatest migrations in recent history, could be prevented today by the judicious use of modern pesticides.

Since the discovery of DDT, dozens of pesticides of new chemical classes have come to the forefront. The highly potent parathion and its relatives must be handled only by those skilled in the use of hazardous chemicals. Malathion and carbaryl, on the other hand, are little more hazardous than aspirin. Though hundreds of millions of pounds of pesticides are used each year in agriculture and public health, surprisingly few people are injured or suffer known ill effects.

But the war on pests is not nearly won. The tsetse fly, carrier of the blood-swimming trypanosome that causes sleeping sickness, occupies and has conquered one-third of the African continent. Large tracts of that potentially rich area are no longer in productive use because of the ravages of Nagana, the sleeping sickness disease of cattle.[2]

Part of the debris of progress, however, is that, pesticides, like drugs, medicines, alcohol, or automobiles, can be harmful when improperly used. DDT and its chlorinated hydrocarbon relatives are found in many places throughout the environment—water and soil—as well as in the tissues of animals and man. The chlorinated hydrocarbons have an affinity for fatty tissues and are recoverable in minute amounts from the fat of human adults almost everywhere, from milk, and from wildlife from the temperate zone to the Arctic. No one knows what the long-range effect of continued use of chlorinated hydrocarbon pesticides will be. Combined with all other chemical exposure—from drugs, detergents, combustion exhausts, industrial pollutants, and radioactive contaminants—pesticides give reason for intelligent concern that they may pervade the environment in ways that will damage plant and animal life and ultimately human welfare. Fear of widespread desolation from pesticides appears to be unfounded and outweighed by the yearning of the hungry and the sick for food and health, yet there is clearly a need for more intelligent use of chemicals of all kinds and for intensified research in the quest for more selective pesticides—more effective against pests while safer to humans and other desirable life.

---

[2] *Based on statements by D. Reed, "The Battle Against Sleeping Sickness,"* Reader's Digest, *pp. 124–127, 1967.*

A Conservationist's Views on the New Insecticides

Clarence Cottam

Problems associated with insect control have long been with us. Ditching, draining, clearing, burning, oiling and the use of various chemicals, particularly arsenicals, have been practiced for years and all have produced problems of a greater or lesser degree. The development of highly toxic, wide spectrum, non-specific, residual insecticides has greatly intensified the problem. With the exception of a few plant products, like pyrethrum and nicotine, all insecticides prior to 1943 were inorganic materials. In 1943, DDT was the only insecticide having a high residual action. Now there are over 100 organic pesticides and thousands of formulations of these complex compounds with a still greater variety of trade names. Not only is there a much greater variety of materials, but these chemical poisons are being used for an ever increasing variety of purposes.

Chemical control agents are now being used as algicides, herbicides, fungicides, insecticides, piscicides and rodenticides. Other highly lethal chemical compounds are also being used to control mammalian predators. Private citizens, organizations, municipalities, and county, state, and federal agencies, are using them for control of flies and other insect pests, as adulticides for the control of mosquitoes, and for the control of diseases and parasites of trees and shrubs. Home owners, farmers, and ranchers use them in their gardens, lawns, farms, and pastures. They are used to control aquatic as well as terrestrial weeds. They are used in astronomical quantities on farms, orchards, range lands, and forests, and the acreages treated are increasing rapidly.

Reprinted from *Biological Problems in Water Pollution,* Public Health Service Technical Report No. W60–3: 42–45 (1960), with permission of the author and the publisher.

The use of airplanes for broadcasting these toxicants has greatly extended and intensified their use and has made possible routine and inexpensive treatment of large areas. Vast areas of the public domain, including both range and forest land, are sprayed or dusted annually. Still, the most intensive use and by far the greatest quantity of pesticides applied are for protection of field, orchard, and truck crops. It has been reported that in the South the amount of technical material (that is, without the dusts, water, oil, clay, or other carrier material) applied per acre of cultivated crops may vary from three to ten pounds annually.

In 1957, America used some 35,000,000 pounds of undiluted arsenical salts, 45,000,000 pounds of copper sulfate, 6,000,000 pounds of organic phosphates, and 130,000,000 pounds of chlorinated insecticides and fungicides.[1] Control agents and formulations are legion and new products appear almost weekly. Today, well over 6,000 brand-name formulations are sold over the counter, and most of these with little more restriction than the rather high price of the concoction, despite the law that pesticides must be registered and properly labelled.

Last year, a billion pounds of chemical pesticides were applied to about 100,000,000 acres of land, or about 5% of the United States. Mixed with dusts, oils, water and other solvents, emulsifiers and carriers, the volume totaled between two and three billion pounds and cost the consumer over 500 million dollars. A four-fold expansion of this program is expected within the next ten or fifteen years. Currently, more than ⅙ of our crop lands and millions of acres of forest and range lands are treated annually with pesticides in quantities of a few ounces to 25 or more pounds per acre.

The magnitude of this problem is tremendous and points to the urgent need for close cooperation between those directing the control operations and those whose interests may be affected by the program. It suggests to me that ultimately legislative action by the Congress may be necessary to give more effective protection to man and his resources against over-zealous operations that may be inclined to rush into drastic and widespread operational eradication or control programs without necessary research to guide them. The public need of widespread control should be well determined. Knowledge needs to be

---

[1] *James B. DeWitt, "Effects of Chemical Sprays on Wildlife,"* Audubon Magazine, 60(2): 70–71 (1958).

available concerning the probable or possible indirect as well as the direct effect of the projected operational program.

The current widespread fire ant program of the southeast is a case in point. It is my considered opinion that this program calls for more maturity of judgment than has yet been demonstrated by those directing this irresponsible and unnecessarily damaging operation.

Many crops would be jeopardized if pesticidal protection were withheld. Wisely directed control is a part of the American life and is here to stay. However, it is not unreasonable to insist that controls be applied with understanding, judgment, and a realization of the indirect as well as the direct effects that are likely to follow. Intellectual integrity by those directing it is to be expected. An informed public will not long tolerate a procedure that is so poorly directed that it does serious or unnecessary damage to other public resources.

It has been recognized that most control chemicals are more or less toxic to vertebrates and particularly to man. Consequently, steps have been taken to afford some protection to man and his domestic animals. Under Public Law 518 of the 83rd Congress, tolerances have been established for pesticide residues in foods and produce that enter interstate commerce, and those exceeding these limits are judged unsafe for human consumption. Users of pesticides are advised to allow suitable periods of time to elapse between application and the harvesting of crops or pasturing of treated areas.

These protective measures are quite ineffective as they relate to wildlife because the poisons are placed out in wildlife habitat, and usually these poisons are placed on wildlife foods. Birds, mammals, fishes, and other wild creatures are likely to be exposed to the sprays and other forms of control agents. Water, in which aquatic forms live, and wildlife foods at times are dangerously contaminated. Consequently, damage to fish and terrestrial wildlife often is known to be serious and extreme.

Many of the toxicants are particularly damaging to fish and other cold-blooded creatures. The poisons reach our ponds, reservoirs, lakes and streams by direct application, by drift from areas being treated, or by being washed in from treated areas. Alarming and severe kills of fish and food chain organisms are much too common in many parts of the continent—particularly in the United States. Furthermore, it has been demonstrated that these materials can and do exert a long-time effect and can wipe out entire populations of fish. The amounts of these pesticides now used and the tremendous extent of areas covered are such that they are becoming water pollutants.

These poisons are different from most conventional pollutants in that they are highly toxic; they are surprisingly stable and are not readily subject to breakdown. Furthermore, their toxicity usually is not greatly influenced by the quality of the receiving water. These toxicants compound the problem of stream pollution because they do not enter streams or lakes at just a single point (or rarely at a few points) but are washed in from extensive areas. It would seem logical to conclude, therefore, that conventional methods of waste treatment cannot successfully be used in their control. Control of these chemical compounds must necessarily be directed at the source through materials and formulations used, the amounts, applied, areas treated and the method, time and frequency of application. Watershed treatment and good soil conserving practices will, of course, help to retard dangerous runoff of polluted soil which obviously carries the lethal pesticides.

In the mid and late 1940's it was found that flies became resistant to DDT, especially when DDT was used both as a larvicide and adulticide. Later it became evident that a variety of insects became resistant to a number of insecticides. A report of the Executive Board of the World Health Organization in June of 1956 states: "The conclusion was that the development of resistance of insect vectors to insecticides has become a serious public health problem. Thirty-two countries have reported insect resistance to DDT and other new insecticides. About 35 species of insects, including various types of malaria-bearing mosquitoes, show immunity to DDT in some areas of Greece, Lebanon, Indonesia, Saudi Arabia, Panama and Mississippi. Body lice, vectors of typhus, can no longer be controlled with DDT in Korea, and five other countries report that satisfactory control is becoming difficult. Fleas, responsible for plague, are manifesting resistance in certain parts of South America. But worse still, a strain of mosquitoes that spread yellow fever has shown itself extremely resistant to DDT in Trinidad. The destruction of flies with DDT and other chemicals is no longer possible in almost all countries where these materials have been used in recent years. The new insecticides that have become available in the last three years are too few, too limited in efficiency, and too toxic."

The development of resistant insect strains has led to a program of research to develop many new and ever more toxic materials. Most of these have been highly toxic, wide spectrum, residual insecticides that are surprisingly stable and long lasting in effect. The wide-spread use of these chemicals has had serious effects on aquatic as well as upon terrestrial wildlife in many areas. No one knows what will be the extent of the indirect effects upon mankind, domestic and wild animals, soil organisms or aquatic life. It is well to remember that the dangers to human health and to animal life will of necessity be a delayed action and some of this probably long delayed.

Illness and death may come after long repeated ingestion or consumption of minute daily intake of poisons. There is evidence to support this. The shallow argument that all is well because we have not died yet is little comfort for those who are stricken.

Martin[2] states that "We have much experimental evidence in animals to show that any interference with the oxidative enzyme system of the fetus during the early embryonic stage of development will cause structural changes in the tissue and organs of the body, as well as a marked increase in congenital deformities . . . It has been recently discovered that the brain of a mentally sick person uses a lower than normal amount of oxygen." He adds that many of the pesticides in the fatty tissue of the body act as inhibitors of the oxygen supply to the cells. He concludes that "The physical and mental strength of our Nation is being lowered daily by the effects of these insecticides on our body metabolism, and there is reason to believe that the effects will be increased with their future use . . ."

I believe that our past approach to the pesticide problem needs a new look. It seems to me that instead of seeking ever more toxic, broad spectrum compounds we should strive to develop materials which are selective or specifically toxic for particular insect pests that must be controlled. It is not improbable that such an approach will result in more economical and more effective control. At the same time, it will result in much greater protection for other organisms in the biota. I am convinced we have given this field of research far too little consideration. While it is probable there is still more work needed and improvements yet to be made, this general approach has proven feasible and most efficient in the control of lamprey, house rodents and mammalian predators. I understand it is also being used here at the Taft Center in

---

[2] W. Coda Martin, "Insecticides Today and Tomorrow," Address before the 1957 N.F.A., published in the Congressional Record by the Hon. Lee Metcalf, pp. A4616–A4618 (June 4, 1957).

the search for algicides which are specific for those algae which cause problems in the provision of a potable water supply. Some such method must be used if we are to avoid pollution of our waters and serious damage to our aquatic and terrestrial wildlife. It is no secret that insecticidal poisons have already been found, even at the mouths of many of our major river systems. With present and contemplated control and "eradication" programs for various insects and other organisms (such as the wholesale broadcasting of poisons ostensible to "eradicate" fire ants), we may be sure this pollution will rapidly increase unless more selective and wiser methods of approach are followed.

Many of these chemicals are extremely toxic to fish. I understand that several of them have 96 hour TLm values below 10 ppb, and for endrin it is less than one part per billion. If the present trend continues, it is probable that we will get amounts of highly lethal toxicants in our streams that definitely will be limiting to some important forms of aquatic life. I trust you will agree with me that this is a field that warrants our serious and objective consideration.

This is an age of specialization; therefore, it is to be expected that pesticide operators would have as their objective the effective control of pest species. Experience teaches that all too often these specialized workers look for immediate effectiveness, efficiency and economy of control, without regard to other organisms in the biota. Control, when conducted with chemical agents alone, is a repetitive process and normally very costly. Consequently, such an approach is often abandoned sooner or later. Biological control, wherever feasible, has proven most satisfactory and should be the aim wherever and to whatever extent is possible. A combination of the biological and chemical approach to control, at times, is the most advantageous. Chemical controls should not be stressed over good sanitation practices and environmental control.

Those directing as well as those engaged in operational control should be well-grounded in ecology and should understand the environmental approach to these land-use problems. The environmental effects of a proposed treatment should be thoroughly studied and effects upon the entire biota well understood before launching a large scale control or "eradication" program. When such programs are initiated and directed by government, there is an added responsibility to see that the public interests of all the people are appropriately considered and evaluated. Foresight is much more difficult to attain than hindsight, but to a public-spirited, intelligent citizen, it is much more rewarding and satisfying. The Federally directed "fire ant eradication" fiasco should afford a splendid object lesson of how not to proceed to make friends, influence people or attain a satisfying degree of success in a public service.

Our wildlife species are public property and protected by international treaty and by federal, state, and local laws and regulations. Aside from all benefits and interest in our various species, control operators, particularly government workers, have a moral obligation to protect this resource. Wildlife resources are of high economic, social, aesthetic and recreational value and certainly should be protected and wisely managed. Unnecessary destruction of valuable species should not and will not long be tolerated by an informed public. As our population increases, and especially at times like the present when it is skyrocketing explosively, the value of our aquatic as well as the terrestrial resources correspondingly increase. With increased population, pure water becomes even more of a national and individual necessity. Preservation and conservation is far better than costly restoration. Let us remember always that willful waste makes woeful want.

I do not agree with the defeatist attitude that to protect our agricultural crops we must inevitably sacrifice wildlife values. If we take a positive rather than a negative approach and develop procedures and techniques through appropriate research, I believe we can have both good crops, clean water, and wildlife. Surely we can find selective and specific pesticides which we can use to control pests without significant detrimental effects to other public values or to other members of the biota which are of high economic, social, or recreational importance. It has been done before. The possibilities are there and the promised rewards are worthy of our best efforts.

Pesticides: A Report on Residues in Food

R. E. Duggan
Keith Dawson

Civilization advances proportionate to man's ability to overcome the problems associated with securing the essentials of survival: food, water, and shelter. He competes with other forms of life for these essentials, and he has developed complex and inter-related scientific mechanisms resulting in the most bountiful supply of food and fiber ever known.

By contrast with past ages, today's average man has little direct knowledge of the sophisticated means employed to obtain food. Modern society has had to provide a control mechanism to protect his interests.

In the United States the Food and Drug Administration has a unique responsibility to act in the individual's interest. The Agency has no conflicting interests or responsibilities in the production or marketing of foods and allied products. There is an equally important responsibility to recognize and accept technological advances resulting in more and better foods.

To this end the use of chemicals is not new. It probably began when a cave dweller first observed that food left in the smoke of the fire or the salty residue of sea water did not disappear into a mass of insects before he could eat it.

If we were to correlate chemical discoveries with the resulting effects on food production, especially when accompanied by similar advances in other sciences, we would most likely find that our bountiful supply of food and fiber was made possible by such advances.

Reprinted from *FDA Papers*: 4–8 (June 1967) with permission of the authors and the publisher.

There are many uses for pesticide chemicals for purposes other than food production. Large quantities of these chemicals are used in disease prevention, such as mosquito control; in fiber production, such as cotton dusting; in forest conservation; in highway weed control. Pesticides do not stay put. They drift through the air and are contained in the dust and dissolved or suspended in the water systems of the world. The possibilities for potentiation and interaction are innumerable. When drugs, food additives, air pollutants, and other similar factors influencing man's total environment are added to the list of pesticides, there is reason to exercise caution and to maintain control. It becomes imperative when the individual cannot exercise a choice concerning exposure to these factors.

The comparatively simple chemicals, lead, arsenic, mercury, bromides, sulfur, of a quarter century ago have been augmented by several hundred complex, synthetic, organic, chemical compounds. They come in a wide variety of basic chemical structures: chlorinated ring compounds, organic phosphorus, carbamates, and some whose chemical identity is not fully known. They are recommended for a multitude of uses, ranging from highly specific to broad spectrum applications. Some decompose or dissipate rather rapidly. Others are remarkably persistent.

There is a wide variation in the acute toxicity levels and in the "no effect" levels of various pesticide chemicals as measured by test animals. The interpretation of data obtained on laboratory animals to humans is not a precise mathematical exercise, although it is generally acceptable. By nature, however, pesticides are toxic and, quite naturally, there is a substantial and growing public interest in toxic residues from all sources in man's environment and, more specifically, in food.

Historically, the Food and Drug Administration has exercised control of such residues in foods. The almost explosive use of toxic chemicals in agriculture, beginning in the 1940's, led Congress to pass an amendment to the Food, Drug, and Cosmetic Act in 1954. This amendment directed that FDA establish safe and legal tolerances for pesticide chemicals on raw agricultural products, after USDA approved the usefulness of such chemicals. Tolerances have been, and are being, established on the basis of raw foods as shipped in interstate commerce.

A tolerance is granted only on the showing that the residues on the food are safe by pharmacological tests at levels greatly exceeding those remaining on the food. Furthermore, a tolerance will not be granted for levels exceeding those necessary in the production of the food even though the pharmacological data shows that a higher level is safe.

Tolerances are not additive. For example, if two similar chemicals each have a tolerance of 1 ppm on a food, this means that both chemicals combined may not exceed 1 ppm. Specific regulations have been promulgated for those instances where more than one pesticide chemical is present. Section 408 of the FDC Act is applicable only to raw agricultural products. Residues remaining in foods after processing are subject to Section 409 which concerns food additives. Regulations provide that processed foods will be legal if prepared from raw foods containing legal residues and if the residue in the ready-to-eat food does not exceed the tolerance on the raw product. One of the factors given consideration in establishing tolerances is the total amount of pesticide chemicals and combinations which might be consumed over extended periods of time.

Every year, the FDA determines the amount of pesticide chemicals in thousands of samples of food in the enforcement of the tolerances. These analyses are made on foods as shipped in interstate commerce. Shipments containing excessive residues may be removed from the market by seizure and the shipper may face legal proceedings.

In the surveillance program, samples are collected throughout the year at producing, shipping, and destination points. Figure 1 shows the geographic representation of 49,044 domestic objective samples obtained during the period July 1, 1963—June 30, 1966.[1]

Objective samples are surveillance-type samples; there is no reason to suspect that residues will be found. FDA differentiates between objective samples and those selected for examination because of information or other causes indicating the presence of excessive residues. Figure 1 shows that general nationwide coverage was obtained. For all practical purposes, these can be considered as "random" samples. The total number of samples provides a high degree of reliability in the results.

Modern pest control often requires use of more than one chemical to achieve the desired result. The FDA has been instrumental in developing and perfecting multiresidue methods, which permit the examination of a sample for many residues by a single test. The analytical procedure used on all samples will detect the presence of the following 54 pesticide chemicals:

---

[1] *A total of 49,356 domestic samples and 3,836 import samples were examined during this period.*

1. Aldrin	28. Isobutyl ester 2,4,D
2. BHC	29. Iso-octyl ester 2,4,5,T
3. Bulan	30. Iso-octyl ester 2,4-D
4. Butyl ether esters 2,4,D	31. Isopropyl ester 2,4,5,T
5. n-butyl ester 2,4,D	32. Isopropyl ester 2,4,D
6. n-butyl ester 2,4,5,T	33. Kelthane
7. Chlorbenside	34. Lindane
8. Chlorbenzilate	35. Malathion
9. Chlordane	36. Methoxychlor
10. Chlorothion	37. Methyl parathion
11. CIPC	38. Ovex
12. Dacthal	39. Parathion
13. DDE	40. PCNB
14. DDT (o,p+p,p; Op; pp)	41. Perthane and olefin
15. Diazinon	42. Prolan
16. Dichloran	43. Ronnel
17. Dieldrin	44. Strobane
18. Dilan	45. TCNB
19. Dyrene	46. TDE
20. Endrin	47. Tedion
21. Ethion	48. Telodrin
22. Ethyl hexyl ester 2,4D	49. Tetraiodoethylene
23. EPN	50. Thimet
24. Folpet	51. Thiodan I
25. Heptachlor	52. Toxaphene
26. Heptachlor Epoxide	53. Trithion
27. Hexachlorobenzene	54. Vegadex

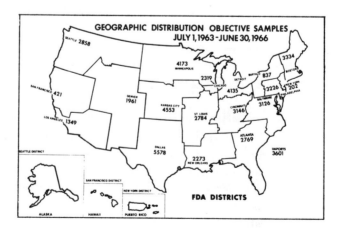

Figure 1

Any one, or combination of chemicals, present in the sample will be detected and measured.

A selected portion of the samples are examined for residues of carbamates, chlorophenoxy compounds, and carbaryl. Although these are important pesticide chemicals, analytical resources are not equal to examining all samples for these compounds. The number of objective samples examined for these chemicals, plus the knowledge gained through inspections in the growing areas, provides assurance that no serious problem will develop without recognition and followup for control purposes.

During this 3-year period almost half (49.5 percent) of the objective samples contained residues and 29 percent contained more than one pesticide residue. See Figure 2. The picture is approximately the same when these rates are computed on an annual basis from fiscal year 1964 through fiscal year 1966.

The 10 most commonly found pesticide chemicals in domestic samples and the 10 most commonly found in import samples follow in order:

Domestic Samples	Import Samples
DDT	DDT
DDE	DDE
Dieldrin	Dieldrin
TDE	TDE
Heptachlor Epoxide	BHC
Lindane	Lindane
BHC	Aldrin
Endrin	Kelthane
Aldrin	Heptachlor Epoxide
Toxaphene	Endrin

Frequency of residues of these chemicals in terms of percent of samples examined is shown in Figure 2. Their percentages will add to more than 100 percent of the samples because about 30 percent contain more than one residue.

Tolerances have been established for a number of specific chemicals on various foods. The relative toxicity of the residues is quite important as is the relative consumption of the food item.

Although a detailed report and analysis of amounts of specific chemicals found on specific foods is beyond the scope of this paper, some general observations are pertinent. A total of 81 different chemicals were found in domestic samples during the 3-year period. Thirty-three chemicals were common to all years.

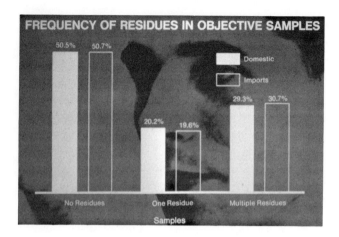

Figure 2

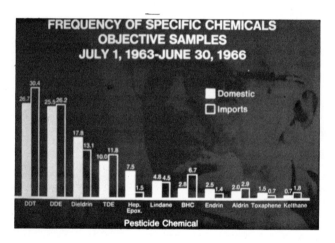

Figure 3

Irrespective of tolerance levels, it can be seen from Figure 3 that about 42 percent of the residues on domestic samples and about 55 percent of the residues on import samples exceeded 0.03 ppm. About 22 percent of the domestic samples and about 35 percent of import samples contained residues exceeding 0.1 ppm. Also, it can be seen that total residue levels on imported foods are higher than those on domestic foods, and that similar chemicals are found at about the same frequency.

These general findings show that a relatively high frequency of many

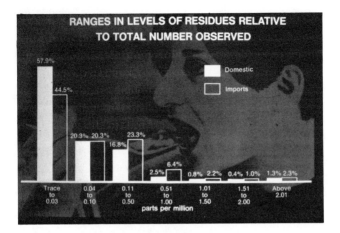

Figure 4

different pesticide chemicals are in foods as shipped in interstate commerce.

In contrast to the finding that imported foods generally contain higher levels of residues, approximately 3 percent of domestic objective samples and 1.5 percent of import samples contained residues in excess of the tolerances or analytical guidelines. The total percentage is somewhat misleading, since this percentage varies substantially within broad food categories, such as fruits, vegetables, cereals, fish, and dairy products. For example, only 1.5 percent of the domestic raw fruits, vegetables, and cereals, and 0.9 percent of the import samples of similar products, have contained excessive residues. Many tolerances are in effect for these products. On the other hand, excessive residues are found more frequently in products for which there are no tolerances, such as shell eggs and fish, and particularly those where indirect sources affect residue levels.

The primary objective of FDA is to protect the consumer from eating foods containing significant amounts of these poisonous substances. The tolerance procedure and the surveillance program with accompanying regulatory control provides information only on the foods as shipped. Foods are washed, trimmed, cooked, and prepared in many different ways which affect the remaining residues. For this reason, tolerances are established on the food as shipped in interstate commerce, because it is not practical to establish tolerances at other points in the food processing procedure.

As an additional precaution and as final assurance that the primary objective is being reached, it is necessary that information be obtained on food as it is actually consumed. The tolerance concept does not anticipate, as a practical matter, that all foods will contain residues at the tolerance level for all chemicals for which a tolerance has been established, or even that all of a single food will always contain a residue at the tolerance level. Actual experience throughout the years proves this to be a valid concept. The safety factor included in establishing tolerances does take care of isolated situations of this nature.

Several investigators have stated that foods are the major sources of pesticide chemicals in man. There has been relatively little information concerning the kind and amounts of residues in foods as they are eaten. The "market basket" or "total diet" studies by the Food and Drug Administration provide the most reliable index of the residues being consumed in the diet in the United States.

Briefly, these studies consist of purchasing in retail food stores, as would any consumer, a diet list of 82 foods in a quantity sufficient to satisfy the Nation's largest appetite, a 17- to 19-year-old male, for 2 weeks. The diet list was developed by the Household Economic Research Division of the USDA.

The food is prepared for the table by dieticians. It is separated into 12 similar kinds or classes of foods to avoid problems in analysis and, more important, to minimize the dilution factor. A composite consists of all food items within a class mixed together for analysis. Each class composite of food is examined at a much lower sensitivity level than that used for the samples described earlier. This lower sensitivity requires much more care during the analysis.

Each year a total of 30 diet samples are examined in 5 geographic regions, and 30 different cities are represented. This level of sampling was not achieved during the first year of the study. A detailed evaluation report of data obtained through April 1966 is in manuscript for future publication.

The data indicates that a well-balanced diet in the United States contains pesticide chemicals as follows:

        chlorinated organic chemicals—0.02 ppm
        organic phosphate chemicals—0.003 ppm
        chlorophenoxy chemicals   —0.003 ppm
        carbamate chemicals   —0.05 ppm

Statistically, there was no difference in the findings when each year of the study was considered separately.

The chlorinated organic chemicals are the most widely used and persistent pesticides. Irrespective of the statistical interpretation, there was a finite increase from 0.08 mg/day to 0.12 mg/day in the total amount of chlorinated pesticides found in the second year of the study, indicating a need for continued surveillance. The average frequency of the 14 most commonly found chemicals is shown in Figure 5. This percentage is calculated from the total number of food composites examined. Organic phosphate compounds were not found until the second year of the study. In our opinion, this is due to improved methodology, and does not represent a change in the residues present.

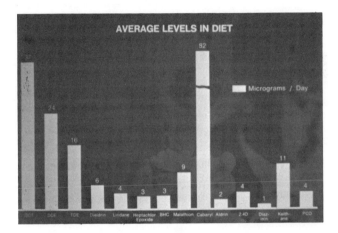

Figure 5

Except for carbaryl, the levels of residue are closely related to the frequency with which the residues are found.

The kinds of specific chemicals and the relative amounts present are important because of wide variations in toxicity. DDT and its analogs, DDE and TDE, account for about three-fourths of the daily intake of chlorinated organic compounds at a total intake of 0.077 mg/day in the diet used in this study. Residues of dieldrin, lindane, and heptachlor epoxide follow in order of frequency. The six most commonly found residues account for 90 percent of the total intake. However, consumption of 4 kilograms (8.8 lbs.) of food a day is almost twice the consumption of 2.2 kilograms (4.8 lbs.) of food by the "average" individual. Therefore, the actual intake of pesticides in a well-balanced diet will be substantially lower than those reported.

Acceptable daily intakes of specific pesticide chemicals in foods have been jointly proposed by the FAO of the United Nations and by the WHO Expert Committee. The following compares these levels with the findings calculated from the total diet samples:

	Acceptable Daily Intake	Calculated from Total Diet Samples
	(mg/kg body weight)	
DDT	0.01	0.0005
Lindane	0.0125	0.00006
Malathion	0.02	0.0001
Carbaryl	0.02	0.0012

One of the factors given consideration in establishing tolerances is the percentage of the food supply affected by the action. The following comparison has been made of the findings in this study with the intake calculated on the basis that the specific chemical residue would be present at the tolerance level in the foods for which there is a legal tolerance:

	Calculated from Tolerance	Calculated from Total Diet Samples
	(mg/kg body weight)	
Dieldrin	0.006	0.00009
Heptachlor Epoxide	0.0006	0.00004
2,4-D	0.017	0.00005

These figures show a substantial margin still remains before residues in ready-to-eat foods even reach the currently acceptable levels.

Major components of the diet will affect the consumption of pesticide chemicals. For example, meat, fish, and poultry composites and dairy products composites, when combined, account for more than half of the intake of chlorinated pesticides. Most of the residues in these foods result from indirect additions through animal food, water, or other environmental factors.

Recently, a tolerance has been established for DDT and its analogs in dairy products, not because of direct application but because DDT is so widely distributed in the environment that it is impractical to prevent exposure of dairy animals to this chemical. It is well recognized that continuing use of other persistent pesticides will aggravate this situation. The uses of such chemicals are being critically examined to minimize or avoid such situations.

From the above, we can conclude in general terms that currently the incidence and levels of pesticide residues in the Nation's food supply are not approaching dangerous or even alarming levels. The frequency and levels of residues in the Nation's food supply must not be permitted to increase unnecessarily. Additional measures are needed to avoid increases in specific food items where indirect sources result in residues; specifically, dairy products, eggs, and fish. Surveillance and control must continue at current levels to detect and eliminate problems arising from unexpected, unanticipated, and unavoidable sources, as well as from misuse. There are instances where residues remaining in the soil from previous crop treatment have migrated into subsequent crops. The usual degradation or disappearance of a chemical due to weathering may be delayed because of climatic conditions.

Improved analytical procedures may demonstrate conclusively the presence of a residue where, earlier, less sensitive procedures had failed. There are no "marker" foods that can be used as common denominators from which to judge the food supply as a whole.

The information on ready-to-eat foods obtained from the market survey is most reassuring, and supplements the interpretation of the data obtained on samples examined for compliance with tolerances. This kind of surveillance serves as a final check on the effectiveness of controls being exercised throughout the food production and distribution system.

In summary, there should not be alarm or complacency concerning pesticide residues in food. Continued responsible judgment and caution are required of those who use pesticide chemicals for whatever purpose. Additional research will provide better information concerning the total effect on man of environmental exposure to pesticide chemicals. Continued vigilance is required of those having the responsibility for the public's interest.

A Socio-Economic Evaluation

James G. Horsfall

Perhaps a sociologist, a psychologist, or even a psychiatrist should have been asked to discuss the socio-economic phases of the role of pesticides in the nation. These matters surely fall within their purview. It is said that education is too important to be left wholly in the hands of educators. And the problem I am discussing is too important to be left in the hands of sociologists.

fantastic interaction of social and economic pressures

This problem has given us a fantastic array of interacting social and economic pressures. I would like to consider it with respect to (a) the social taboos about insects and disease that pervade our society, and (b) the equally strong set of taboos that permeate our society about poisons. The interaction of these two deep-seated sets of taboos generates the maelstrom that is tossing us about. It surely creates eddies, countercurrents, and upwellings in the stream that are confusing to contemplate and even more confusing to attempt to navigate.

I shall approach the problem by exploring what happens when the tabooed poisons are used to combat the tabooed bugs. Let us first consider the taboo on bugs.

the social taboo on bugs

Take any picnic of city people. Here the bug taboo is clearly evident. Mothers are running after their babies, telling them not to put their

Reprinted from *Research in Pesticides,* pp. 3–16, C. O. Chichester, Ed. (New York: Academic Press, 1965) with permission of the author and the publisher.

hands on the bugs—those nasty little critters might sting or bite. In our folklore, pests are equated with devils. The Wassons, man and wife, have published two beautiful tomes on the folklore of mushrooms. In an elegant paragraph that deals with insects in our folklore, they say "Bugs, flies, moths . . . in short the insect world constituted for our ancestors until recent times an order of nature with supernatural powers, mostly malevolent and always awesome . . . the fly was demonic . . . the neighbors of the Israelites in the Old Testament worshipped Beelzebub, whose name meant the Lord of the Flies. . . . In English the word 'bug' until the seventeenth century meant an evil spirit. . . . Then the word came to designate a creeping insect."

In folklore, however, "bug" has never lost its connotation of the devil. The use of "bug" in the sense of the devil still appears all through our culture. It shows up in our language in all kinds of ways: for example, bogeyman; bogey derives from the same root as bug. During World War II, when the fighters saw an enemy airplane they called it "a bogey." "Bogey, two o'clock," they would warn; or, "Bogey at 10 o'clock." I need only remind you of some other words in the language that reflect our concern with the devilish qualities of the word bug. We say "bug house," "bugaboo"; we speak of removing the "bugs" from a new machine. We say that the American Embassy in Moscow has been "bugged." Falstaff, as he lay dying, saw a fly on Bardolph's nose and called it "a black soul burning in hell."

A translation of the Bible dated 1549 had one of its Psalms say, ". . . thou shalt not be afrayed of any bugges by night nor for the arrow that flyeth by daye." And, Shakespeare in the *Taming of the Shrew* said, "Tush, tush, fear boys with bugs," that is, frighten boys with bugs.

Of course, the fear of bugs has a perfectly solid biological background. In ancient days people did not know intellectually that bugs transmitted disease, but I am sure that the treatment of bugs came close to recognizing this in a folklore sort of way. If one avoided the bugs, one automatically avoided the diseases that were transmitted by them. The folklore dictum to build one's house on a hill undoubtedly has some basis in the fact that on the hilltops there are fewer mosquitoes from the swamps, and therefore less yellow fever and malaria. The ancients, of course, knew that bugs would bite, creating welts on the skin; and undoubtedly they knew that wasp stings could kill a man and that the stings of scorpions and of some spiders were poisonous.

There is no doubt about it: in our culture bugs are Beelzebub, and

they have been since early times. The Egyptians attempted to deal with
this in their religious system by creating a special God to the bugs—the
sacred scarab beetle.

the social taboos on disease
and decay

There has always been a related taboo on human disease. Stay away
from it. Likewise, there has been a taboo on diseased and decayed
plants. Undoubtedly, since the beginning of civilization we have avoided
spoiled food whenever possible. Women in the kitchen are very careful
indeed to trim off all diseased spots. They do not allow their families to
eat food that has been around too long. The ancients did not know it
intellectually, but this folklore recognized that botulinus and salmonel-
lae produce food poisoning. The Middle East taboo on pork derives
from the same source.

If you think that the bug taboo no longer exists, just recall the
experience that probably most people have had of seeing someone in a
restaurant find a worm in his broccoli or lettuce and become almost
nauseated and perhaps get up and leave or raise "holy rim" with the
proprietor. You will remember the old gag: What is worse than finding
a fly in the cake you've been eating? And the answer is, "To find half a
fly."

taboos find a way into the law

Social taboos find their way into the laws that govern society. The
pure-food laws were enacted back about 1906 by that wily old character Wiley, who was a missionary of the first order. These laws contain
one very picturesque phrase ". . . filthy, putrid, and unfit for human
consumption." This is powerful language, and I doubt not that Wiley
wrote it originally. When I got my first job in the protective science of
plant pathology, I remember so vividly being amused that the Food
and Drug Administration (FDA) had set a tolerance of 7 cherry
maggots per can. The farmers could not get all the maggots out of
the cherries; so if the citizens were to have any canned cherries whatsoever, the FDA had to set a tolerance. Of course, the FDA had no
alternative. Every law must have a tolerance, implicit or explicit.
Speed laws have an implicit tolerance of about 5 miles perhour. Filth
laws, too, have a tolerance.

the solution to pollution is dilution

Tolerances recognize the fundamental concept in biology that the *solution to pollution is dilution*. Few things are deleterious at low concentration. Strychnine, a deadly poison, is a wonderful heart stimulant at low concentration.

Seven maggots per can was somebody's decision that the maggots would not be harmful at that dilution. Tolerances for pesticides too can be and have been established.

In Connecticut we have a good example of taboos written into law. Many years ago the gypsy moth was declared a public nuisance. It was taboo, and the [Connecticut Agricultural] Experiment Station was instructed to get rid of it. The fact is we did not and could not get rid of it, but the law nevertheless continued to instruct us to do so. It said, in effect, "kill the devils," the gypsy moths.

In Washington the law takes another form. I refer to the quarantine laws. The quarantine laws called into being a whole new bureaucracy, now called the Plant Pest Control Division. One of their jobs is to keep the gypsy moth devils from crossing national and state boundaries. In California there is an iron curtain, ostensibly to keep out the bugs. Through this the tourists must pass and their luggage be searched for bugs. The quarantine people seek to enforce the social taboo on insects. I doubt if they keep many insects bottled up, but they try hard.

the rise of sciences to protect against these taboos

Another interesting result of the social taboos on bugs and disease is the establishment and cultivation by society of the protective sciences of entomology and plant pathology. Weed science has come in recently. My whole professional life rests on the fact that the public is willing to pay for plant pathologists to protect them from food that is "filthy, putrid, and unfit for human consumption." And, similarly, my brother is in the field of entomology. Society, in effect, has said to the sciences of entomology and plant pathology, "Extirpate Beelzebub!" and "Down with the devils and diseases!"

As a result, we in these sciences were flattered and stimulated to get on with the job of extirpating the devils. We were Sir Galahads riding in seach of the Holy Grail.

And so we began to fight the bugs and the blights with all the tools
we had. When I was working in New York State, we bought tons of
California ladybugs collected from high up in the Sierras. We liberated
them in the pea fields of New York State to eat up all the aphids. I do
not think the California ladybug liked New York State aphids very
well, because the aphids continued to feed on the peas. But for five or
six years in the 1930's it was a popular thing to do.

In other cases, we drained the swamps for the mosquitoes; turned
over the tin cans and scrap tires to deal with this pesky insect. We bred
new varieties of plants to avoid plant diseases. We bred millions of
parasites and liberated them in the farmers' fields. We plowed under the
corn to get rid of the corn borer. But on came the bugs! We never did
find parasites that gave good commercial control of the codling moth or
the pea aphid. We found no really resistant varieties that would control potato blight and apple scab and so we turned to poisons.

The organisms that we fight are alive, and so we said to ourselves,
"We will poison them. We will do it selectively. We will use poisons that
will poison the pest under the conditions of use but will not poison
people under the conditions of consumption." Our job was to produce
clean food both for everyday living and for the festive table.

We did poorly for a hundred years or so after the sciences of
entomology and plant pathology were established. We had available to
us the ancient remedies: arsenic, mercury, sulfur, copper, and zinc.
More recently we acquired from the savages the use of derris and
pyrethrum, but these did not give us *really* good control of insects.
They were the best we had, we used them, and we did get some control of
the target organisms. But, still, on came the bugs!

The Colorado potato beetle marched from the Rocky Mountains to
the East Coast across the bridge of potatoes that we had planted as we
moved west. A scale insect came out of California to attack apples and
made San Jose famous.

success beyond our dreams

And then, in about 1940 came success—success beyond our wildest
dreams. The control of insects and plant diseases we obtained seemed to
us to border on the miraculous. I can remember the first potatoes I saw
in the Connecticut Valley that had been sprayed with DDT and zineb. I
had not dreamed that potato plants could look so beautiful in the latter
part of August. Until then they had always died by the latter part of

July, and there they were at the end of August or even into September, just as green and lush as ever.

Our medical friends had sulfanilamide and penicillin. We had DDT and zineb and phosphates. We controlled the typhus epidemic in Italy during the war. We kept down malaria and other dangerous diseases in the Pacific so that our troops could fight the Japanese, and not disease. Mosquitoes disappeared from the salt marshes along the east shore of the United States. There were no more bedbugs in the theater, no more flies in the cow barn, no more maggots in the cherry cans.

We in the protective sciences fairly "busted our buttons." The yields of potatoes were tripled. Agriculture became efficient. For the first time in the history of man, a culture could produce more food than it could consume—a position of rare luxury indeed in the long history of famine and malnutrition extending back to the farthest reaches of history. Society forgot the seven lean years of the 1930's when the grasshoppers and rust ate the wheat. The years were now fat years. We thought they would always be fat. Perhaps they will be. Boys grow taller than their fathers; athletes run a mile in less than 4 minutes. They are obviously well nourished. *Newsweek* magazine, in July 1964, referred to the "outworn Malthusian theory." The world "never had it so good!"

No longer did the bugs sit down first at the table and consume our food before we had had a chance at it. We were pretty proud of ourselves, and the grateful world gave Müller a Nobel Prize—the highest social honor that can be bestowed by a grateful society on a scientist. The taboo on DDT was yet to be called down. The field of entomology had reached the peak of social kudos. We had fulfilled our charge. We had Beelzebub on the run.

the balance of nature

In the balance of nature, so dearly beloved of the ecologists, things that go up must come down; things that rise must be clawed down. This is as ancient a concept in our culture as the bug taboo. It does entomologists and plant pathologists no good to decry the use of this dictum by modern man. It is built into our religion. The Chinese call it Yin and Yang; the Hindus call it Brahma and Shiva; the Christians call it God and Mammon—the creator and the destroyer. There must be a destroyer for every creator. And, in this sense there must be a destroyer for the very high position to which the protective sciences had reached with their powerful control of insects and plant diseases.

the social taboo on poisons

The force that would claw down this achievement would arise from the taboo on poisons. Many of us were so flushed with our success that we forgot this fundamental taboo. The taboo on poisons is built just as deeply into our culture as the taboo against insects or the concept of the balance of nature. People still shudder when they think of the Borgias, the old masters of the use of poisons. The fear of poisons is so deep that it is easy to think of entomologists as modern Borgias. Every school boy knows about Socrates and how he was poisoned by the hemlock tea. Everybody knows about poisonous mushrooms, poisonous snakes, the deadly nightshade, and the poison ivy. These are taboo in our culture. Mushrooms we allude to by vile-sounding names like toad-stools. And as for the snake, he tempted Adam's wife—and the Garden of Eden disappeared.

the dictum that "it might be"

"Don't eat that," says a mother on a picnic, "*it might be poisonous.*" Please note, she does not *know* it is poisonous. She just says "It might be poisonous." So don't eat it, it might poison you.

The social pressures against the poisons we were using for bugs and blights built up slowly, but build up it did.

For one thing, people woke up slowly to the fact that some pesticides are, in fact, poisons. They knew that pesticides were poisonous to insects, but did not realize that they might be poisonous to people. This was due in part to the fact that city people are far from agricultural reality. They think that food comes out of the supermarket and that chocolate milk comes from brown cows. It is no wonder, then, that they did not at first apprehend that "they could be poisoned." Eventually, however, they came to follow the dictum of the mother at the picnic. They said to themselves, "Don't eat that sprayed food. *It might be poisonous.*" Pleast note, they did not say that it *was* poisonous; they said it *might* be poisonous.

There seems to be a deep-seated social satisfaction in being titillated by the "*it might be's.*" Children's stories are full of examples of this sort of thing. The wolf in sheep's clothing; the wolf might eat you. Little Red Riding Hood; the wolf might eat her. Newspapers carry stories all the time on what might be. It gives us a vicarious sense of living dangerously. The writers of "whodunits" keep us in suspense as to who poisoned the victim. They think of fabulous new ways of concealing the identity of poisons.

And so, we were very excited indeed when somebody came along and said, "You may be eating poisoned food." Vast numbers of people did not really think they were, but they were frightened just the same, because they *might* be.

we "didn't know the territory"

Now, we in the protective agricultural sciences did not really sense early enough this rise in importance of the poison taboo. The opening song in the "Music Man" show castigated a feckless salesman because "He didn't know the territory." Or, if I may be allowed to use the phraseology of the communications experts, I would say that we didn't hear the signal for the noise. The signal was there, but we were so confused by the noise of the plaudits for our success in quelling the Beelzebub taboo that we did not hear very plainly the signal from the poison taboo.

the signal from nova scotia

The first faint signal that I remember came to us in about 1938. It was very weak. Perhaps not many people remember the arsenate of lead on apples shipped to Britain before the war. There was a big hullabaloo because the British discovered that apples from the United States and from Nova Scotia contained arsenate of lead. Not long before, the British had been through the harrowing experience of discovering that the ritualistic beer they drank in their pubs was loaded with lead from the lead pipes between the barrels under the bar and the spigots on top. The habitués of the pubs had been having painter's colic—that is, lead poisoning. So, when the British heard about the arsenate of lead, the social pressure was on. Authorities in Britain had to shut out Western apples because of the arsenate of lead. Not only did they contain lead —they contained arsenate as well!

The pressure was exaggerated, of course, because British apple farmers wished to shut out Western apples so their own apples would sell better on the British market. Here the economic aspects reinforced the social taboo, and it became essentially impossible to ship Western apples to Britain. This almost killed the Nova Scotia apple industry, which depended almost 100% on export to Britain, because arsenate of lead was their only control for worms in apples.

This is an early example of a signal from the poison taboo. And we did not catch it! We just put it down that the British farmers were trying to shut off American and Nova Scotian apples. We did not see it as the rise of the social taboo against poisons.

Another signal came in during the mid-1950's with the passage of the Miller Bill and, later, the Delaney Amendment to the Food and Drug laws. This was social pressure to get the poison that *might be there* out of the food.

a strong signal in 1957

The nation got a very strong signal in 1957 when the Plant Pest Control Division sprayed DDT over all of Long Island and over Westchester County, near New York City, for the control of gypsy moth. The Plant Pest Control Division of the U.S. Department of Agriculture had persuaded Congress a year or two earlier to appropriate a large sum of money to "eradicate" the gypsy moth in the Northeast. Mind you, this was not a pest of the food supply; it was a pest of the forest. It had been in the country for almost a hundred years. It had been sprayed intensively. Eradication programs had been tried on Cape Cod and failed. Nevertheless, the Division put on a very strong campaign that year to "wipe it out" of the westernmost reaches of New Jersey, Westchester County, and Long Island. These are densely populated areas.

The Plant Pest Control Division ignored the rising social pressure from the conservationists, who had been objecting loudly for several years. The Department of Agriculture sprayed those people from the air; sprayed their babies in the backyards; sprayed their clothes hanging on the line.

It seems hard to believe that officials would "beard the lion in his den" and spray in those densely settled areas. Conservationists could look up and see the DDT come streaming from the belly of the airplane and falling on them. And they had no place to hide. To my mind, this was probably the most powerful incident in provoking the rapidly rising opposition to the use of poisons. By 1962 this opposition had frozen into a book on the injudicious use of sprays: no birds sang in the "poison rain."

The Department of Agriculture was promptly sued by irate citizens.

Even while this suit was going on, and the pressure was rising in the Federal Court in Brooklyn, the Plant Pest Control Division came to Connecticut and said, "Next year we will spray the entire state of Connecticut." Mind you, spray the *entire* state of Connecticut with DDT whether gypsy moth occurred over the entire state or not. "Now that we have eradicated it from New York State," they said, "we will eradicate it next from Connecticut and then Massachusetts and Rhode Island, and thereby squeeze all the gypsy moths into the sea." It is amazing that they would dare take the campaign from the thickly settled areas of New York State, where they were being sued, into equally thickly settled areas of Connecticut.

It was my statutory responsibility to sign a paper to give permission to spray Connecticut, and I refused to sign. I had already heard the signal, I think, in my own Legislature. There had been a tremendous outcry two years before about the gypsy moths, and I could see that if the Plant Pest Control Division sprayed Connecticut, the fire then raging in Westchester would become a conflagration in Connecticut.

The Department of Agriculture won the suit in the court in Brooklyn, and thought it had won the war. Actually, it had won only a very minor skirmish indeed. The trouble is, it could not read the signal for the noise; it did not see the social ramifications of its actions. It ignored a taboo—which is dangerous.

You could repeat this story with eradication of the fire ant in the South, or the white-fringed beetle in Norfolk, Virginia.

I emphasize again that Westchester was sprayed for a forest insect that had nothing to do with food-producing agriculture, but it was food-producing agriculture that was to suffer a few years later when the fire raged out of control. And it is to be noted that the aim was biologically impossible of achievement with the chemicals available. All of us who had been involved in the experimental work on gypsy moth were convinced that DDT could not eradicate it. All in all, it was a fiasco, a mass misuse of a very good pesticide.

the very loud cranberry signal

The signal became raucously loud in the cranberry crisis in 1959. I know how raucously loud it was, because I served on the Panel of the President's Science Advisory Committee to examine the cranberry crisis.

Most of us in agriculture missed the signal even here. We were inclined to explain this as an effort to make political hay. We did not seem to realize that politicians sense social change. The Secretary of Health, Education and Welfare merely mirrored the crescendo of social pressure motivated by the taboo on poisons. He raised the question just before Thanksgiving, and he raised it with a food that has ritualistic importance. Cranberries are a symbol of the thankfulness of the nation for bountiful harvests. Everybody eats cranberries at Thanksgiving time. To say that the cranberries were poisoned was almost the equivalent of saying that the vintners had put strychnine in the sacramental wine. This was extraordinarily dramatic, and it created an uproar from the citizens. It undoubtedly fanned the flames that eventually scorched us in 1962.

I have simplified, I know, this problem of failing to hear the signal. We did hear the signal. We knew as well as anyone that the indiscriminate use of pesticides was to be avoided, and yet the Government flew its airplanes into the teeth of the opposition.

zero in on DDT

One very interesting social aspect has always fascinated me. The anti-spray people zeroed in on DDT. It so happens that DDT is probably the least poisonous to man of all the powerful insecticides. W. J. Hayes' definitive work on volunteers has shown that men can walk around with 200–300 parts per million in their fat without showing any symptoms whatsoever.

By and large we discovered empirically, almost accidentally, that DDT is reasonably safe. DDT started small, like everything else, but it was so effective against bugs that it was sprayed all over the troops in the South Pacific during the war. My entomologist brother was involved in that. It was dusted on practically every citizen of Italy in the typhus epidemic, because winning the war and the control of typhus were more important than the outside possibility that somebody would get the trembles from the effect of DDT on his nerves. Nobody got the trembles, and such widespread use made it reasonably clear that DDT was not very poisonous to human beings. One cannot say this about the phosphates and dieldrin and endrin, but DDT is probably the least poisonous of the lot. Yet Miss Carson zeroed in on DDT. The social reason for this is quite simple. DDT had climbed the highest on the totem pole and everybody could see it; it was a widely known compound. It had a euphonious name; it was easy to see and easy to shoot down.

socio-economics of year *III*

Socio-economic aspects in the third year after Miss Carson's attack are of interest in terms of the psychology of the various groups that are concerned.

the psychology of the farmer

The farmer is more careful about pesticides than he used to be. He does not want to poison the citizens. He occupies a high position in social thinking because he feeds the citizens. Food is ritualistically important. When a family wants to celebrate, its members get together for dinner and kill the fatted calf. So, the farmer will do his best to keep the poison off the food.

In addition, the farmer is subject to very strong economic pressure from the purveyors and consumers of food to keep the food so it is not "filthy, putrid, and unfit for human consumption." Most city people do not associate the requirement of food that is free of filth with the need for pesticides. When a lady goes to the market, her social taboos against contaminated food force her to buy pest-free food. If, therefore, the farmer, in attempting to deal with the taboo on poisons, lets his food go to market with pests in it, he runs hard into the taboo against contaminated food. Very often he is between the devil and the deep blue sea.

Besides that, a farmer may be subjected to other economic pressure. If he does not put pesticides on and control his pests, his neighbors will; their crops will move to market, but his will not. So he is under a very tight socio-economic pressure.

the psychology of the *FDA*

The people of the Food and Drug Administration have similar psychological problems. It is they who coined the phrase "filthy, putrid, and unfit for human consumption." They have to guard against food of that description. If the cherry maggots in the cans go up again, the FDA must close in on the canner. Then the canner must close in on the

farmer, and the farmer must close in on the maggots with an insecticide. The circle is vicious. How far will the FDA go in insisting on
maggot-free cherries and zero tolerance on residues to control the pest?
The position of the FDA administrators is not enviable.

the psychology of those whose
need changes

The psychology of those whose need has changed over the years is
interesting to me. When we were having our difficulties with gypsy moth
in Connecticut, large numbers of city people who now live in our
mountains were violently opposed to spraying the woods with DDT to
control gypsy moths. The vacationer who comes to Connecticut is
repelled by denuded hills and by the droppings of larvae on his picnic
table. So he does not return, and this affects the holiday businesses.

There are those who fight gypsy moth spraying when it is not on
their property. "Don't kill the wildlife," they say. The gypsy moth
strikes in different places in different years; when it occurs on the
property of the man who has opposed spraying, his tune is likely to
change.

We have an elegant example of a lady who changed her mind. She
writes a column for a local weekly. I would like to read you an excerpt,
"We don't know how other sections have fared during the past few
weeks but the gypsy moth has descended upon our part [of the state]
in a dark tapestry of destruction. They hang from the trees like bead
curtains, pattern the buildings, get in the hair, on the person. . . . The
other morning we found one on the living room table, thumb to nose,
getting a good laugh out of The Connecticut Agricultural Experiment Station's [bulletin] 'Control of the Gypsy Moth.' Heretofore we
have been firmly anti-spray and have given tongue to the same patter
as all the rest of the anti-spray faction. . . . Right now the most
beautiful sound in the world is the drone of the helicopter as it works
back and forth over adjacent woodland. We can't wait for it to get
overhead and give us our money's worth of purification. Coincidentally,
we have just found, with great amusement, the first draft of a long-
winded and sober article prepared for this column some time ago on this
gypsy moth spray-or-not-spray question. It was full of bombastic
facts, the high-toned prose edging into the pseudo-scientific and
trimmed with some dandy heart-throbs. We tore it up with the greatest

of pleasure and relief. . . . Anybody want some fine anti-spray propaganda only slightly used?"

This column was written back in 1955, seven years ahead of the articles in the *New Yorker*. Her psychology had changed. It was all right to put social pressure on to stop the spraying when somebody else's fields and forests were involved, but it was different when the gypsy moths were eating the trees in her yard. She changed her mind.

the psychology of the plant pest control division

The psychology of those in the Plant Pest Control Division has changed, too. They are not so anxious now to eradicate the gypsy moths. They realize that the social aspects of the problem have changed, that people are not as anxious to keep the bugs out of the fields as they are to keep the poison out of their food. So, the Division is having more trouble with their psychology than they had five or six years ago.

the psychology of the scientists

The psychology of the scientists has changed drastically. Entomologists have suffered dreadful blows. They have been called Stone Age scientists, inadequate, incompetent, poor in judgment, devoid of any spark of human kindness in their systems, guilty of having sold their souls for a few paltry dollars. This has undoubtedly hit entomology very hard indeed. My guess is that it will be difficult to recruit young men to come into a field so harried and beaten about. However, the entomologists are rushing into biological control. This course is politically smart, and it may save them from too much attrition.

isolation of city people from agricultural reality

Where do we go from here? Probably the greatest problem that confronts us in agriculture is the tremendous isolation of the city man from the reality of food production. As we have said, he thinks chocolate milk comes from brown cows. He has been so far away, and so long away, from the problems of producing food that he has little compre-

hension of the details involved. His opinions are reflected in the operations of agriculture, but he does not even know how they are reflected.
The demands for pesticide-free food and for disease-free food are hard
to reconcile, but the city man does not even know that a need for
reconciling them exists. The editor of *Newsweek*, referring to the "outworn Malthusian doctrine," showed how far from reality these fellows
really are. One letter to the editor proposed a novel advantage of
abandoning all pesticides. The writer said that such a change would
create thousands of new jobs. As one of my friends remarked, that
writer was proposing to let the nit pickers pick nits.

The thousands of new jobs that would be created by the loss of
pesticides could conceivably reverse the downward trend in the percentage of citizens required to produce food. If the numbers of people
needed to produce food were to go up, our society might very well be on
the road back to an agrarian society and away from an industrial
society. If we let pests run rampant, we could not possibly keep up the
standard of living that we have provided for ourselves.

Social pressure will certainly change the laws. Congressmen like to
get into the act. State legislators like to get into the act. The laws will
be tightened, and it will be more difficult to produce new pesticides just
at the time when we need much safer ones. The President's Science
Advisory Committee rather naïvely said that we needed specific insecticides. The more specific they are, the smaller the market; the smaller
the market the less the return; the less the return, the less likely the
companies are to embark on developing specific pesticides. And this is a
serious problem that confronts us.

conclusion

How I conceive of the socio-economic aspects of the situation we find
ourselves in has been set forth above. Today we are in the eye of a
hurricane generated by the opposing forces of the social taboos against
bugs and pests and the social taboos against poisons. I have faith that
we will not be destroyed by the hurricane, though I am sure that we are
going to be buffeted around considerably.

Devitalizing Composition of Matter

Paul Müller

This invention relates to insecticides.

For combatting insects of all kind such as flies, stinging flies, moths, beetles, plant-lice and so on, there are mostly used petroleum solutions of pyrethrine or rotenone or aqueous emulsions of such compounds. Nicotine is, in spite of its poisonous character, also used for the protection of plants, but it cannot be used in inhabited rooms.

Both the first mentioned agents show the disadvantage of smelling disagreeably in spite of the admixture of strong perfuming agent, when they are used in form of petroleum solutions. In aqueous emulsions they are however stable only for a short time, as their activity already strongly decreases after a short time.

All experiments for inventing artificial substances acting very rapidly and positively, but being nearly or completely odorless and having no irritating effect upon human beings have given until now no essential result. Thus for example the use of halogenated nitriles, especially of trichloracetonitrile, is limited to uninhabited buildings or to closed receptacles, as these halogenated compounds, even when extremely diluted, irritate very strongly the mucous eye-membrane.

Therefore, it is very surprising that the condensation products of 1 molecule of choral with 2 molecules of certain compounds with replaceable hydrogen from the benzene series, show, beside the sure killing effect on insects, only a very weak and not at all a disagreeable odor and do not exert even in finely dispersed form any irritating effect on the mucous membranes of the eyes, nose or throat.

Reprinted from *United States Patent Re. 22,700* (Reissued September 30, 1947) with permission of the assignee and the U.S. Patent Office.

The said compounds correspond to the following general formula

$$X_3C-CH\diagdown\begin{matrix}Y\\\diagup\\\diagdown\\Z\end{matrix}$$

wherein X represents chlorine atoms and Y and Z mean certain aromatic radicals of the benzene series.

The said compounds can be used as powder or, when dissolved or emulsified, in solvents or diluents, but they can also be used together with other inert substances inactive by themselves or in combination with fungicide, bactericide or insecticide agents.

They are very stable in neutral as well as in acid or weakly alkaline solutions and their preparation is technically very simple.

The preparation of the described compounds is known [O. Zeidler, B.7, 1181].

The following example illustrates the present invention. The parts are by weight, unless otherwise stated.

example

By treating, while strongly stirring, a mixture of 2 molecules of benzene or chlorobenzene with one molecule of chloral or chloralhydrate with an excess of concentrated sulfuric acid (of 100 percent strength) heating takes place after some time, which first increases up to about 60° C. and then slowly decreases again. Stirring is continued until the reaction mass has cooled down to room temperature and contains solid particles. Then it is poured into much water whereby the raw condensation produce separates out in a solid form. It is well washed out and, after being recrystallised from alcohol, it is obtained in form of white, fine crystals which show a weakly fruit-odor. The formulae of these compounds are the following ones:

The first-compound melts at 64° C, the second one at 103–105° C [about the preparation see also O. Fischer, B.7, 1191]. These two diphenylmethane compounds react surely against flies, by spraying 5 ccm. of an alcoholic solution of 5 percent strength per cubic metre of room. Death takes place, for flies, within 2 hours; already after 10–15 minutes nearly all flies are so paralyzed that they can no longer fly.

Moths, plant-lice or other pests are also destroyed within a very short time by the sprayed compounds. Instead of solutions in alcohol, petroleum or similar solvents one may, in many cases, also use aqueous emulsions. Their efficiency does not thereby decrease even on long storage, which is the case for many known insecticide preparations.

What I claim is:

1. An insecticidal composition of matter comprising the combination of the active ingredient α,α-di(p-chlorophenyl)-β,β,β-trichlorethane of the formula

$$Cl_3C-CH \begin{array}{c} C_6H_4Cl \\ \\ C_6H_4Cl \end{array}$$

and an insecticide carrier selected from the group consisting of powder, solvent free from ether, and aqueous emulsion.

2. A contact insecticide comprising the chemical compound α,α-di(p-chlorophenyl)-β,β,β-trichlorethane in the form of powder and a carrier therefor.

3. A contact insecticide comprising a solution of the chemical compound α,α-di(p-chlorophenyl)-β,β,β-trichlorethane in a petroleum solvent.

4. A contact insecticide comprising the chemical compound α,α-di(p-chlorophenyl)-β,β,β-trichlorethane and a carrier therefore consisting of an aqueous emulsion.

5. A contact insecticide comprising a solution of the chemical compound α,α-di(p-chlorophenyl)-β,β,β-trichlorethane in a solvent free from ether.

10

Molecular War

You've got to know what to brew
and how to brew it.

—LOLA, IN *Damn Yankees*

Since the time when the first Neanderthal-like creature dimly rational-
ized that someone stood in the way of his pursuit for a better life and
bashed in the head of his selected victim with a blunt rock, the weapons
of war have grown progressively more lethal and destructive. The
current weapon of terror is the outcome of nature's compulsion for
growth and man's search for the ever bigger bang. Yet despite the
incredibly intricate instruments of death that man has devised, the goal
of absolute dominance over the enemy and perfect protection from the
invader remains as elusive as when the spear was the ultimate weapon.

While it may seem that nothing could make modern warfare more
brutal or inhumane, the potential for misuse of poisons was recognized
early in the era of chemical technology. World leaders feared the use of
projectiles containing poison gas. Beginning with the Hague Gas Declaration of 1899 and more importantly the Second Hague Conference
at which the United States was a signatory, nations solemnly promised
to kill each other only with more primitive weapons.

The agreement did not survive the first world war. In fact the
desperation effort by the Germans to use poison gas in World War I
was a dismal and depressing example of tactical blunder and fumbling
technology. Actually, both sides "experimented" with poison gas.
Early in 1915, Germany made a gas attack against the Russians, and
the French tried tear gas against the Germans. Later in the same year,
Germany released chlorine gas from cannisters in an attack on both

British and French troops, resulting in 15,000 casualties including 5,000 dead. The Allied forces retaliated in kind, and before the war's end the chemicals in use had been modified to include more poisonous and more painfully disabling toxicants.

The expression "chemical warfare" has a restricted meaning.[1] Actually nearly all weapons consist of or use chemicals. Salt was used, and condemned, by the ancients to incapacitate cropland. Gunpowder delighted the thirteenth century populace with "a noise like thunder and flashes like lightning,"[2] but about a hundred years later began to be used in firearms. Gunpowder consisted of sodium nitrate, charcoal, and sulfur. Since then, many refinements have produced propellents of varying properties. Guncotton, made by the action of nitric acid on cellulose, was discovered in 1846 in Switzerland and later, in 1891, was used by British Ordnance in the powerful explosive cordite, a mixture of guncotton, nitroglycerin, and petroleum jelly. Alfred Nobel, working in the family explosives works in Sweden, had discovered in 1863 a safer way to use the powerful force of nitroglycerin in the form of dynamite. He left most of his fortune to be used for the famed Nobel prizes.

By World War II, Germany had successfully conducted extensive research in chemical warfare agents and had discovered and stockpiled the highly effective "nerve gases," which the United States later adopted and also stockpiled. Neither side used nerve gas, but a direct outgrowth of the German discovery was the development of several insecticides, including the highly effective, though dangerous parathion, which along with its relative methyl-parathion constitutes a major share of the agricultural insecticides in world-wide use.

Incendiary bombs and napalm were used during World War II and the Korean conflict to wipe out bunkers. Napalm is jellied gasoline, the name being derived from the jelling agents that originally were naphthenic acid and palm or coconut fatty acid soaps. Napalm-B, which has replaced the soap gel, consists of 50 percent polystyrene, 25 percent benzene, and 25 percent gasoline. White phosphorus, itself a viciously painful incendiary, is used to ignite the napalm, which burns at nearly 4800 degrees Fahrenheit and produces asphyxiating concentrations of carbon monoxide. The material is used in flame throwers

---

[1] *Some perfer to lump all unconventional nonnuclear weapons into the "CBW" (chemical-biological warfare) bag.*

[2] *Roger Bacon, "De mirabili potestate artes et naturae" (1242).*

and land mines as well as in aerial bombs. Napalm is an effective agent for saturation bombing and is credited with burning out 60 percent of Tokyo in 1945 and of causing more deaths than the atomic bombs dropped on Hiroshima and Nagasaki.

The use of defoliants by the United States in the Vietnam conflict has introduced a new dimension in chemical warfare. Many people have expressed fear that dissemination of herbicides over large areas of forest and cropland may cause prolonged if not permanent impairment in soil productivity. Part of their fear is based on the nature of a type of soil called *laterite*, common to the tropics. Upon exposure to the air, such as by removal of the forest cover for agriculture, laterite turns into a form of rock with the characteristics and durability of brick. For centuries, laterite has been used as a construction material in tropical parts of the world. The temple of Angkor Thom of the ancient Kmer civilization in Cambodia is a well-known example of laterite construction. Milpa farming, practiced throughout the tropics —while suitable for small-scale, primitive agriculture—exhausts the soil within a few crop cycles and, may leave large areas of land permanently lost for productive use. The Kmer civilization, as well as that of the ancient Maya, may have perished largely as a result of lateritic deterioration.

The popular aversion to chemical warfare agents may stem partly from the centuries-old taboo against "poisons" and partly from the inhumane chemical weapons of World War I and napalm of later times. Lost in the emotion of revulsion and fear is that the most useful of the chemical warfare agents, exclusive of napalm, do not kill but temporarily disable the enemy.

The continuing effort to "humanize" warfare is grim, if negative, evidence that the aggressiveness that permeates all races may persist for the thousands of years of future existence to which *Homo sapiens* can hopefully look forward. It may be too much to expect that man's ambition to eliminate greed and brutality could overcome his contentious nature within the span of historical perspective. However, it may not be too much to anticipate that the ingenuity that created nuclear and nonnuclear explosives might also give birth to nonlethal and nonviolent means of controlling adversaries. If massive death and destruction can become nonprofitable, perhaps victory in war will no longer belong to the most destructive combatants but, rather, to those who succeed in controlling their enemies by more subtle methods. One might imagine a livable, though contentious, world in which nonlethal molecular bullets would be the weapons of choice for "civilized" people.

Chemical and
Biological Warfare (I):
The Research Program

Elinor Langer

Biological warfare is the intentional use of living organisms or their toxic products to cause death, disability, or damage in man, animals, or plants. The target is man, either by causing his sickness or death, or through limitation of his food supplies or other agricultural resources. Man must wage a continuous fight to maintain and defend himself, his animals, and his plants in competition with insects and microorganisms. The object of BW is to overcome these efforts by deliberately distributing large numbers of organisms of native or foreign origin, or their toxic products, taking full advantage of the ability to utilize more effective methods of dissemination and unusual portals of entry. BW has been aptly described as public health in reverse. ["Effects of Biological Warfare Agents," pamphlet published by Department of Health, Education, and Welfare, July 1959].

Recently, the University of Pennsylvania has from time to time been the unhappy object of national attention arising from disclosures that the university is conducting secret research for the Army and Air Force on chemical and biological weapons. In an interview with *Science* last fall, one troubled university official complained that Penn's participation in CBW was being unfairly singled out. "There are a lot of people in this game," he said. He was right.

The chemical and biological weapons program is one of the most secret of all U.S. military efforts—not because it is the most important of our military R&D activities, but because the Pentagon believes it is the most easily misunderstood and because it provokes the most emotional distress and moral turbulence. Official secrecy makes a complete portrait of the CBW program difficult to construct. Rumors fly freely around the security wall that separates the "ins" from the "outs." In some portions of the scientific community the . . . administration's "credibility gap" has taken its toll and there is readiness to believe

Reprinted from *Science, 155:* 174–76, 178–79 (1967) with permission of the author and the publisher. Copyright 1967 by the American Association for the Advancement of Science.

that, every time someone in Vietnam sneezes, it is because the United States is distributing the germs. In the defense establishment the CBW program is represented as being some kind of cross between defensive preparations, on the one hand, and peaceful by-products in preventive medicine, on the other.

Defensive preparations are only one part of the program, for the United States is engaged in a comprehensive and flourishing R&D effort in chemical and biological weapons. It involves non-military as well as military agencies, industry as well as the academic community, and it has received cooperation from some of the major scientific institutions of the United States. Stockpiles of chemical and biological weapons produced by this program provide a far-ranging offensive capability. Furthermore, U.S. policy concerning the use of chemical and biological weapons is ambiguous and contradictory, and is rendered even more so by the use of chemical weapons in Vietnam.

The current CBW program is the product of decisions made and steps taken during the late 1950's and early 1960's. Before that time the old-line Army Chemical Corps was regarded by the nuclear-age military establishment as custodian of a particularly controversial and probably useless emporium. The Chemical Corps had a message it had been repeating since World War I—that its wares were unusually humane—but no one was buying. The Corps existed on budgetary dregs, usually around $35 million a year. Its most active support came from the Armed Forces Chemical Association, a group of military and industrial executives supported by chemical companies and "dedicated to scientific and industrial preparedness for the common defense in the fields of chemical, biological, radiological and related technology commonly referred to as chemicals." The Corps felt continually threatened with the possibility that it would be abolished.

In 1959 the Corps took matters into its own hands and went to the public with a full-scale publicity campaign known as "Operation blue skies." It was a period of fascination with the possibility of "incapacitating" weapons, particularly psychochemicals, and, putting aside its more lethal products, what the Chemical Corps advertised—in articles, speeches, lectures, symposia, and Congressional appearances—was "war without death." Within a short time the Corps' hopes for expansion had won endorsements from a variety of outsiders, from the American Chemical Society to the House Committee on Science and Astronautics.

At the same time, the Kennedy administration came into office, concerned about the military inflexibility imposed by over-reliance on nuclear weapons. New Frontiersmen were interested in acquiring a more versatile weapons "mix." And they were especially interested in systems that, like CBW, seemed to offer particular promise in fighting limited wars. In the nuclear stalemate between the great powers, there began to be a reorientation in conceptions of how the U.S. would conduct its war against smaller nations, and CBW was just one beneficiary of the reorientation. Fantasies about battles in which whole populations would fall asleep while being captured provided a comforting alternative to the known, stark destructiveness of nuclear weapons, and also helped to establish the appeal of CBW. The relative cheapness of CBW systems played a role as well.

By 1961 CBW had ceased to be scorned, and a comprehensive program for improving U.S. capabilities was underway. In fiscal year 1961 the R&D budget for CBW for all three military services was about $57 million. By 1964 it had risen to about $158 million, with the Army's share being about $115 million. It is now roughly at that level or slightly lower. In 1961 only the Army had money for procurement—about $46 million. In fiscal year 1964 the Army received a little more than $117 million for procurement related to CBW; the Navy, $11 million; and the Air Force, $8.7 million. Procurement figures for more recent years are classified. (These sums for procurement are additional to the amounts spent for research and development.)

In addition to these annual budgets, there is a large standing capital investment in CBW activities. Fort Detrick alone, the center of biological warfare research, occupies 1300 acres of land near Frederick, Maryland, and has a building complex valued at $75,000,000. According to an employee-recruitment brochure, it has "one of the world's largest animal farms" and its "facilities for conducting research with pathogenic organisms are among the most advanced in the world."

Were it not for two things, Detrick might pass as nothing more than the particularly well-endowed microbiological research center it advertises itself to be. Research on basic characteristics of microorganisms seeks the same knowledge and is carried on in the same fashion whether the agency paying the bills is Detrick or NIH. Some of the research undertaken has a defensive motivation—an effort to discover means of combatting biological weapons that might be used by an enemy. Some of the research is neutral—not susceptible to utilization by a weapons program at all. But much of the work inescapably has a special character, an inverted quality like that of medicine turned inside out.

It consists in part, for example, of efforts to breed into pathogenic organisms precisely the characteristics—such as resistance to antibiotics—that medical researchers would like to see eradicated. In the context of biological warfare even life-saving techniques such as immunization take on a strange aspect: immunity among one's own population and troops is a prerequisite to the initiation of disease by our own forces, as well as a precaution against its initiation by others. Some diseases are currently excluded from active consideration as BW agents chiefly because no vaccines against them have yet been developed.

A second factor separating Detrick from other research centers is the restraint placed on its researchers. Detrick's scientific staff consists of 120 Ph.D.'s, 110 M.S.'s, 320 B.S.'s, 34 D.V.M.'s, and 14 M.D.'s. Only about 15 percent of their findings are published through conventional scientific channels; the rest become part of a secret literature managed by the Department of Defense and available to other government agencies and contractors on a "need to know" basis.

While nothing is published that would indicate the relative degree of military interest in, or effort on, a particular agent, Detrick scientists do report in open literature on subjects such as instances of laboratory-induced or accidentally acquired infection, immunization, therapy, routes of infection in man and animals, and various experimental techniques. From these papers and from other sources it is possible to surmise a good deal about the Detrick research program.

Diseases that are at least the objects of considerable research and that appear to be among those regarded as potential BW agents include: bacterial diseases—anthrax, dysentery, brucellosis, glanders, plague, and tularemia; rickettsial diseases—Q-fever and Rocky Mountain spotted fever; viral diseases—dengue fever, several types of encephalitis, psittacosis, and yellow fever; a fungal disease, coccidioidomycosis; and botulism toxin.

In recent years a good deal of attention has been focused on plant diseases also. Recently the Army's Distinguished Service Medal, the highest award the Army gives civilians, was awarded to a Detrick researcher for her contribution to development of a rice blast fungus, a disease that in its natural form has repeatedly damaged Asian rice crops.

To make the jump from naturally occurring organisms to usable weapons, biological agents must possess certain characteristics: they must be highly infectious; they must be able to maintain viability and virulence during production, storage, transportation, and dissemination; they must be sturdy enough to withstand injury during dissemination and have a minimum decay rate; and they must be capable of being produced on a militarily significant scale. Judged from what has surfaced, a substantial portion of fundamental research at Detrick has been devoted to development of these characteristics in the organisms producing the diseases listed.

Detrick is also more or less the home of the science of aerobiology—the study of airborne infection—an area of much interest to researchers studying dissemination of disease, whether their interests are causative or curative. Aerobiology is of particular relevance to biological warfare, however, because the idea of disseminating infectious agents by aerosols—suspensions of small particles in the air—seems to be displacing earlier notions about how to transmit disease. Conventional images of biological warfare—the covert "man with the suitcase" or the poisoning of water supplies and ventilation systems—seem to have been discarded, partly because the number of people who could be subjected to infection at any one time is too small.

Two out of the three times Detrick has emerged to participate in a conventional way in the affairs of the scientific community, it has cosponsored conferences on airborne infection. (Its intellectual debut was a 1959 symposium on "Nonspecific resistance to infection," held in collaboration with the American Institue of Biological Sciences.) The first "Conference on airborne infection," held in Miami Beach in December 1960, was supported jointly by Detrick and the National Institute of Allergy and Infectious Diseases (NIAID), of the National Institutes of Health, and sponsored by the National Academy of Sciences. Detrick papers included "Viability and infectivity of microorganisms in experimental airborne infection," "Techniques of aerosol formation," and "Airborne Q-fever."

Detrick's third meeting was the second International Conference on Aerobiology, held in Chicago last March and sponsored jointly with the Illinois Institute of Technology, a Detrick contractor. Papers by Detrick researchers included "Antibiotic prophylaxis and therapy of airborne tularemia;" "Physical and chemical stresses of aerosolization;" "Infection of pigeons by airborne Venezuelan equine encephalitis virus;" and "Attenuation of aerosolized yellow fever virus after passage in cell culture." Two papers reflected collaboration between Fort Detrick and NIAID: "Effect of route of inoculation on experimental respiratory viral disease and evidence for airborne transmission" and "Assessment of experimental and natural viral aerosols." A cooperative project between Detrick and the University of Maryland Medical School was a study of "Aerogenic immunization of man with live tularemia vaccine." A researcher at Ohio State University College of Medicine, supported by a Detrick grant, reported on "Aerosol infection of monkeys with *Rickettsia rickettsii*," the organism that causes Rocky Mountain spotted fever. Detrick, the University of Arizona, and the Public Health Service all cooperated in a study of "Experimental epidemiology of coccidioidomycosis," an infectious fungal disease.

PHS involvement

The Public Health Service has also cooperated with Detrick in other ways. In 1960, for example, the PHS received more than $380,000 in funds transferred from the Army Chemical Corps, and, according to a PHS spokesman, annual transfers of funds measure only a fraction of the real cooperation between the two agencies. The PHS says that it does not take Army money to conduct research that it would not otherwise undertake, but only to bolster ongoing projects in fields in which it has an independent interest. Its policy is that none of the research results obtained in collaborative projects may be classified. However, the subject matter of an Army—PHS transfer of funds cannot always be discussed because—even though it may concern an area in which the PHS is studying openly—the mere fact of military interest in it may be classified.

Apart from the transfer of funds, there is active liaison between the two agencies—communication on several levels, and efforts on both sides to avoid duplication. And the PHS has also cooperated with Detrick by delaying required reporting to international health authorities of quarantinable diseases occurring at Fort Detrick. One such instance took place on 1 September 1959 when a 22-year-old enlisted technician named Ralph Powell became ill with pneumonic plague. The following day Detrick informed the Frederick County Health Officer, and on the second day it informed the Public Health Service. Its memo to the PHS, classified secret, stated that "no press release has been made or is contemplated by any DOD agency, unless death occurs. In such a case, the cause of death would not be announced." Powell recovered, the report was downgraded to "for official use only," and on 6 November the PHS reported the case. If the PHS is assured that no epidemic hazard exists, it allows the military's declaration of "national security" to take precedence over its international obligations.

Another source of advice for the biological warfare effort is the National Academy of Sciences. In addition to occasional formation of special groups to consider particular problems, the NAS has for several years sponsored a program of postdoctoral "Resident research associateships" designed in part to help bring talent into Detrick. The fellowships are supported by Detrick for research at its laboratories, but candidates are screened by the Academy. Appointees, who must be investigated and cleared, are subsequently permitted to describe themselves as having received an NAS–NRC fellowship.

Additional intellectual assistance for Detrick comes from the American Society for Microbiology, which maintains a permanent Detrick advisory committee. In 1966 the President of the ASM was Riley D. Housewright, scientific director of Fort Detrick. Detrick also uses the part-time consulting services of a number of individual researchers drawn largely from the academic community.

a million dollar secret

A number of universities and research institutes aslo have come into the CBW constellation. The terms of the research sponsored by Detrick or by its chemical-weapons counterpart, the research laboratories of Edgewood Arsenal, vary. Some of it is secret, some open. Some of it amounts to support for basic microbiological research in which Detrick and university-based investigators happen to have simultaneous interest; some is closer to a straight purchase of manpower for a particular task. The scale and magnitude of university-based CBW research is also variable, occasionally running—as at Penn—into large projects but most often consisting of a few researchers together with perhaps a handful of graduate students.

Between 1955 and 1963, as an example of one end of the spectrum, John Hopkins received over $1 million for work described as "studies of actual or potential injuries or illnesses, studies on diseases of potential BW significance, and evaluation of certain clinical and immunological responses to certain toxoids and vaccines." Hopkins reports that its work, which is continuing at a reduced level, produced no results published in open literature. At the other end of the spectrum is the Duke University Medical Center, where researchers have been working since 1958 to develop a vaccine against *Coccidioides immitis* and have made several contributions to professional journals. Some of the CBW work, such as that performed in the late 1950's at Stanford University, is strictly classified; or, like that done at Brooklyn College, the New York Botanical Gardens, and the Midwest Research Institute, at least does not contribute to open literature. Most of the research seems to occupy an ambiguous middle ground where at least some fraction of the results may be publishable, but only with clearances, releases, and so forth from the Department of Defense. Among the institutions where researchers recently performed or are now performing work in this category are the Southern Research Institute, the University of Maryland, the Illinois Institute of Technology, and Hahnemann Medical College.

Another group of institutions has done or is doing research, supported by the CBW program, that is not classified; it includes the universities of Chicago, Minnesota, Michigan, and Texas, Ohio State University, and M.I.T.

Cooperation, including joint support of graduate students, seems particularly flourishing between Detrick and universities in the Washington area, such as the University of Maryland and George Washington University. GW had Detrick contracts totaling $1,202,000 in 1960, and from 1952 to 1959 it conducted a comprehensive research program relating to the "physical and biophysical factors incident to the explosive dissemination of biological aerosols." The annual report of the dean of sponsored research for 1959 reported "phenomenal success improving the efficiency of dissemination of liquids" and noted that, "While it is quite obvious that the end result . . . will be a new weapon," GW's role was limited to research and did not include development. GW maintained a special laboratory at Fort Detrick during that period. Similarly close relations appear to exist between the Dugway Proving Ground and academic institutions in its area. In 1960 the University of Utah had eight contracts with Dugway, totaling $1,570,000. Utah State University also has worked with Dugway.

Finally, it should be pointed out that many more institutions than those cited have contributed to the CBW program. While the Army has turned to academic organizations for basic research, especially on the biological side, industrial contributions to the chemical-weapons program have been substantial. At times nearly 65 percent of the military R&D money in CBW has gone to industry, which is reported to be the most productive source of new compounds. Arthur D. Little, Inc., and DuPont are among companies mentioned as prominent contributors to the CBW program. From outside the chemical industry, many aerospace companies now devote some fraction of their efforts to CBW.

beyond basic research

During the past few years the Army and the Air Force together have moved into another area of CBW research. It goes by a lot of contemporary-sounding titles but boils down to evaluation of chemical and biological weapons and delivery systems. The controversial contracts at the University of Pennsylvania are of this type. But, although Penn is a crucial cog in this phase of the CBW program, it is not the only one: New York University also is performing such studies, under an Air Force contract, and a Pentagon official recently stated that related studies are being conducted by, among other organizations, RAND, the Stanford Research Institute, and the Institute for Defense Analyses.

Research Analysis Corporation, a small firm located near Washington, in a brochure designed to reflect past support by government as well as to attract more, lists the following "research capabilities." Under the heading "Agricultural warfare" are "Study of biological and chemical attacks on crops and some analyses of effects on livestock," "Covert attack on a food crop," and "Impact of chemical attack on guerilla food crops." Under "Guerilla warfare and counter-insurgency" are "Evaluation of counter-insurgency requirements in Southeast Asia," and "Southeast Asia environmental-data collection." And under "CBR warfare" are "Military potential of GB" [a toxic nerve gas], "The feasibility of chemical warfare in defense of a perimeter in the Naktong Valley basin," and "The value of toxic chemicals in ground warfare."

Another leading entry in the field of CBW is the Travelers Research Center, an outgrowth of the Travelers Insurance Companies. Its most recent brochure reports studies of military operations that are "highly sensitive to the natural environment." Chief among these, the report continues,

. . . are chemical and biological weapons systems, which exhibit a high degree of dependence on meteorological, terrain, and vegetative factors. The extensive experience of the TRC staff in research on turbulent diffusion and transport of atmospheric contaminants provides a firm base for TRC's participation in the nation's CB weapons analysis program. The Center's interest in this field stems not only from the importance of understanding the environmental phenomena involved, but also from our desire to support and assist the United States in acquiring effective, humane, incapacitating (non-lethal) systems for coping with proliferating limited war and counter-insurgency. One study was undertaken for the Army to identify the most effective approaches for contending with difficult military situations with a minimum loss of human life to both sides. Another study conducted for the Navy provided an updated review of the influence of micrometeorological factors on chemical warfare in the form of a technical manual to assist in the identification, observation, and prediction of relevant meteorological factors and processes. In another study for the Army, TRC began comprehensive research on dosage prediction techniques to provide up-to-date knowledge of dispersion processes in the lower atmosphere, and with a critical evaluation of the capabilities and limitations of present quantitative techniques for predicting the behavior of atmospheric contaminants. This study is similar in many respects to those being conducted on urban and regional air pollution.

Travelers has branched out in another new direction: "Because modern military planning must often consider technical and strategic goals in relation to their political, sociological and psychological implications, particularly with respect to limited war and counter-insurgency," the brochure states, "a study was undertaken for the Air Force to assess not only the military potential of non-lethal CB weaponry, but also the psycho-political reaction to its use."

This is the chain of research. The United States government is developing chemical and biological weapons. It is learning how to use them effectively. And, finally, it is inquiring into the public reaction to their use.

Chemical and Biological Warfare (II): The Weapons and the Policies

Elinor Langer

Until I retired . . . I was not able to speak of a chemical or biological weapon without prefacing my remarks with the statement that the enemy might use it. I was never able to speak of the offensive, only of the defensive. [Brig. Gen. J. H. Rothschild, USA (Ret.), former Commanding General, U.S. Army Chemical Corps Research and Development Command, *Tomorrow's Weapons* (McGraw-Hill, New York, 1964)]

The United States' program in chemical and biological weapons does not stop in the laboratory. Weapons are accumulating and military manuals describe in detail a variety of circumstances and conditions in which they might be used.

It has to be remembered that, because of restrictions in the government's information policy, a great deal of data would probably be held just as secret if CBW production were floundering as if it were successful. Nevertheless, although the magnitude and precise ingredients of the CBW arsenal cannot be known by those outside the security establishment, the weapons-production program does support an apparatus of several thousand people.

Fort Detrick, in addition to its research activities, is involved in process development, small-scale production, and design and operation of pilot plants. Closely related to Detrick is the Dugway Proving Ground, which employs about 900 people and occupies an area in Utah larger than the state of Rhode Island. Dugway is the principal station for field assessment and testing of chemical and biological munitions.

According to Pentagon officials, there is no large-scale field testing of chemical and biological agents on human subjects. Limited testing is

Reprinted from *Science 155*: 299–303 (1967) with permission of the author and the publisher. Copyright 1967 by the American Association for the Advancement of Science.

done on volunteers at Detrick—Seventh Day Adventists who serve in the Armed Forces only as noncombatants—and occasional experiments have been performed on prisoners. But the military logic of real testing is evidently outweighed by fear of injury and contamination, and field trials are reportedly limited to animals or to nonpathogenic simulated agents. (During World War II the British conducted BW experiments with anthrax—spores of which remain in soil for a long time—on the small island of Gruinard, off the northwest coast of Scotland. According to a recent statement by G. E. Gordon Smith, director of Porton, the British equivalent of Detrick, when the island was recently revisited it was concluded that "it may remain infected for 100 years.")

Biological munitions are produced at Pine Bluff Arsenal, a 15,000-acre installation outside Pine Bluff, Arkansas, which employs about 1400 people. Pine Bluff also produces toxic-chemical munitions and riot-control munitions. Its job runs from manufacturing the agents to filling and assembling weapons. Research and development on chemical weapons, and some production and assembly of them, take place in a number of subunits of the Edgewood Arsenal, in Maryland. Various chemical munitions, reportedly including nerve gas, mustard gas, "incapacitants," and anticrop weapons, are produced at Rocky Mountain Arsenal in Denver. The U.S. also operates a major manufacturing plant—at an estimated annual cost of $3.5 million—in Newport, Indiana, where Sarin, a lethal nerve gas, is produced and loaded into rockets, land mines, and artillery shells. The plant is managed under contract by the Food Machinery Corporation, has 300 employees, and is reported to have been operating 24 hours daily since 1960. Additional chemicals were manufactured during the middle 1950's at another plant in Muscle Shoals, Alabama. A few years ago the Pentagon entered into contracts with about ten chemical companies for research and development on improved defoliants and dessicants; the chemical defoliants used in Vietnam are for the most part purchased commercially.

Chemical weapons are produced in forms designed to meet the requirements of all services. They are available in a variety of forms from regular artillery shells to the Sergeant missile (which has a range of 139 km), the Honest John and Little John rockets, and chemical land mines. They are also available as bombs for delivery by conventional military aircraft. Detailed information on delivery systems for biological agents is classified, but unclassified manuals suggest that biological weapons are available as warheads for missile systems (for large-area attacks), as cluster bombs, and as spray tanks and dispensers mounted on aircraft. (In his book promoting CBW, General Rothschild qualifies his discussion of the availability of chemical and biological weapons with these words: "Whether or not they have been procured in sufficient quantity for combat use is another matter. However, this information cannot be released to the public.")

Useful attributes of chemical and biological agents, from a military point of view, are that they can penetrate structures, cover large areas, and produce a range of effects for varying periods—severe illness for a brief time or less-severe illness for a long time, tears or hallucinations, paralysis or death. A useful quality of biological weapons, according to the unclassified military field manual *FM 3-10*, is their ability to "accomplish their effects . . . with little or no physical destruction. This constitutes an advantage both in combat operations . . . and— from a longer range viewpoint—in postwar rehabilitation, where over-all rebuilding requirements would be reduced." The utility of chemical weapons is described in similar language. (The manual, entitled *Employment of Chemical and Biological Agents*, has classified counterparts.)

the chemical arsenal

Components of the arsenal change from time to time, reflecting both technical progress and military judgment. The current manual lists seven chemical agents now standardized for use. They include two nerve agents, one blister agent, an incapacitant, a vomiting agent, and two riot-control agents.

The nerve gases were discovered in Germany in the course of research on insecticides. At the end of World War II the Russians captured a German plant that manufactured Tabun, a highly toxic chemical known by the military symbol GA. They moved the plant to Russia, and are said to have made Tabun their standard nerve agent. The United States adopted a related chemical, Sarin, known as GB, which is said to be four times as toxic as Tabun and 30 times as toxic as the previously favored lethal agent, phosgene. Sarin is colorless, odorless, and poisonous in minute quantities. According to the Army technical manual *TM 3-215, Military Chemistry and Chemical Agents*, its effects, in order of appearance, are:

> . . . running nose; tightness of chest; dimness of vision and pinpointing of the eye pupils; difficulty in breathing; drooling and excessive sweating; nausea, vomiting, cramps, and involuntary defecation and urination; twitching, jerking, and stagger-

ing; and headache, confusion, drowsiness, coma, and convulsion. These symptoms are followed by cessation of breathing and death. . . . Although skin absorption great enough to cause death may occur in 1 or 2 minutes, death may be delayed for 1 or 2 hours. Respiratory lethal doses kill in 1 to 10 minutes, and liquid in the eye kills nearly as rapidly.

The other standard nerve gas, VX, is of the same general type as GB and has similar effects, but it evaporates more slowly and therefore remains effective longer.

The blister agent available for use is distilled mustard, or HD, a purified version of the mustard gas used in World War I. Moderate concentrations of mustard burn the eyes and produce skin irritation that may include blistering and ulceration. High concentrations may have systemic effects—nausea, vomiting, cardiac arrythmia, and shock. Long-term effects may include aplasia of bone marrow, dissolution of lymphoid tissue, and ulceration of the gastrointestinal tract.

Both the nerve gases and distilled mustard are recommended for use to cause direct casualties, to harass the enemy by forcing troops to wear protective clothing ("thereby impairing his effectiveness as a result of fatigue, heat stress, discomfort, and decrease in perception"), and to hamper or restrict the use of terrain. They may also be used to complement other munitions, or for, among other purposes, "engaging numerous small, individual targets not militarily worth the use of a nuclear munition."

"incaps"

Research on incapacitating chemicals, known informally to some CBW researchers as "incaps," began in the middle 1950's, with emphasis on consciousness-altering drugs, or hallucinogens. In 1964, General Rothschild remained enthusiastic. "Think of the effects of using [LSD-25] covertly on a higher headquarters of a military unit or overtly on a large organization!" he says in *Tomorrow's Weapons*. "Some military leaders feel that we should not consider using these materials because we do not know exactly what will happen and no clear-cut results can be predicted. But imagine where science would be today if the reaction to trying anything new had been 'Let's not try it until we know what the results will be.'" However, fear of inducing irrational and unpredictable behavior in an enemy—especially one who controls nuclear weapons—evidently outran scientific curiosity. Research shifted to agents causing temporary physical disability such as discomfort, anesthesia, paralysis, or immobility. One compound reportedly regarded as promising produces temporary ascending paralysis. The victim first loses the ability to stand, then becomes unable to move his arms. He remains alive but cannot fire a weapon or otherwise function in a military capacity.

The incapacitant now standardized for use is known as **BZ**. It has both physical and mental effects, but its precise nature is not clear; unclassified information is notably less ample than for other chemical agents. The Army technical manual (*TM 3-215*) lists the following effects: interference with ordinary activity; dry, flushed skin; tachycardia; urinary retention; constipation; slowing of physical and mental activity; headache; giddiness; disorientation; hallucinations; drowsiness; maniacal behavior (sometimes); and increase in body temperature. The weapons-employment manual warns that there are "critical limitations to the use of BZ" but cites the usefulness of incapacitants against intermingled enemy and friendly military units and against mixed populations of friendly, enemy, and civilian personnel.

The three remaining agents are sometimes placed together in the "riot control" category, although one—DM—is a vomiting agent. It causes sneezing and coughing, nausea, vomiting, severe headache, and acute pain and tightness in the chest; symptoms may last up to 3 hours. Another agent, CS, is one of the more recently developed agents of the general tear-gas type. It causes extreme burning and tearing of the eyes, difficulty in breathing, tightness of the chest, stinging of the skin, running nose, dizziness, and—in heavy concentrations—nausea and vomiting. The third, CN, has effects generally like those of CS, but it also causes burning, itching, and, occasionally, blisters. Effects of these two agents last for a few minutes.

The agent DM alone "is not approved for use in . . . any [riot-control] operation where deaths are not acceptable." However, the field manual reports that it may be used combined in munitions with CN and in "military or paramilitary operations, in counter-insurgency operations, or in limited or general war . . . where possible deaths are acceptable. Chemical agents CN and CS may be used to flush "unmasked enemy troops from concealed or protected positions, to reduce their ability to maneuver or use their weapons, and to facilitate their capture or their neutralization by other weapons." They are also regarded as useful "in the conduct of raids and ambushes against guerrilla forces and in defense against insurgent or guerrilla attacks and ambushes." All three, DM, CS, and CN, have been authorized for use—and used in many of these ways—in Vietnam.

biological possibilities

The identity of the biological agents standardized for use is classified, but unclassified references testify to their existence. Characteristics of the diseases that might be employed vary considerably. Brucellosis (undulant fever), for example, begins with aching, headache, loss of appetite, and stiffness, and produces constipation, loss of weight, and fever accompanied by severe sweating. It lasts for months and sometimes years, and may produce severe depression. Tularemia (rabbit fever) is characterized by sudden onset of chills, nausea, vomiting, fever, and prostration; it sometimes produces ulcerations and pneumonic complications, and may become a chronic condition. Mortality of untreated victims is as high as 30 percent. Rocky Mountain spotted fever is an acute infectious disease producing fever, joint and muscular pains, aversion to light, and sometimes delirium, coma, convulsions, tremors, muscular rigidity, and jaundice. Persistent effects may include deafness, impaired vision, and anemia. Mortality in untreated cases averages about 20 percent but can run as high as 80 percent. Psittacosis, or parrot fever, causes acute pulmonary infection, chills, fever, sore throat, constipation, weakness, and, sometimes, delirium. Mortality in untreated cases is about 10 percent; death is more common among persons over 30. Coccidioidomycosis occurs as an acute, disabling disease resembling flu, and as a chronic malignant infection that may involve any or all organs—including skin and bones—and produces abscesses. From the second form, mortality is about 50 percent. Botulism poisoning produces vomiting, constipation, thirst, weakness, headache, fever, dizziness, double vision, and dilation of the pupils. In the United States, death occurs in about 65 percent of the cases.

Particular diseases are not recommended for particular uses in unclassified Army publications, but the anticivilian character of biological weaponry is suggested: "While these agents might be employed against selected individuals, their main value appears to lie in producing mass casualties over large areas with resultant physical and psychological effects that could weaken or destroy the target group's ability to wage war."

Projections of the military utility of chemical and biological weapons now in the arsenal are not based on experience. Chinese allegations that the United States used biological weapons in Korea were never substantiated. During the Korean war some U.S. commanders sought permission to use chemical agents; they were refused, and after the war did considerable public griping. Riot control agents were used against North Korean prisoners of war during outbreaks in POW camps, however, which may have been the source of stories that chemicals were employed in combat. In addition, American planes are reported to have dropped propaganda leaflets in converted gas cannisters that were left over from earlier wars.

The Italians used mustard gas against the Ethiopians in 1936, and the Japanese are believed to have used chemicals against the Chinese between 1937 and 1943. But apart from these cases there are no authenticated instances of intentionally lethal chemical gases being employed since World War I, and there are no authenticated instances of modern use of biological weapons.

U.S. policies

According to the unclassified field manual *FM 3-10*, "the decision to employ lethal or incapacitating chemical or biological agents is a matter of national policy." That policy is now in a somewhat unsettled state.

During the 1920's the United States took the lead in promoting international prohibitions of chemical and biological warfare. One effort, the 1922 Treaty of Washington outlawing "the use in war of asphyxiating, poisonous or other gases" was ratified by the U.S. Senate but rejected by France because of provisions, unrelated to chemical warfare, that placed strict limitations on submarines. The treaty never went into effect. In 1925 the United States tried again with the Geneva Protocol, which repeated the earlier ban on chemical weapons and added a prohibition of "bacteriological warfare." It was sent to the Senate in January 1926, where it met a returning wave of isolationism and a wall of opposition led by the American Legion and the American Chemical Society. A majority of the Senate became convinced of the need to keep the CBW option open and to avoid offending the treaty's enemies. The Geneva Protocol was returned to the Senate Foreign Relations Committee and never again emerged.

Since that time, American rejection of chemical and biological warfare has rested chiefly on a statement issued by President Roosevelt in 1943:

From time to time since the present war began there have been reports that one or more of the Axis powers were seriously contemplating use of poisonous or noxious gases or other inhumane devices of warfare. I have been loath to believe that any nation, even our present enemies, could or would be willing to loose upon mankind such terrible and inhumane weapons. . . . Use of such weapons has been outlawed by the general opinion of civilized mankind. This country has not used them, and I hope that we will never be compelled to use them. I state categorically that we shall under no circumstances resort to the use of such weapons unless they are first used by our enemies.

This policy was fortified by the universal abstention from CBW in World War II, and by U.S. restraint in Korea. Roosevelt's statement was reaffirmed in January 1960 by President Eisenhower, who said, in response to a question at a press conference, "so far as my own instinct is concerned, [it] is not to start such a thing as that first."

Even while Eisenhower was speaking, however, wheels were already turning in other directions. In September 1959 Representative Robert W. Kastenmeier (D-Wis.), alarmed by the Army's emerging CBW campaign, proposed that Congress adopt a resolution opposing first use of these weapons. The resolution, its language echoing Roosevelt's, said:

Congress hereby reaffirms the longstanding policy of the United States that in the event of a war the United States shall under no circumstances resort to the use of poisonous or obnoxious gases unless they are first used by our enemies.

Kastenmeier's resolution was opposed by the State and Defense departments in September 1960 in language that testified to the reevaluation that was under way, and on grounds remarkable for their avoidance of the "first use" issue. According to the State Department, in its official response to the resolution:

As a member of the United Nations the United States . . . is committed to refrain from the use not only of biological and chemical weapons, but the use of force of any kind in a manner contrary to that Organization's Charter. Moreover, the United States is continuing its efforts to control weapons through enforceable international disarmament agreements. Of course, we must recognize our responsibilities toward our own and the Free World's security. These responsibilities involve, among other things, the maintenance of an adequate defensive posture across the entire weapons spectrum, which will allow us to defend against acts of aggression in such a manner as the President may direct. Accordingly, the Department believes that the resolution should not be adopted.

The Pentagon said:

It must be considered that biological and chemical weapons might be used with great effect against the United States in a future conflict. Available evidence indicates that other countries, including Communist regimes, are actively pursuing programs in this field. Moreover, as research continues, there is increasing evidence that some forms of these weapons, differing from previous forms, could be effectively used for defensive purposes with minimum collateral consequences. These considerations argue strongly against the proposed resolution, which appears to introduce uncertainty into the necessary planning of the Department of Defense in preparing to meet possible hostile action of all kinds.

Most recent official statements on CBW have arisen in the context of Vietnam. In a news conference held in March 1965, Secretary of State Dean Rusk told reporters, "We are not engaged in gas warfare. It is against our policy to do so. . . ." At about the same time, Deputy Defense Secretary Cyrus Vance wrote to Representative Kastenmeier that "national policy does proscribe the first use of lethal gas." In addition, the United States last month went along with a move of the United Nations General Assembly, initiated by Hungary, and endorsed a resolution calling for strict observance by all states of the principles of the Geneva Protocol. (Hungary's original version, which also condemned "any actions aimed at the use of chemical and bacteriological weapons" and termed their use an "international crime," was opposed by the U.S. as "subject to contention, misinterpretation, and distortion.")

These statements by U.S. officials have had a common theme. The Johnson administration maintains that its operations in Vietnam do not involve the "asphyxiating, poisonous, or other gases" outlawed by the Geneva Protocol, and that they do not constitute "chemical and biological warfare." Whether they do or not is something that scholars of international law can perhaps argue in many ways. But it has to be faced that despite their civilian analogues—to which the administration repeatedly has called attention—the destruction of crops by chemical or biological means, and the use of non-lethal chemicals to achieve military objectives, fit in naturally with most descriptions of CBW written before current operations in Vietnam began.

According to the latest information supplied by the Pentagon on request from *Science*, more than 500,000 acres of jungle and brush and more than 150,000 acres of cropland have been, in DOD's language, "treated with herbicides." While the Pentagon points out that this area is a negligible fraction of Vietnam's arable land, the program is now tripling in capacity, to 18 planes. (Correspondents in Vietnam report that, lettered above a room in the headquarters of the men who fly the missions is a motto: *Only We Can Prevent Forests.*) In other operations, the use of what the Pentagon still terms "riot control agents," after a period of being closely monitored in Washington, has passed to the initiative of local commanders. The Pentagon told *Science* that it no longer knows how many times and for what purposes they have been employed.

Apart from Vietnam itself, and the issues, raised by many scientists, of the effects of these chemicals on Vietnamese civilians and on the countryside, there is another question: Will what we are doing there, however the government chooses to label it, lead to further CBW operations—by the U.S. or by others, during this war or the next— about whose character there could be no semantic quibble? Officials of the Pentagon and the State Department deny that we are setting a precedent or that there is a risk of escalation. On historical grounds alone, their position is weak. The first use of gas in World War I was not the German attack with chlorine in 1915 but a French attack in 1914—with tear gas. United States officials find the Vietnam war an especially bitter and frustrating one. There is constant search for a technological breakthrough—with some suggestions bordering on the bizarre—that will produce a political victory in the fight against elusive guerrillas. We appear headed for involvement in guerrilla warfare for a long time. Proposals to reach further into the waiting CBW arsenal provided by research have traveled high into the Pentagon. Until now they have been resisted. But, if the record of the Vietnam war demonstrates anything, it is that frustration and a sense of futility can make even desperate measures seem attractive. What is "unthinkable" at one moment may be policy the next.

11

Radiation Roulette

But if you be afeared to hear the worst,
Then let the worst unheard fall on your head.
—BASTARD, IN *King John*

One of the most dramatic, and most traumatic, events in man's 1.5 million years on earth was the discovery that the submicroscopic speck of an atom embraces energy and power beyond most men's imaginations. Moreover, the prospect of poisonous atomic radiation conveys panic to life-loving people who have little influence over the machines of science or political leaders who hold the power of world decisions.

Men grope for a way to disentangle the nuclear web spun by their clever minds. Yet, despite our fears, the unthinking atom continues to yield grudgingly the wherewithal to use its awful power for the betterment of mankind. While someone may someday push the nuclear button to blast the world into a fireball of eternity, the very horror of the prospect might preclude it from human experience. The greater hazard of the nuclear age may more likely be the creation and release of radioactive poisons accompanying the experimental and useful release of energy from the atom.

Medieval alchemists experimented diligently to unravel the mystery of the atom. Sensing that matter is not immutable, they sought ways to create gold from base elements. They were a thousand years ahead of their time; in 1942 Enrico Fermi was led to the discovery of even greater power than gold. In the legendary squash court under the bleachers of Stagg Field at the University of Chicago, Fermi and his group of investigators shot neutrons from splitting uranium atoms into a critical mass or "pile" of uranium and brought about a chain reaction that proved once and for all the incredible energy of the atom.

A single atom of uranium explodes with the release of 195 million electron volts (Mev), and an atom of plutonium disintegrates with similar violence. Unfortunately, part of the energy is given off as lethal radiation. Moreover, products are produced by atomic disintegrations that also release these energetic rays and toxic particles, some of them for extremely long periods of time.

Forms of radiation that adversely affect living organisms are:

Gamma rays and *x-rays*, similar to light, are electromagnetic radiations at the short end of the light spectrum. As the wave length of electromagnetic radiation decreases from infrared, through red, orange, green, blue, ultraviolet, and finally x-rays and gamma rays, the amount of energy increases. Radiation in the highly energetic end of the spectrum is disruptive to living cellular functions at the molecular level.

Beta particles are electrons traveling at high speeds. Electrons are components of all elements and therefore abundantly present in all living things. Many radioactive substances, however, during their decay to less energetic materials, expel some of their electrons with great force. These high-speed electrons, though lacking the penetrating power of gamma rays and x-rays, are damaging to living tissue. If a long-lasting beta emitter gets into the system, it can cause serious damage.

Alpha particles are energetic helium nuclei (helium atoms minus their electrons). They do not have the penetrating power of electrons and, because they are larger, are more readily scattered. The precise effect of alpha particles on living tissue is not well known, but exposure to them is not as dangerous as to beta and gamma rays.

As gamma, beta, and alpha rays and particles hurtle through the spaces of materials and tissues, they bounce from atom to atom knocking off pieces, or ions, as they go. Hence, these rays and particles are called *ionizing radiation*.

Excessive exposure to ionizing radiation results in severe burns or radiation sickness, which may cause death in hours, days, or weeks. However, it is low-level radiation about which we are most concerned because of its less obvious contaminative effects, as well as the danger of inadvertent exposure from medical or industrial applications.

The most serious biological effect of low-level radiation is on the genetic material contained in the chromosomes of living cells. The hereditary features of living organisms are determined by material in little packages or *genes*, which one can think of as strung like beads to make up the chromosomes. The genes, in turn, contain smaller components, the DNA,[1] which in turn is a double string of smaller units (nucleotides), twisted like a helix or spiral staircase. The twisted helix contains the "genetic code" in the form of key letters (the nucleotide molecules) arranged in groups of threes to spell out instructions for creating and maintaining the intricate complexities of each kind of living thing.

The genetic code, while remarkably dependable, is not infallible. Its operation can be disrupted by highly unfavorable influences such as radiation or biologically active chemicals. Changes in the genetic code are not uncommon and, when they occur, cause changes (mutations) in the vital functioning or physical form of the organism. Background radiation from the sun and space, as well as from radioactive materials present on Earth, in ground, water, and air, is the cause of many of the naturally occurring mutations. However, the number and frequency of mutations can be greatly enhanced by exposing the organism to a radiation source. Such radiation, by the impinging of energetic rays or particles near or on DNA, may foul up the genetic code with disastrous results to the organism or more likely to its offspring, since the dividing cells of the sex organs during formation of the sperm or eggs are most highly susceptible to ionizing radiation.

Some of the most dangerous radioactive elements are those that emit radiation during a long decay period. Calcium-45 has a half-life of 164 days; sodium-22, 2.6 years; cobalt-60, 5 years, and carbon-14, 5,568 years. Strontium-90, which collects in the bones of animals in place of calcium, has a half-life of 27.7 years.

Clearly, from both short- and long-range viewpoints, problems of radiation control and radioactive waste disposal are of immediate and urgent concern to mankind. The solution and successful handling of these problems necessitates a thorough understanding of the sources, types, and intensity of radiation and their effects on biological systems.

---

[1] *Deoxyribonucleic acid.*

The Genetic Damage
Produced by Radiation

H. J. Muller

Genetics seems to be the field of "natural" science which is most abused with political and other special interests, in their attempts to fabricate theoretical bases for their practices, as in the case of Hitler's racist obsessions and Stalin's Michurinism. Although these two perversions are now gradually weakening their hold, they served in their day as tools in the wreaking of untold harm. In these two situations, those of us scientists who were in or near the field concerned felt it incumbent upon ourselves to speak up in the defense of science as we knew it, even though it was certainly not the force of our own words which finally turned the tide.

And now today, even in our own country, we see certain versions—or is it perversions?—of genetics raising their heads, not primarily among geneticists, but among groups who wish to create a semblance of scientific support for some preconceived policy. The matter at issue now is that of the genetic effects of radiation. This is a subject on which this writer has given his only previous talks before this Academy, one of 27 and one of 14 years ago.[1] At the present time, in view of the grave danger to which the growing distortions of this subject may lead, it would seem to be in the spirit of the Kimber Genetics Award for this occasion to be used, not for another purely academic treatment, but for a frank discussion of the matter in relation to current affairs.

Wide circulation has recently been given to statements by certain prominent publicists, including physicians and others working on government projects, alleging that the bombings of Hiroshima and Nagasaki have left the descendant populations unharmed, or possibly even

---

[1] *H. J. Muller,* Proc. Natl. Acad. Sci. U.S., 14: *714 (1928)*; Science, 93: *438 (1941)*.

Reprinted from *Bulletin of the Atomic Scientists 11* (6): 210–12, 230 (1955) with permission of the publisher.

improved. Opposed to these are other voices, calling loudly, and in some cases in a suspiciously vitriolic tone, for an end to all nuclear test explosions, on the ground that even the tests are already seriously undermining the genetic basis of all mankind. To geneticists, both of these contrary claims appear so far from the truth that they can be interpreted only as special pleadings, dictated by ulterior motives.

It is no longer a matter of doubt among scientists working in this field that radiation, of the types derived from radioactive substances or x-ray machines, does produce permanent changes, mutations, in the hereditary constitution of living things of all kinds. The most numerous and important of these changes, occurring in the individual hereditary particles or genes and therefore called gene mutations, arise with a frequency depending proportionately on the total dose of radiation. For instance, one-tenth of a given dose produces one-tenth the number of gene mutations, no matter in how long or short a time that total dose was received. Thus, no exposure is so tiny that it does not carry its corresponding mutational risk.

inconclusiveness of hiroshima and nagasaki data

It is well established that the overwhelming majority of mutations (over 99 percent) are harmful, causing some functional impairment. However, any given harmful effect is usually too small to be recognized by ordinary means, especially when it is inherited from only one parent, as is almost always the case, and when, as in any human population, it occurs in the midst of a motley throng of variant characteristics, differing from person to person, which arose as natural mutations among many generations of ancestors. For these reasons, statistics on human populations, like those obtained at Hiroshima and Nagasaki, are ill suited for finding out whether mutations have been produced by a given exposure.[2] That is why the group of responsible scientists who signed the official report on these investigations in Japan, published in *Science*, November 6, 1953,[3] stated that it had "always been doubtful whether significant findings" could be obtained by the methods there used, and pointed out that the inconclusive results, while not definitely

---

[2] H. J. *Muller*, Science in Progress, 7: *93* (*New Haven: Yale University Press, 1951*); Acta Radiologica, 41: *5* (*1954*); Amer. J. Obstet. and Gynec., 67: *467* (*1954*); Radiation Biology, 1: *Chap. 7 and 8* (*New York: McGraw-Hill, 1954*).

[3] *J. V. Neel et al.,* Science, 118: *537* (*1953*).

positive, were at the same time "entirely consistent with what is known of the radiation genetics of a wide variety of other material." In other words, there could well have been as many harmful mutations produced in these human populations but lying undetected, as experiments with other animals have shown to be produced in them by such exposure.

Each detrimental mutation, even though small in effect and lost to view in the jumble of a heterogeneous population, tends to continue from generation to generation and to hamper successive descendants, until at last it happens to tip the scales against one of its possessors, and that line of descent then dies out in consequence of the inherited disability. This involves either the premature death of the affected individual, or his failure to reproduce.

A significant attack on the problem of how many mutations are produced by a given dose has required refined genetic tests, utilizing reasonably uniform biological material in precisely controlled crosses. This has meant experimenting on animals and plants. The notable recent work of W. L. Russell at Oak Ridge, on mice,[4] shows that at least ten times as many gene mutations are produced in them by a given dose of radiation as my co-workers and I had found to be produced at a corresponding stage in fruit flies, which had previously been the best studied material. Since humans are so much closer to mice than to flies in all important respects, we must take Russell's figure as a closer approximation to that for humans than the one obtained for flies.

Working on this premise, we find that, on a conservative estimate, a dose of 200 reps,[5] such as many Hiroshima survivors must have received, would probably have caused each of their offspring to inherit, on the average, at least one mutation produced by the exposure, in addition to the several or many natural mutations, mostly derived from long past generations. It is only wishful thinking to regard the inconclusive statistics gathered on the Hiroshima population as casting any doubt on this conclusion.

Since the numerous disabilities and deaths thus occasioned will be spread out very thin, over a large number of generations, the over-all cost, although great, will be much too scattered and insidious to affect the population as a whole noticeably. And the individual sufferers will be unable to trace their troubles to the source. At long last, the damaged heredity must become eliminated from the race by the painful

---

[4] *W. L. Russell*, Cold Spring Harbor Symp. Quant. Biol. 16: *327 (1952)*.
[5] *That is, Roentgen equivalents, physical.*

process of extinction of lines. But modern high standards of living and of medical practice tend greatly to delay this elimination.

Among fruit flies, the elimination can be much faster, because it is the usual thing for more than one hundred young to die for every one that survives. Thus even after massive irradiations, repeated for generations, as in the experiments carried out by Bruce Wallace at Cold Spring Harbor, the population may recover relatively soon. In fact, it may even be benefitted by the rapid multiplication, at the expense of both the weaklings and the original type, of the extremely rare beneficial mutations that the radiation had produced. But such treatment would be ruinous to a modern human population, with its already extreme variability, its very low rate of multiplication, and its artificial hindrances to selection.

genetic effects of test explosions

To calculate the genetic damage caused in this country by all the nuclear tests to date (including both those in the USA and those in the Pacific and Soviet Union), we will provisionally take the AEC's published estimate of a tenth of a roentgen as the average for each American. In the statement that this amount is about equal to that of a chest x-ray it is doubtless meant that the total dose reaching the reproductive organs from all the tests is about as much as reaches the interior of the chest from one chest x-ray. This amount seems minute, but we must multiply it by 160,000,000, representing the population. It is curious that the product which we then obtain, 16,000,000 "man-r's," is the same as that obtained when we take 100 r, assuming this to be not far from the average dose received by Hiroshima survivors, and multiply it by 160,000, the approximate number of those survivors. Hence, the number of harmful mutations which will be inherited by our own descendants as a result of all test explosions turns out to be not far from the number among the Japanese as a result of the Hiroshima fission explosion.

This number of mutations is certainly in the tens of thousands at least (our reckoning gives about 80,000 as the number present in our successor population), and it will mean, in the end, several times this number of hampered lives. Yet, far more than Hiroshima, the effects will be so scattered, in this case not only in time but also in space and separated by many more individuals who have mutations of natural origin only, that, as a group, the effects will be completely lost to sight. That is, their connection with the radiation will not be traceable. It is nevertheless true that each individual casualty, though concealed, must be regarded as a significant evil, which we have no right to dismiss lightly.

On the other hand, when the effects here in question are taken in relation to the total American population (numbered in billions) of the scores of generations in which they find expression, and to the total number, much larger still, of natural mutations contained in that population, it is evident that *relatively* to these totals the damage is in this case minute. It cannot be said to involve a significant undermining of the hereditary constitution of the population as a whole, for it results in an increase of much less than one percent (possibly less than one hundredth of one percent) in the number of mutations contained in that population.

It is true that the AEC's figure of one-tenth roentgen received by each of us from the tests seems to represent only the gamma radiation penetrating us from the outside. Until we are given more information about how much "soft" radiation we may be getting from fall-out substances that have entered our bodies, about its persistence, all estimates of the genetic damage must remain subject to much revision upward. Yet unless the amount of radioactive material that we take into ourselves in this way turns out to be far greater than we have been led to suppose, our general conclusion could not be altered that, relatively to the natural mutations already present, those produced by the test explosions would form but a minute contingent.

In order to decide whether a continuance of the tests are justified, it is necessary first to admit the damage, and then to weigh our estimate of it against the potential benefits to be derived from the tests, or rather, against the probable damage which would follow from the alternative policy. It is only by this kind of criterion that we can justify the use of so lethal a device as the automobile, for example. In fact, automobiles kill and maim tens of thousands of us, not over a period of hundreds of years like the test explosions, but every single year. On the other hand, automobiles in many indirect and direct ways help to save lives, as well as to bring many other benefits that outweigh the accidents.

The same kind of reasoning is necessary to justify the use of carefully controlled x-rays and radioactivity in medicine. A recent Public

Health Service survey[6] indicates that our people are annually receiving much more radiation in these ways than as a result of nuclear test explosions. Unfortunately, however, the majority of physicians have for twenty-eight years closed their eyes to the genetic damage. Hence they neglect, as a rule, to provide shields over the reproductive organs of their patients, and to take other elementary precautions for limiting the exposures and keeping track of the total exposure of each patient throughout his life. These practices result in the committing of entirely unnecessary and indefensible genetic damage, far greater in its totality to date and probably per year, than that caused by all test explosions. It is largely this reckless attitude on the part of physicians which has encouraged extremists to claim that nuclear explosions are genetically harmless or beneficial.

the weighing of alternatives

So many of the public are already aware of the genetic damage produced by radiation that their morale is weakened and their apprehensions are increased when they see that the damage is denied by prominent sponsors of our national defense. Thus the door is opened for their acceptance of the defeatist propaganda which alleges that even the tests are seriously undermining the biological integrity of mankind. In this situation, the only defensible or effective course for our democracy is to recognize the truth, to admit the damage, and to base our case for continuance of the tests on a weighing of the alternative consequences.

I submit that we do not need to fear the results of this appeal to our better judgment. Have we no right to expect individual sacrifices when the stakes are democracy and intellectual freedom themselves? Surely there is good evidence that ruthless antagonists would long since have imposed totalitarianism on all the world if we had not pushed the development of our nuclear arms, and that in fact the development of our more conventional arms, as well as of measures for reducing our vulnerability to nuclear attack, are today no less important? Is not this procedure, even though it is fraught with direst peril and requires monumental self-control, nevertheless indispensable at this stage, before we can pass to the further stage at which both sides alike will recognize the long-term futility of this unstable equilibrium, and will at last agree

---

[6] *D. W. Moeller et al.,* Public Health Reports, 68: *57* (*1953*).

to that globally controlled disarmament, necessarily embracing not only nuclear but also conventional arms, short of which humanity will never be safe?

It is natural that those in opposition to us should be making every effort to have nuclear arms prohibited *selectively*. For that would change the military balance greatly in their favor, in view of the fact that at present we are ahead in nuclear arms and they in conventional arms and armies. Some of the critics who demand a ban on test explosions are so silent on this point that one wonders whether they are not actually aiming at this very result. But for many of us who abhor totalitarianism, that form of slavery appears to be a condition as miserable and as hopeless, if grown worldwide, as the barbarism which total war might bring. Another reason why those who sincerely desire a reduction of human suffering should not limit their demand for disarmament to the more radical mass-destruction techniques is that today weapons of the more traditional types have been so developed that they also, in the full-scale use occasioned by a world war, would bring about wholesale catastrophe. Our own tactics therefore should be to continue the development of both nuclear and other arms, as well as means of protection, while at the same time earnestly offering to join in a really balanced and controlled reduction of all kinds of armaments. If we steadfastly insist on this proposition, it is unlikely that any group would be in a position to refuse it indefinitely.

the need for perspective

If we may look forward to a time when our present international tensions have become less acute, we may anticipate that in that situation the public will be in a better mind-set for viewing the whole question of the genetic damage from radiation in a still wider perspective, based upon a fuller realization of genetic processes in general. They may then come to see that even the considerable toll of genetic deterioration that a nuclear war might bring is probably not as great as that resulting from a couple of centuries of our modern peacetime civilization. It is probably an undervaluation to suppose that in each generation we today succeed, by means of our advanced medical, industrial, and social techniques, in saving for reproduction only half of the people who in past times would have had their lines of descent extinguished as a result of their genetic shortcomings. On the basis of this conservative premise, our population would in the course of some eight generations (not much more than 200 years) have added to its habitual "load of mutations"[7] about as many more as would have arisen naturally in $\frac{1}{2} \times 8$, that is, in four generations. On a provisional estimate, this would be about the same as the number of mutations that would have been produced by the irradiation of every member of one generation with 320 roentgen units. This is a dose much greater than that received by the average Hiroshima survivor. It is not, however, as great as what would be received by a person occupationally exposed for 25 years to radiation given at the rate which conforms to what has been officially termed the "permissible dose" (0.3 r per week).

A mutation is just as bad no matter whether its presence results from the action of a previous generation in having perpetuated one that was already in existence in consequence of natural causes, or whether it had been artificially produced by application of radiation or of mustard gas. The first of these two means of getting it represents the boomeranging effect whereby our highly developed techniques result in the visiting of more of our own biological plagues upon our descendants. The only way in which such an aftermath can be avoided is by the development of more understanding and a more socially directed motivation among the public at large in regard to matters of genetics and reproduction.

Here again the way out requires us frankly to admit and to face the problem, in the hope that the public will not wish indefinitely to continue favoring practices that lead to its genetic deterioration. Of course this does not mean that we should abandon modern technology —far from it. It means that, in order to enable our descendants to retain the benefits of our technology, we must match it with a higher conception of our duties to subsequent generations. According to this more advanced morality, the saving of a life does not automatically justify its production of offspring, for the chief criterion on which to base decisions in the planning of parenthood would be the welfare of the descendants themselves.

Such a revision of outlook involves the development of a new and more intelligent type of idealism in regard to genetics: one that consciously strives to bequeath to each succeeding generation as good an outfit of genes as it can manage to. It is true that we might here dispute at length about the meaning of the word "good," as used in this connection. However, this question also is one that must be tackled

[7] *H. J. Muller,* Amer. J. Human Genet., 2: *111* (*1950*).

eventually. There are indications that it will be found to be by no means
a hopeless question, still less a meaningless one as some critics contend,
and that even genetics, through evolution science, will have some contribution to make in regard to it. If all this comes to pass, then finally, in
the field of human genetics, even as in that of nuclear war, the old words
of Edwin Markham may prove to have been prophetic:

> The world is a vapor, and only the vision is real;
> Yea, nothing can hold against Hell but the winged ideal!

Food Supplies
after A-Blast

Food supplies in the aftermath of an atomic attack could become as critical a problem as that of medical supplies—at least that was the feeling of many civil defense people. To find how critical, the Federal Civil Defense Administration called on the Food and Drug Administration to supervise an experiment with foods for AEC's blast in Nevada in May, 1955.

As a result of these tests, FDA now knows that:

- All foods recovered intact one mile or further from the target are safe for immediate consumption
- All foods and their containers exposed within a quarter of a mile of ground zero are subjected to radioactivity from gamma rays and neutrons
- Consumption of foods from the close-in area within two to seven days after exposure can only be tolerated for short periods
- Use of the radioactive foods should be restricted to disaster situations
- All foods containing phosphorus or sodium chloride become permanently radioactive

E. P. Laug, reporting FDA's findings to the annual meeting of the Association of Official Agricultural Chemists in Washington, said there is little doubt that phosphorus contributes the most serious radioactivity. The Bureau of Standards Handbook No. 52 sets the permissible phosphorus radiation level at 2×10^{-4} microcuries per gram of water intake. FDA, assuming the same tolerance in foods, found that 15 days after exposure in the 0.25-mile radius, 23 of the 28 bulk and retail foods tested exceeded this limit. Milk powder, cheese, oatmeal, navy beans, and baking powder headed the list. Of the 54 canned foods

Reprinted from *Agricultural and Food Chemistry*, *4* (11): November 1956, 910–912. Copyright 1956 by the American Chemical Society. Reprinted by permission of the copyright owner.

tested, activity was excessive in all but eight, with seafoods showing the highest counts.

Even in an emergency situation, foods containing radioactive phosphorus in these amounts could obviously not be eaten for long. However, concludes Laug, "in the face of possible mass starvation, consumption of such radioactive foods would certainly constitute the preferable risk."

Conversion of stable chlorine-35 to the long-lived radioactive chlorine-36 is also of interest chemically. Because of this action, all exposed foods containing sodium chloride will show a slight but permanent trace of radioactivity. Table salt, for example, maintains measurable activity even after a year.

The Food and Drug Administration tested 100 different types of commodities—about 1500 tons. Included were heat-processed foods packed in cans and glass; frozen foods; beverages; semiperishable fruits and vegetables; fresh and processed foods; and bulk staples.

In one series of tests, FDA stored foods in on-the-site homes, store-type structures, and industrial buildings one to three miles from ground zero. Here damages were physical and similar to those caused by other disasters—heavy explosions and hurricanes. Shelving attached to walls at right angles to the blast lost their contents by drumhead action of the walls. Shelves on walls in line with the blast suffered less displacement. Food stored in basements was not moved, and any missile damage occurred on shelving in a direct line with windows or doors.

The second test series was set up in the quarter-mile area closest to the blast. In this radius, buildings were not available for test storage, so FDA stored the test foods in shallow trenches and covered them with a layer of dirt, one to two inches deep. These foods received maximum irradiation and maximum force of pressure waves, but were shielded from burning in the heat flash. Induced radiation at this distance is of the order 10^{12} neutrons per square centimeter. Samples from this area furnished the significant findings on irradiation effects.

Pressure waves caused some physical damage to foods in the trenches. Glass breakage and splitting of wooden panels were extensive, and losses from crushing and distortion of cans amounted to 5%. Semiperishables were badly crushed and bruised. As might be expected.

On recovery of the food samples two days after the blast, all glass containers were discolored (clouded) and highly radioactive. However, this irradiation was never extended to the contents of the containers,

Effects of Irradiation on Foods Placed ¼ Mile from Target

	Radioactivity	Taste and Odor	Other Effects
Dry milk solids	Excessive P^{32} after 15 days	Distinct off-flavors on reconstruction with water	American cheese and skimmed milk showed excessive P^{32} activity after 13 days.
Butter and Margarine	Excessive P^{32} after 13 days	Butter was "cheesy" or "oxidized"; margarine, "stale"	Deterioration similar to aging under poor storage conditions
Meats:			
Fresh	Low	Meats were dry and coarse after cooking; flavor and odor unacceptable	Cooked beef was "medicinal" or "liverish"; lamb darkened
Cured and processed	Higher than fresh meats; lunch meats and frankfurters, excessive P^{32} after 10 days	No detectable taste defects	Frankfurters were bulged and curled; dried beef decreased in riboflavin after storage
Canned Foods:			
Soups, vegetables, fruits, juices	Lowest of all canned foods	Only apple juice was inferior in taste	Catchup with 3% salt was more active than salt-free tomato juice
Seafoods	Excessive P^{32} after 15 days		
Baby foods	Excessive P^{32} after 10 days		
Pork and beans[a]	Excessive P^{32} after 10 days		
Semiperishable fruits and vegetables	Low	No detectable effects	Raisins showed excessive P^{32} after 13 days
Frozen Foods	Low, except cod fillets	No change in flavor, odor, or taste	Frozen foods had added protection of insulated containers
Flours[b]			
Without additives	Low	Some deterioration of flour in small packages	
With baking powder, salt, etc.	Higher due to P^{32} and sodium chloride	Cornmeal had bitter taste when baked	Cornmeal deterioration due to accelerated aging effect
Cereals	Low	Only rolled oats developed "burnt" flavor and poor aroma	Oats showed no loss of thiamin, riboflavin, or niacin after storage

Effects of Irradiation on Foods Placed ¼ Mile from Target
(*Continued*)

	Radioactivity	Taste and Odor	Other Effects
Beverages	Low, except beer with salt content	Slight loss of sweetness in soft drinks; coffee and tea flavors unaffected	Should be potable at any time

[a] Navy beans showed excessive P^{32} activity after 15 days
[b] Macaroni showed excessive P^{32} activity after 13 days

and after five days, less than 1% of the activity due to sodium-24 remained. Plastic packaging films except polyethylene showed some activity (attributed to mineral plasticizers), but this decayed rapidly.

Metal cans also became moderately radioactive, but this activity, primarily from coatings, lasted much longer than that in glass. There is evidence that some of the activity is due to tin—a particular isotope having a half life of approximately 100 days. Can liners themselves were radioactive, especially "C" enamels used to prevent discoloration by black iron sulfide. Since liners contain zinc, activity was also traced to zinc-64 with 250-day half life and to food-derived sulfur that combined with the zinc.

There was no sign of toxic by-products being formed in any of the foods, and nutritional values remained good after the test. Considering the normal variations in vitamin content of foods, these losses were relatively unimportant. Vitamin losses from vitamin-rich foods were insignificant; foods considered poor sources showed largest losses.

Chemical analyses, as evidence for changes, were conducted only if samples showed organoleptic or physical effects. One of the most striking chemical changes was the yellowing of table salt, originally believed to be due to liberation of free iodine. Analysis, though, did not support this belief, nor did it provide any other clue to the reaction.

Foods from the quarter-mile area were made into diets for rats. No deviation from normal growth and development was noted even after one year.

Laug stressed the fact that these test conclusions apply only for fission-type explosions. He and the FDA believe, however, that some of the findings may be related qualitatively to larger explosions of the thermonuclear type tested in the Pacific.

Radiobiological Studies at the Eniwetok Test Site and Adjacent Areas of the Western Pacific

Lauren R. Donaldson

The nuclear experiments conducted at Bikini and Eniwetok Atolls in the Marshall Islands are more than experiments to measure physical forces; they are unparalleled scientific experiments involving a great number of scientific disciplines. Among the disciplines represented, biology is taking a leading role.

Biologists have been a part of this scientific team activity since the inception of the atomic tests at Bikini in 1946. Studies with the radioactive materials resulting from the weapons tests and deposited in the sea and on the islands have made it possible to follow the biological cycling of these materials even where they have become diluted to infinitesimal quantities, by standards of ordinary chemical analysis. Hines (1951) [1] has described the general problem of evaluation of this research.

Much attention has been given to the more immediate effects of the weapons tested upon the fauna and flora of the atolls but such studies, important as they are, have not occupied the total planning, thinking and execution of the program of biological studies. Extensive investigations using the facilities, personnel, and equipment available at the test organizations and test sites have answered many questions relating to the economy of the sea, have opened up new knowledge of the life zones of coral atolls, and have reshaped in important ways some of the basic

Reprinted from *Biological Problems in Water Pollution*, Public Health Service Technical Report No. W60-3, compiled by C. M. Tarzwell: 1–7 (1960), with permission of the author.

concepts of biological science. By using the radioactive or "tagged" minerals available and the methods of microchemist and physicist, biology has advanced to a more exact science.

Since the pre-test preparations for Operation Crossroads in 1946, representatives of marine biology, oceanography, and geology have made intensive studies at some of the atolls in the northern Marshall Islands, with the result that few oceanic areas have been studied as intensively by such a variety of specialists as have Bikini and Eniwetok Atolls.

Notable contributions have been made to the knowledge of the geology of atolls by Tracey et al. (1948) [2] and Ladd (1952) [3]. Von Arx (1954) [4] has reported on the water circulation in Bikini lagoon, and the action of ocean waves on Bikini reefs has been described by Munk and Sargent (1954) [5]. Robinson (1954) [6] made studies of the sea temperature in the Marshall Islands. Barnes et al. (1948) [7] reported on the ocean circulation in the Marshall Islands area, and Mao and Yoshida (1954) [8] described the physical oceanography of the same region. Schultz et al. (1953) [9] have described the fishes of the Marshall and Mariana Islands. The plants of Bikini, etc., were studied and reported on by Taylor (1950) [10], Fosberg (1953) [11], St. John (1949) [12], and Biddulph (1952) [13]. Dawson (1957) [14] has reported on the algae of Eniwetok Atoll.

Studies on the distribution of radioactive minerals produced by the atomic tests conducted in the Marshalls have been published by the Laboratory of Radiation Biology,[1] University of Washington [15].

An atoll may be described as a roughly oval, coralline reef rising 15,000 feet above the ocean floor. Within the surrounding reef there is enclosed a shallow lagoon generally with a maximum depth of about 180 feet. The lagoon is open to the ocean by one or more passes cutting through the reef, most of which is awash except at low tides. Emergent land consists of low sandy islands with an elevation seven to ten feet above sea level; elevations as high as twenty feet are rare. The islands occupy only a small fraction of the total area of an atoll. Bikini lagoon covers 229 square miles (Handbook on the Trust Territory of the Pacific Islands [16]) and has a dry land area of two and a third square miles divided among some thirty-six islands and islets; Eniwetok lagoon covers 388 square miles, has a dry land area of two and one-fourth square miles, and forty islands.

---

[1] *Formerly the Applied Fisheries Laboratory.*

These atolls lie in a zone of the northeast trade winds. Because of the constancy of direction of the winds, there are distinct differences in reef form between the windward and leeward sides of the atoll. The windward side is generally considered the region of most rapid growth and is characterized by a narrow, slightly elevated ridge near the reef edge, the *Lithothamnion* ridge, which is lacking on the leeward side. The latter drops off vertically to depths of 100 to 200 feet on the seaward side, while the seaward slope of the windward reef falls away at an angle of about forty-five degrees.

On the reef and in the lagoon there is an abundance of colorful plant and animal life in which the keen competition between different species for space, and food is very evident. On every hand there is evidence of rapid growth and simultaneous destruction. Masses of reef-building coral are competing with each other and with the coralline marine algae for space one often overgrowing the other. Schools of green parrotfish gnaw wide scratches on the coral. Fleshy patches of algae are pressed tightly against the surface of the coral to hold against the surges of the water pushed across the reef by the crashing breakers. Sea urchins and clams grind niches into the hard coral, some of them constantly feeding on the cover of bacterial and algal film which is as constantly being replaced. The clams, the corals, some small fish and other forms are ceaselessly removing from suspension in the water the small, often microscopic, plants, animals, and bits of debris which make up the plankton. In regions of quieter water, where sand has been deposited, sea cucumbers and spider snails, among the larger forms, turn the sand again and again in their gleaning for food.

Large schools of goatfish, mullet, surgeonfish, and other plant and plankton feeders are a common sight. Preying on unwary or disabled members of these schools are the carnivorous fish—the groupers, tuna, jacks and sharks. Ultimately the waste products and carcasses of these and other carnivores are returned to the lagoon and reef to complete the cycle.

Little or no time is lost between steps in the biological cycling of materials for there is not only an abundance of organisms but also a wide variety of species—some 700 among the fishes alone (Schultz et al. (1953) [9])—so that whatever is not utilized by one is quickly taken by another. There is here a perfect economy of use of substances essential to life.

Available substances are rapidly taken up by the biota, never remaining long in the water to be diluted and washed away. This is dramatically demonstrated following an atomic test in which radioactive materials are deposited in the water. Within hours, the great bulk of these materials is to be found in the living organisms. Plankton and some of the algae, which are the key organisms in the food chain, may concentrate within themselves more than a thousand times the amount of radioactive substances found in the sea water. The herbivorous fish and invertebrates have lower concentrations of radionuclides at any given time than do the plants on which they feed, and progressing along the food chain to the carnivores the concentrations become lower and lower. Within each organism there is a differential concentration from tissue to tissue, the digestive organs having a higher concentration than the other tissues, where a more selective deposition as to specific isotopes has taken place.

More specifically, plankton, the oceanic plants and animals that drift about passively with little or no resistance to water movements, may influence greatly the distribution of radioactive materials in the sea. These forms include many groups of organisms from the simple one-celled plants to the larval forms of vertebrates.

Plankton acquire radioisotopes by absorption, adsorption, or both. Plankton, especially phytoplankton, present a greater absorptive surface to the environment than any other group of marine organisms. Thus, the major initial concentration of radioactive isotopes probably occurs in the phytoplankton—the same organisms which comprise the foundation of the food chain in the sea. The isotopes especially concentrated by these forms are, for the most part, representatives of those elements which tend to form strong complexes with organic material. They include most of the anionic radioisotopes, with the exception of iodine, and the cationic radioisotopes produced by neutron induction including radioactive zinc, cobalt, iron and manganese. All of the cationic radioisotopes concentrated in the plankton are biologically important elements comprising the essential parts of enzyme systems and, in one case at least, an essential vitamin.

The levels of radioisotopes present in the plankton vary with time after release of the radioactive materials, mainly because of the variation in availability due to physical decay of the individual radioisotopes [17]. In general, however, plankton contain the three radioactive isotopes of cobalt. Co^{57}, Co^{58} and Co^{60}, at a level of 11 to 50 percent of the total radioactivity. Zn^{65} is present at a level of 12 to 47 percent; Fe^{55-59} at a level of 1 to 40 percent; Mn^{54} in trace amounts, and the fission products Zr^{95}-Nb^{95} at levels of 3 to 44 percent; Ru^{106}-Rh^{106} from 0 to 7 percent; Ce^{144}-Pr^{144}, 0 to 13 percent; and Cs^{137} in trace amounts, if present at all [18]. Sr^{90}-Y^{90} has not been found in plankton.

Once the radioactive materials have been absorbed or adsorbed by the plankton, their distribution is likely to be greater both vertically and horizontally than if distribution were solely dependent upon the surface currents. One reason for a greater distribution would be that absorption by plankton makes the radionuclides available to larger organisms which can move beyond the current's boundaries. Similarly these materials also become available to the local resident populations and, as they are recycled through the food chain, the effect is a delay in their distribution away from the original area of contamination. Another factor influencing the distribution of radioactive materials by plankton is their diurnal vertical migration. If this migration were great enough to take the plankton below the current stream, it would extend the vertical distribution and also slow down the horizontal distribution, because the plankton would be moving horizontally more slowly than the water.

Plankton may carry radioactive materials from the deeper waters of the lagoons to the surface or even up onto the reefs and eventually to the islands by vertical migration. At Bikini it has been observed, for example, that these materials were picked up by the plankton in the deeper waters of the lagoon during the daytime. The concentrated radionuclides in the plankton were then transported to the surface by the diurnal vertical migration of these minute forms. At the surface, their presence at night caused the surface radiation content to increase measurably over the daylight readings. The fouling organisms on the bottoms of the ships and the plankton feeders on the reef became increasingly radioactive at night as the transport of the radioactive products continued.

It can be said then that plankton may cause the distribution of radionuclides in the sea to be different from that which would be expected from the distribution by currents alone in the following respects: (1) a delay in the movement from the area of original contamination, (2) a slower down-current movement, (3) a limited dispersion up-current or beyond the currents' boundaries, (4) a greater vertical distribution, and (5) an over-all greater dispersion of relatively lower concentrations.

Aquatic plants or algae may be free-floating (as are the phytoplank-

ton), attached to the reefs, or growing in the shallow water. Just as do
land plants, the algae contribute to the food supply of animal populations. Minerals as well as organic materials, concentrated and incorporated into the algae, are passed on in the food chain to the animals that
feed upon them. Thus the radioactive materials pass through the algae
to the animals in the normal course of food gathering.

The affinity of algae for some of the radioisotopes is well known. For
example, *Asparagopsis*, a marine alga found on the reefs at Bikini and
Eniwetok, has a great affinity for iodine [19]. In the presence of I^{131}
Asparagopsis becomes radioactive. This alga is a succulent morsel
sought by fishes; thus the I^{131} passes to the fish and along the food
chain.

The land plants of the tropical islands of the Pacific atolls become
contaminated with radioactive materials in two ways: (1) by fallout of
material from the air or from the rain water with direct absorption
through the leaves, and (2) by absorption from the soil.

The soils of the atolls are generally deficient in potassium. This
deficiency speeds the uptake of Cs^{137} by the plants. Although Ce^{144} is
present in the soils it is so firmly bound there that little is available to
the plants.

The radioisotopes remain concentrated in the top two inches or less
of soil. The rooting habits of the plants, therefore, are associated with
uptake of the radioisotopes. The plants with feeder roots close to the
surface thus take up more of the radionuclides than do those with
deeper root systems.

While all of the tissues of the plants may contain radioisotopes, the
major concentrations are to be found in the leaves, bark, seeds, corms
or nuts. Since these are the most used portions of the plant for animal
foods, the plants pass the radioactive materials on to the animals where
they are incorporated into the animal tissue, only to be released in the
normal biological cycle and passed back to the land for reabsorption.

The invertebrates, or animals without backbones, make up the great
bulk of the animal life of an atoll. The role of these animals in the
cycling of radioactive materials in an atoll is as varied as the inverte-
brate forms. Sea cucumbers have been compared with earthworms in
their ceaseless turning of the gravel and sand as they obtain their
nutriment from bacteria and algae. Corals and clams remove microorganisms and particulate matter from the water and also are host to the
unicellular algae, Zooxanthellae, which are found in their tissues. The

Zooxanthellae may be thought of as a vast reservoir of trapped plankton. Their relationship to their host is not completely understood but it is probable that they play an important part in the removal of phosphate wastes. Corals and clams are eroded by algae and sponges, which bore holes in the skeleton or shell, thus contributing to a return of carbonates to the water. Crabs, sipunculid worms and others also attack the skeleton of the corals. Some of the land crabs contribute to the deposition of radioisotopes from the sea onto the islands by dragging fish and algae ashore when feeding. In short, within the invertebrates and their symbionts alone complete biological cycles occur from land to sea and back again, from inorganic substances to organic and back again.

The fishes of the waters in and about the Marshall Islands have received a major share of the attention in the study of the biological cycling of radioactive materials [15, 20, 21, 22, 23, 24]. Despite detailed study, the great variety of fishes with a correspondingly great variation in feeding habit make this a very difficult area in which to summarize results.

In general, the fishes may be divided by feeding habit into three groups: the herbivores, omnivores and carnivores. Since the herbivores feed directly on the algae, the radioisotopes concentrated from the water by the algae are passed on directly to the fish, and from the fish to the animal eating the fish. The herbivores, represented by such fishes as the surgeonfish and parrotfish, have the greatest amount of radioactivity of the three major groups.

Omnivorous fish such as the damselfish have less contamination than have the herbivorous fish, for they feed on more complex organisms.

The herbivorous and omnivorous fish tend to concentrate the same isotopes found in the plankton except for the radioisotopes which are taken up only in trace amounts by these animals. Zn^{65} usually accounts for 50 percent or more of the total radioactivity in the organs of these fish and Fe^{55-59} comprises a major part of the remaining activity. The radioactive isotopes of cobalt account for 7 to 20 percent of the radioactivity and Mn^{54} 2 to 6 percent.

The minimum concentrations of radioactive material are found in the carnivores, for these fishes, like the reef-dwelling groupers, or the roaming carnivores, like the tuna and barracuda, obtain their "tag" of radioactive material only after it has been passed through a number of living forms which select, retain, or reject various radioisotopes. With the passage of time longer-term studies indicate that several years after a single contamination of an area the carnivorous fish contain the greatest amount of radioactivity.

The carnivorous fish such as tuna and bonito, caught in the open ocean, contain Zn^{65} at the highest levels of any of the three groups of fish. In these animals Zn^{65} accounts for 75 to 92 percent of the total radioactivity; Fe^{55-59}, 6 to 25 percent; the cobalt radioisotopes, 1 to 3 percent; and Mn^{54}, less than 1 percent.

In all species of fish, the greatest amount of radioactivity is found in the alimentary tract, with liver, skin, bone and muscle having lesser amounts in descending order. Skin and bone are quite similar in the amounts present, and usually the radioactivity averages about twice that found in the muscle. The liver may have two to nine times as much radioactivity as the bone or skin, and the alimentary tract contains two to four times as much as the liver.

Unlike the fishes—the aquatic vertebrates—the land vertebrates are limited in both kinds and numbers on the islands of the atolls used for the experiments. Two kinds of birds, the fairy or white tern and the common noddy tern, and the insular field rat are sufficiently abundant and have adequate distribution to be useful as study material.

The terns gather their food from the sea, where they feed mostly upon small pelagic fish, which in turn feed upon plankton. Radioisotopes not absorbed and retained by the birds may be dropped upon the islands in the resting and nesting areas. This transfer of radioactive materials from the sea to the land by the fish-eating birds is a useful way to measure the reverse flow or "uphill" transfer of minerals from sea to land. An indirect effect is the change of availability of radioactive materials following fertilization of the soil by the birds.

Studies of the rats on the islands near the detonation sites have proven to be extremely useful in evaluating the over-all effects of atomic weapons. Since they are confined to the small islands and must both live and eat on the contaminated areas, they may receive both external as well as internal exposure to radiation.

The highest concentration of radioactive materials in the rats is in the bone, with liver and kidney somewhat lower. The skin, muscle, lung and intestinal tract are, in general, lowest in radioactive content. The relative levels in the various tissues vary with time, although the general pattern is that noted above.

This species of rats is essentially herbivorous; they obtain their food from the land plants, seeking out and eating the seeds of grasses, sedges, sand burrs, and leaves of some of the succulent plants.

The plants upon which the rats feed concentrate Sr^{90} and Cs^{137}. These radioisotopes account for approximately 100 percent of the radioactivity within the organs of these animals except immediately after shot when additional short lived radioisotopes are also present. During this time, I^{133}, I^{131} may be present in very high levels in the thyroids.

By following the pattern of gross radioactivity it has been possible to delineate the broad trends in the distribution of radioactive materials in an atoll and its surrounding area. There remains much that can profitably be done to amplify this area, but enough is now known to point the need for increased attention to the task of following the distribution of specific isotopes. Thus, more can be learned about selective absorption of elements by different organisms, and an unparalleled opportunity is presented to study the role of trace elements in the marine environment.

In the remote atolls of the Marshall Islands important contributions to biology have been made; the need now is to apply the knowledge, techniques and skills to increase the productive capacity of our freshwater areas. There is every evidence that the rewards in increased food production from *aquatic* resources will rival or exceed the spectacular results that have been obtained from applying these new concepts to agriculture.

In short, the Pacific testing areas comprise a laboratory in which the biologists have worked with the secondary but long-range problems incident to the peaceful employment of atomic energy. Conditions there are exceedingly fine for the study of the disposition and distribution in nature of the radioactive by-products of such employment.

Biologists have been participants in this scientific team activity since the inception of the atomic tests at Bikini in 1946. This participation has been of almost revolutionary importance to the biologists, for it has given them unprecedented opportunity to observe the biological cycling of radioactive materials deposited on sea and land in the detonation of atomic weapons. But twelve years of field and laboratory work also have demonstrated that the problems of the biologists are those that have fundamental significance in the larger matter of proper planning for the future use of atomic energy. Experience in the Pacific has permitted the biologists to develop new techniques of investigation and has suggested other areas in which the techniques may be tested and applied. The program in the Pacific, permitting the biologists to use the facilities of the test organizations at the test sites, has answered many questions relating to the economy of the sea, has opened up new knowledge of the life zones of coral atolls, and has reshaped in important ways the basic concepts of biological science.

references

1. N. O. Hines. 1951. Bikini report. *The Scientific Monthly*, v. *72*, No. 2: 102–13.

2. J. I. Tracey, et al. 1948. Reefs of Bikini, Marshall Islands. *Bull. of the Geol. Soc. of America 59:* 861–78.

3. H. S. Ladd. 1952. Foundation of Eniwetok atoll. *Bull. Geol. Surv. Amer. 63:* 1273. Abstract.

4. W. S. Von Arx. 1954. Circulation systems of Bikini and Rongelap Lagoons. Bikini and nearby atolls, Part 2. *Geol. Sur. Prof. Paper 260-B, C, D.*

5. W. H. Munk and M. C. Sargent. 1954. Adjustment of Bikini atoll to ocean waves. Bikini and Nearby Atolls, Part 2. *Geol. Sur. Prof. Paper 260-B, C, D.*

6. M. K. Robinson. 1954. Sea temperature in the Marshall Islands area, Bikini and nearby atolls, Part 2. *Geol. Sur. Prof. Paper 260, B, C, D.*

7. C. A. Barnes, et al. 1948. Ocean circulation in the Marshall Islands area. *Am. Geophys. Union Trans. 29:* 871–76.

8. H. Mao and K. Yoshida. 1954. Physical oceanography in the Marshall Islands area. *Geol. Sur. Prof. Paper 260-R.*

9. L. P. Schultz, et al. 1953. Fishes of the Marshall and Marianas Islands. 1, *Bull. 202.* Smithsonian Institute, U.S. Natl. Mus.

10. W. R. Taylor. 1950. *Plants of Bikini and other northern Marshall Islands,* Univ. of Michigan Press, Ann Arbor.

11. F. R. Fosberg. 1953. Vegetation of central pacific atolls. *Atoll Research Bull. 23:* 1–26.

12. H. St. John. 1949. Report on botanical studies on Eniwetok atoll. U.S. Atomic Energy Commission Donaldson Expedition.

13. O. Biddulph and R. Cory. 1952. The relationship between Ca[45], total calcium and fission product radioactivity in plants of *Portulaca oleracea* growing in the vicinity of the atom bomb test sites on Eniwetok atoll. Off. Tech. Services, U.S. Dept. Comm. *AEC Report UWFL-31.*

14. E. Dawson. 1957. An annotated list of marine algae from Eniwetok atoll, Marshall Islands. *Pacific Science.*

15. Applied Fisheries Laboratory. 1950. Radiobiological survey of Bikini, Eniwetok, and Likiep atolls—July-August, 1949. Off. Tech. Services, U.S. Dept. Comm. *AEC Report AECD-3446.*

16. *Handbook on the trust territory of the Pacific Islands.* 1949. Navy Department, Office of the Chief of Naval Operations.

17. K. Bonham. 1958. Radioactivity of invertebrates and other organisms at Eniwetok atoll during 1954–55. Off. Tech. Services, U.S. Dept. Comm. *AEC Report UWFL-53.*

18. F. G. Lowman. 1958. Radionuclides in plankton near the Marshall Islands, 1956. Off. Tech. Services, U.S. Dept. Comm. *AEC Report UWFL-54.*

19. R. F. Palumbo. 1955. The uptake of iodine-131 by the red alga *Asparagopsis taxiformis.* Off. Tech. Services, U.S. Dept. Comm. *AEC Report UWFL-44.*

20. L. R. Donaldson, et al. 1956. Survey of radioactivity in the sea near Bikini and Eniwetok atolls—June 11–21, 1956. Off. Tech. Services, U.S. Dept. Comm. *AEC Report UWFL-46.*

21. A. H. Seymour, et al. 1957. Survey of radioactivity in the sea and in pelagic marine life west of the Marshall Islands, September 1–20, 1956. Off. Tech. Services, U.S. Dept. Comm. *AEC Report UWFL-47.*

22. A. D. Welander. 1957. Radioactivity in the reef fishes of Belle Island, Eniwetok atoll, April 1954 to November 1955. Off. Tech. Services, U.S. Dept. Comm. *AEC Report UWFL-49.*

23. F. G. Lowman, R. F. Palumbo, and D. J. South. 1957. The occurrence and distribution of radioactive non-fission products in plants and animals of the Pacific proving ground. Off. Tech. Services, U.S. Dept. Comm. *AEC Report UWFL-51.*

24. A. D. Welander. 1958. Radiobiological Studies of the fish collected at rongelap and ailinginae atolls, July 1957. Off. Tech. Services, U.S. Dept. Comm. *AEC Report UWFL-55.*

bibliography

E. E. Held. 1957. Land crabs and radioactive fallout at Eniwetok atoll. Off. Tech. Services, U.S. Dept. Comm. *AEC Report UWFL-50.*

T. Ichikawa and Y. Hiyama. 1954. Adsorption of radioactivity on mucus of fish. *Report III-5 on the effects of radioactivity to the Special Committee of the Science Council of Japan.* Tokyo.

R. F. Palumbo and F. G. Lowman. 1958. The occurrence of Antimony-125, Europim-155, Iron-55, and other radionuclides in rongelap atoll soil. Off. Tech. Services, U.S. Dept. Comm. *AEC Report UWFL-56.*

Glossary

acetylcholine   hormone-like substance that initiates transmission of the nervous impulse at nerve or neuromuscular junctions.

acute toxicity   poisonous or deleterious effect from administration of a single dose of a chemical; usually 24-hour effect (see ED_{50} and LD_{50}).

aerosol   suspension of finely divided particles or droplets in air.

α, α-di(p-chlorophenyl)-β, β, β-trichloroethane   (see *DDT*).

alpha particles   energetic helium nuclei (helium atoms minus their electrons).

antagonism   the effect of a chemical (antagonist) on biological activity of another, such as a pesticide or a medicine, so that the toxic or physiological effect of the latter is decreased.

antibiotic   a chemical produced by an organism, usually microorganism, that has a toxic or inhibiting effect on another organism.

ATP   adenosine triphosphate nucleotide; the source of immediate energy in cellular functions.

beta particles   ionizing radiation consisting of high-speed electrons.

biosynthesis   production of an organic compound by a living organism.

carcinogen   chemical or physical initiator of a carcinoma (a malignant epithelial growth). Sometimes broadly referring to an initiator of any malignancy.

CBW   chemical and biological warfare.

chromosome   a threadlike body in the nuclei of cells, containing the genes or carriers of hereditary characteristics.

chronic toxicity   poisonous or deleterious effect from prolonged exposure or repeated administration of a chemical.

corpora allata   glands at the base of the brain in insects that secrete the juvenile hormone.

DDT   the insecticide dichloro-diphenyl-trichloroethane; chemically, 1, 1, 1-trichloro-2, 2- bis (p-chlorophenyl) ethane.

deoxyribonucleic acid (see *DNA*).

detergent   cleansing agent, usually a mixture of surfactant (surface active agent) and water softeners such as phosphates.

detoxication   degradation of a poisonous chemical in the organism to less injurious compounds.

DNA   a polynucleotide making up the hereditary material of chromosomes.

ecology   study of the relation of animals and plants to the environment; interrelationship of organisms.

ED_{50} dose of chemical required to produce a specified effect to 50% of organisms exposed or treated.

enzyme   a proteinaceous substance produced by a living organism that speeds up chemical reactions; a biological catalyst.

estrogen   one of the female sex hormones.

eutrophication   the changing biota of a body of water characterized by dense algal growth, depletion of oxygen in bottom layers, odor and discoloration.

FDA   the U.S. Food and Drug Administration of the Department of Health, Education and Welfare.

gamma rays   electromagnetic radiation similar to light, at the short end of the wave length spectrum.

G.C.   abbreviation for gas chromatography, a highly sensitive analytical method for small amounts of organic chemicals.

gene   a unit of chromosome regarded as carrying a specific feature of heredity.

half-life   time in which half the atoms or molecules decompose; in reference to radioactive elements the time required for half the atoms of an unstable isotope to decompose to its next lower energy state.

hallucinogen   a chemical compound which causes hallucinations (see also *psychedelic*).

hormone   substance produced by secretory tissue (endocrine gland) that affects the function of other tissues or organs.

isomer   a chemical compound which differs slightly from another structurally though identical in atomic weight and elemental makeup.

isotope   a form of a chemical compound which differs from another in atomic weight but not in atomic number, therefore differing physically but not chemically.

juvenile hormone   secretion of the corpora allata in insects that prevents or inhibits molting to a more mature form.

LD_{50} dose of chemical required to be lethal to 50% of organisms exposed or treated.

LSD (also *LSD-25*)   lysergic acid diethylamide, derived from an extract of ergot, a form of the fungus *Claviceps purpurea.*

mutagen   a chemical or physical causative agent for mutation or change in a heritable characteristic.

mutation   change in a heritable characteristic, involving a modification in the genetic code of DNA.

mycotoxin   a poisonous substance produced by a microorganism.

neoplastic   pertaining to the formation of new tissue, often referring to cancerous growth of cells.

nucleic acid   a polynucleotide such as DNA or RNA.

nucleotide   a unit of structure in DNA or RNA consisting of a purine or pyrimidine base, a molecule of 5-carbon ribose sugar (desoxyribose) and a phosphate linkage.

oncogen   a chemical substance or physical stimulus that causes cancer; an initiator of a neoplasm.

parathion   an organic phosphorus insecticide related to the "nerve gases."

pesticide   a chemical used for controlling pests such as insects, fungi, weeds, snails, algae, rodents.

pharmaceutical   of or pertaining to chemicals used as medicines.

photosynthesis   production of carbohydrates from carbon dioxide and water by green plants; process of using radiant energy to synthesize high-energy chemical compounds.

polynucleotide   large molecule such as that comprising DNA or RNA (see *nucleotide*).

progestin   a type of female sex hormone.

psychedelic   "mind manifesting" drug; causing changes in mental processes, perceptions, or attitudes.

purine   a nitrogenous heterocyclic base; the purines adenine and guanine are bases in nucleic acids of DNA and RNA.

pyrimidine   a nitrogenous heterocyclic base in nucleic acids; cytosine and thymine are pyrimidine bases in DNA and cytosine and uracil are pyrimidine bases in RNA.

radioactive   property of a substance that emits radiation such as x-rays, gamma rays, beta particles, or alpha particles, resulting from changes in the atomic nucleus or in the extranuclear electron levels.

residue   chemical remaining, such as a pesticide, on or in food.

resistance   loss of susceptibility of organisms to chemicals such as pesticides and bactericides.

ribonucleic acid   (see *RNA*).

RNA   ribonucleic (or ribosenucleic) acid; a class of polynucleotide related to DNA but also found characteristically in the cytoplasm as well as in nuclei.

side effect   toxic or physiologically injurious effect from a drug or medicine.

steroid   a compound consisting of a molecular skeleton of four fused carbon compound rings, characteristic of sex hormones and other substances found in living organisms.

subacute toxicity   poisonous or deleterious effect from short-term administration of a chemical, in pharmacology usually 21 to 90 days duration.

synergism   the effect of a chemical (synergist) on the biological activity of another, such as a pesticide or a medicine, such that the toxic or physiological effect of the latter is enhanced to an extent that is more than additive.

teratogen   a chemical substance or treatment causing abnormal development or congenital deformation.

tetrahydrocannabinol   one of the active ingredients of marijuana.

tetrodotoxin   toxic substance of the poisonous puffer fish.

tolerance   amount allowed such as residue of a pesticide on or in food; usually expressed as ppm (parts per million).

toxicity   poisonous or deleterious effect of a chemical; side effect (see also *acute, chronic,* and *subacute toxicity*).

trace mineral   elements required in trace amounts in nutrition.

vitamin   organic substance required in small amounts by the organism for growth or maintenance of life; vitamins contribute to the action or formation of enzymes.

x-rays   electromagnetic radiation similar to light, near the short end of the wave length spectrum.

Index